Geoarchaeology, Climate Change, and Sustainability

edited by

Antony G. Brown
Palaeoecology Laboratory University of Southampton (PLUS)
School of Geography
University of Southampton
Highfield Campus
Southampton SO17 1BJ
UK

Laura S. Basell
Palaeoecology Laboratory University of Southampton (PLUS)
School of Geography
University of Southampton
Highfield Campus
Southampton SO17 1BJ
UK

Karl W. Butzer
Department of Geography and the Environment
The University of Texas at Austin
Austin, Texas 78712-3100
USA

THE
GEOLOGICAL
SOCIETY
OF AMERICA®

Special Paper 476

3300 Penrose Place, P.O. Box 9140 ▪ Boulder, Colorado 80301-9140, USA

2011

Published by The Geological Society of America, Inc.
3300 Penrose Place, P.O. Box 9140, Boulder, Colorado 80301-9140, USA
www.geosociety.org

Printed in U.S.A.

GSA Books Science Editors: Marion E. Bickford and Donald I. Siegel

Library of Congress Cataloging-in-Publication Data

Geoarchaeology, climate change, and sustainability / edited by Antony G. Brown, Laura S. Basell, Karl W. Butzer.
    p. cm. — (Special paper ; 476)
  Includes bibliographical references.
  ISBN 978-0-8137-2476-8 (pbk.)
  1. Archaeological geography. 2. Paleoecology. 3. Paleoclimatology. I. Brown, Antony G. II. Basell, Laura S. III. Butzer, Karl W.

CC77.5.G463 2011
551.6—dc22

                                                                    2010046617

Cover: Laser scan of Hodge ditch, Chard Junction Quarry, Dorset, UK. Composite image of multiple scans taken between 2009 and 2011 by Laura Basell using Leica Scanstation.

10 9 8 7 6 5 4 3 2 1

Contents

Preface

Antony G. Brown
Laura S. Basell
Palaeoecology Laboratory University of Southampton (PLUS), School of Geography,
University of Southampton, Highfield Campus, Southampton SO17 1BJ, UK

Karl W. Butzer
Department of Geography and the Environment, The University of Texas at Austin,
Austin, Texas 78712-3100, USA

This Geological Society of America Special Paper is derived from a selection of the papers given at the "Geoarchaeology 2006" Conference that was held at the University of Exeter, United Kingdom, in September 2006. The conference lasted three days and was followed by a fieldtrip within the region. This conference was the first of what have now become regular "geoarchaeology" conferences in the UK (Sheffield in 2009) and marked a formalization of the interest in the field of geoarchaeology in the UK and Europe. The conference had just over 100 delegates from over 20 countries, including the USA, France, Germany, Belgium, the Netherlands, Switzerland, Italy, Greece, and Ireland. The delegates also came from a variety of backgrounds, including archaeology, geomorphology, geology, and the commercial sector (contract archaeology and land-use planning). The field excursion at the end of the conference visited the Exe Valley and fluvial geoarchaeological sites of Holocene age before heading east to the Blackdown Hills and the Axe Valley, which contains a remarkably long and complete stack of Pleistocene fluvial deposits with evidence of hominin presence in the area from the Lower Paleolithic to the Late Upper Paleolithic. The fieldtrip provided fertile ground for interdisciplinary and international discussion and debate. Over three days, 65 papers and 10 posters were presented. Many of these were submitted for publication and the 14 that are published in this volume were those that survived the refereeing process.

The papers presented here cover the typical spectrum of Euro-American geoarchaeology. In a keynote paper, *Karl Butzer* discusses the conceptual basis of geoarchaeology, its relationship to landscape history, and its potential in relation to current debates about adaptive response to environmental change. This is followed by a series of papers on Pleistocene geoarchaeology (*Matthew Pope and Mark Roberts, Laura Basell et al., Robert Hosfield*). Although different in timeframe these papers share common methodologies and address similar problems of temporal resolution and causality. They also illustrate how sand and gravel (aggregate resources) can contain extremely valuable archaeology, a point which is highlighted again at the end of the volume in relation to geoarchaeological management and planning (*Ingrid Ward, Antony Brown*). After the Palaeolithic papers the focus moves east to SW Iran and the use of remote sensing (*Laëtitia Dupin*). Remote sensing is a tool that has revolutionized what we can do, and where. Few self-respecting archaeologists working in the semi-arid or arid parts of the world would now think of commencing work without remote-sensing data, which are getting more technically sophisticated, with ever higher spatial resolution and therefore archaeological value. One such area, the Mediterranean, is also unique in its history of written sources and the paper by *Kalliopi Gaki-Papanastassiou et al.* uses geological data to test theories about the location of the legendary ancient island home of Odysseus described in the writings of Homer. A coastal theme is continued by examining archaeological levels in what are generally thought of as unpromising coastal dune sediments (*Jasper Knight* and *Helene Burningham*) and the pericoastal environment (*Simon Haslett*). Both environments are very valuable in understanding past environmental change and, in contrast to today, were foci of Prehistoric activity due to the proximity and value of coastal resources. Resource distribution is also highly relevant to the following three papers which deal with fluvial geoarchaeological environments. Two originate in the UK and stress the interaction of the changing environment and the location, burial, and destruction of alluvial archaeology (*David Passmore et al.*, *Jenny Bennett et al.*), while the third focuses on the environmental influences on the location of Archaic and Woodland sites on the Nottawasaga River, southern Ontario, Canada (*Mary Thornbush and Joseph Desloges*). Typical geoarchaeological techniques such as coring and radiocarbon dating are then combined with visualization by *Joseph Schuldenrein and Michael Aiuvalasit* in a paper illustrating how valuable geoarchaeology can be even under Manhattan Island, New York City, USA, and how these data are invaluable in archaeological resource evaluation in an urban context. This paper leads the volume into the area of the sustainability of the archaeological resource and what that actually means in practice.

The last two papers (*Ingrid Ward*, *Antony Brown*) are explicitly concerned with the management of geoarchaeological resources in relation to funding sources, planning, and climate change. This brings us back again to the theme of the volume—*geoarchaeology, climate change, and sustainability* both in the archaeological record and today in relation to the preservation of that record. This also brings us back to the other use of "sustainability" and the role of geoarchaeology in testing explanations that involve sustainability or non-sustainability in the past, and particularly in response to climate change. As Karl Butzer emphasizes in the first paper, temporal coincidence is not causality and it is the role of geoarchaeology to test causal explanations and show the mechanisms of climatically or human-driven environmental change.

Acknowledgments

The volume editors, and the "Geoarchaeology 2006" Conference organizers, must thank English Heritage for providing enough funds to allow the invitation of selected speakers and for their support of the conference in a variety of ways. Many of the papers, and indirectly this conference, have benefited from funds raised by a green tax on the aggregates industry in the UK (the Aggregates Levy Sustainability Fund), and this volume is a testament to how vital and rewarding for society and education such expenditure can be.

The Geological Society of America
Special Paper 476
2011

Geoarchaeology, climate change, sustainability: A Mediterranean perspective

Karl W. Butzer*

Department of Geography and the Environment, University of Texas at Austin, Austin, Texas 78712-3100, USA

ABSTRACT

Although geological study of Pleistocene cave sites goes back to the nineteenth century, a new paradigm was set in train during the 1920s, when G. Caton-Thompson and E.W. Gardner established a sequence of prehistoric occupations linked to the changing spatial and ecological contours of fluctuating lakes in Egypt's Faiyum Depression. Subsequent collaborations have carried research beyond geochronology and climate stratigraphy to address human settlement within changing environments, which served both as resource and artifact.

Geoarchaeologists, as they were eventually called, worked at multiple scales and with new skills, exploring new ground such as cultural sediments and the taphonomy of site formation, preservation, and destruction. Others, especially in the UK, investigated human modification of particular watersheds. Forty years of work on Mediterranean soil erosion issues saw researchers continue to wrestle with climate or destructive land use as possible prime movers in ecological degradation. The number of geoarchaeologists, full or part time, has increased by an order of magnitude, and the literature continues to explode in quantity and diversity. Perhaps the overarching conceptual framework for most remains a deep interest in landscape histories and the ways in which they co-evolve with human societies.

This paper encourages our confraternity to engage more assertively in the broader academic debates of the day, as empirical scientists open to interdisciplinary exchange and qualified to argue for competent and reasonable positions. We should play a more effective role in environmental history, alongside historians and political ecologists. The popular "new" environmental determinism centered on civilizational collapse in response to "abrupt" climatic change calls for strong voices of caution, on the premise that coincidence, even when true, does not prove causality. We are qualified to monitor the environmental and adaptive changes critical to future projections of global change, and we all have our ideas, even if intuitive, with regard to alternative ways of thinking about sustainability.

*karl.butzer@austin.utexas.edu

Butzer, K.W., 2011, Geoarchaeology, climate change, sustainability: A Mediterranean perspective, *in* Brown, A.G., Basell, L.S., and Butzer, K.W., eds., Geoarchaeology, Climate Change, and Sustainability: Geological Society of America Special Paper 476, p. 1–14, doi:10.1130/2011.2476(01). For permission to copy, contact editing@geosociety.org. © 2011 The Geological Society of America. All rights reserved.

EARLY GEOARCHAEOLOGY

Collaboration between geologists and archaeologists in the study of Pleistocene cave sites goes back well into the nineteenth century, when disciplinary lines still were fluid. A watershed was crossed in the 1920s, when geologist Elinor W. Gardner began to work with archaeologist Gertrude Caton-Thompson in the Faiyum Depression of Egypt. A series of high shorelines was traced so as to situate a sequence of Neolithic occupations within the changing spatial and temporal contours of a fluctuating lake. First published in the *Geographical Journal* of 1929, this interdisciplinary framework was only superseded by new expeditions to the Faiyum during the 1960s. By building site clusters into a multidimensional landscape, Caton-Thompson and Gardner (1929) had broken new ground, setting a strategic research direction that anticipated geoarchaeology. Equally so, their model of collaborative research showed what could be done and how.

While surveying for Neolithic and Predynastic sites along the desert margins of the Nile Valley in 1958, the Faiyum investigation served to pose and discuss questions that went beyond stratigraphic placement or environmental reconstruction. The outcome was a complex and explicit strategy to address site selection and preservation, physical versus cultural explanations for apparent settlement gaps, and whether the sites identified were representative of their original density (Butzer, 1960, 1961). Further, a morphostratigraphic map of the desert margins attempted to delineate the geoarchaeological potential of different landscape units (redrawn in Butzer, 1982, figure 14-1). This strategy came together during continuing discussion with archaeologist Werner Kaiser.

Although the term "interdisciplinary" has become a meaningless buzzword for the writers of grant proposals, true cross-disciplinary collaboration is essential for geoarchaeology. There always are people on the other side of the fence who are willing to share their ideas and speculations, or listen to yours, despite the artificial boundaries that continue to divide us. That is the way that *Environment and Archeology* (Butzer, 1964a) came about. An exploratory course on "prehistoric geography," that I introduced at the University of Wisconsin, combining earth science and archaeology, was supported by colleagues and students in anthropology and biology. Equally critical components for me personally were new fieldwork opportunities, including three seasons at Clark Howell's Paleolithic excavations in Spain, and almost 7 mo working with an archaeological rescue mission in Nubia and Egypt. Howell generously sponsored my participation at the Wenner-Gren Burg Wartenstein symposia in 1961 and 1963, which included celebrities like Louis Leakey and Desmond Clark. When *Environment and Archeology* appeared in print, it included a half-dozen chapters on archaeological sediments, as well as segments on environmental reconstruction and human-environmental interrelationships in prehistory. Book reviewers from archaeology assured the success of this unorthodox, interdisciplinary presentation, which apparently filled a void. It was this sustained interchange of ideas that led to the conception of geoarchaeology as an engagement between earth science and archaeology, rather than the application of a battery of techniques in an archaeological context.

This paper first singles out a number of research directions that have become durable themes in geoarchaeology. It then turns to the problematic aspects of Mediterranean landscape history as a prime example of the way in which the field has matured, despite persistent difficulties of synthetic interpretation. It subsequently identifies a less familiar set of cultural and behavioral issues that I believe are critical for more effective diagnosis of cause and effect in transformation and change. This cross-disciplinary excursion concludes with suggestions as to why and how we might enter into a broader academic discourse with regard to the "new" environmentalism, the alleged role of climate or environmental degradation in civilizational collapse, and the linkage of geoarchaeology and sustainability.

A COALESCENCE OF GEOARCHAEOLOGY

Empirical research linked to the discipline that came to be explicitly called *geoarchaeology* has been exploding since the 1970s. The term itself was in informal use well before I applied it to the taphonomy of Acheulian artifacts at the South African site of Amanzi Springs, in *Quaternaria* of 1973 (Butzer, 1973a). Also emphasizing this focus on archaeological sites, Colin Renfrew (1976, p. 2) used the designation to argue that "every archaeological problem starts as a problem in geoarchaeology," in his keynote address to a symposium on *Sediments in Archaeology* held in 1973. The chronology of the formal term is an unimportant detail, but the creativity within the emerging subdiscipline is noteworthy. The number of full- or part-time geoarchaeologists has increased by an order of magnitude, while the literature continues to expand in quantity and diversity, and in the number of preferred publication outlets.

There now are a number of textbooks (such as Limbrey, 1975; Rapp and Gifford, 1985; Waters, 1992; Brown, 1997; Goldberg and Macphail, 2006; Rapp and Hill, 2006), as well as quite a few volumes of collected papers, dealing with sediments, soils, or sites (for example, Stein and Farrand, 2001; Boardman and Bell, 1992; Lasca and Donahue, 1990; Holliday, 2004; Goldberg et al., 2001). These works suggest that interdisciplinary research between the geosciences and archaeology has come of age, but the diversity of perspectives or positions is striking. The fundamental dichotomy, however, is about the priority given techniques or goals. I would see geoarchaeology as archaeological research using methods and concepts of the earth sciences (Butzer, 1982, p. 35), whereas archaeological geoscience, at least in the United States, tends to apply earth science findings to archaeology, without directly addressing their implications for the interrelationships between the environment and past societies. In the UK, on the other hand, the interactions between earth scientists and archaeologists are closer and more direct. In fact, given a long and complex Pleistocene archaeological record in the Old World, geoarchaeology in Britain, as documented in the chapters of this volume, typically incorporates archaeology into studies of landscape evolution and environmental history.

These contrasts reflect the distinctive backgrounds of past and present researchers, and the fact that there neither are departments of, nor professorial appointments in geoarchaeology. Despite our individual research trajectories, we all are mainstream practitioners of geography, geology, Quaternary science, or archaeology, as the case may be. It also is a recent subdiscipline, despite its longevity, that only coalesced after the prevailing academic structures had crystallized, a little before or after 1900. However, this very heterodoxy has proven to be healthy, because we all find stimulus, or even excitement, at the various venues we attend, under whatever auspices. There is indeed a close analogy to the spirit of various Quaternary meetings, where everybody does something different, or has a different take on issues or empirical findings, and yet enjoys the opportunity to interact. It is the diversity that is refreshing. Consequently, I think that the big-tent approach to geoarchaeology is a good thing. It brings us together without formal structures, in a way that disciplinary constraints might not have allowed.

The brief discussion that follows attempts to identify some of the salient archaeological subjects being addressed today (also Butzer, 2008), without attempting to do justice to a burgeoning body of literature. Other emphases or interpretations are equally valid, and we should welcome a broader, reflective discussion of what we do and why.

Analysis and Dating of Soils and Sediments

Considerable energy has been and continues to be devoted to the development or application of novel methods to site-specific problems. Relative and quantitative dating has always been a primary concern so that ^{14}C and accelerator mass spectrometry (AMS) remain indispensable. Other, more experimental methods also continue to be tested, and with improving results, for example, optically stimulated luminescence (OSL) (e.g., Fuchs and Wagner, 2005). It need not be emphasized that depositional micro-environments are central to the work of a majority of geoarchaeologists. Interpretive issues of alluvial sites have been discussed by Gladfelter (1981), Abbott and Valastro (1995), and Ferring (2001). Settlement change in response to Holocene fluctuations of sea level in estuarine or deltaic settings has been addressed by Ricklis and Blum (1997), Butzer (2002), and Bell (2007). Soil micromorphology has improved the potential information available from cave sediments (Goldberg and Macphail, 2006, chapter 8). On the other hand, there seems to be a certain reluctance to move from the traditional cave methodologies of Lais (1941) or Laville et al. (1980) toward more sophisticated statistical analyses, which may incorporate analog samples from exterior soils and sediments (Butzer, 1973b, 1981a, 2004; Woodward and Goldberg, 2001). Articles published in various journals illustrate the range of productive examples of geochemical and sediment testing at open-air sites, which has more recently also

turned to the identification of mining residues in alluvial deposits (e.g., Nocete et al., 2005).

Site Patterning and Archaeological Integrity

Of course geoarchaeology is more than the application of a battery of analytical techniques, and we should not lose sight of the wider goal, to address cultural questions directly or indirectly. A prime example of productive collaboration is represented in Pleistocene "open-air" sites that have been sealed and buried by younger sediments. They form a major part of the Old World archaeological record, and significant numbers of such sites have been the subject of elaborate excavations; the early expectation was that sophisticated recovery methods would unearth more or less representative palimpsests of early human cultural behavior.

That illusion has been dispelled by more refined methods (see Behrensmeyer and Hill, 1980; Klein, 1987, 1989). Statistical attention to the orientation and disposition of bones and artifacts can show that lithics and long bones in suggestive associations may well have been reworked by streams, while multiple brief occupations of a site can be conflated by erosion of the finer sediments covering them. As a result of such dispersal, some African Acheulian sites may be no more than point bar accumulations or lags left by flood or lake waters. Bone selection and chew marks show that many bone accumulations were not made by humans, but by large carnivores. Even when a few lithic artifacts are present, such a site may prove to be a natural death or carnivore assemblage, scavenged by early humans.

Preburial or postdepositional disturbance has destroyed the cultural integrity of most formerly "open-air" sites (Butzer, 1982, chapter 7; Butzer, 2008), but such problems can also be encountered in cave sites, where multiple occupations and/or mixing during the course of everyday human activities can simulate occupation levels, such as the thick and rich Mousterian horizons in Spain (Butzer, 1981a, 2008). Unfortunately, that problem is not always recognized by archaeologists, who may be inclined to assume that low-energy cave interiors imply cultural integrity. Perhaps the only means to show that associations are representative is by "refitting" the flakes and chips detached from individual artifacts, a technique that can be applied to both cave and open-air sites (see Pope and Roberts, this volume). A high proportion of animal bones with cut-marks can also be helpful.

Merits of "Secondary Sites"

Must then the majority of Pleistocene artifactual concentrations or incidental lithics be rejected as uninformative "nonsites"? By no means, as several presentations, from the "Geoarchaeology 2006" conference (held at the University of Exeter, UK, in September 2006) that now appear as chapters in this volume have shown. Artifacts, like human fossils, record a human presence and identify a changing biophysical context for human activities (cf. Helgren, 1997). When found in small numbers within a high-energy sedimentary sequence, artifact frequency and depositional structures may allow identification of the original location of the site in a paleolandscape. Bell (2007) suggested that human activity may even have been concentrated during periods of maximum environmental dynamism.

Surface surveys of promising landform elements with the aid of geographic information systems (GIS) can identify sensitive archaeological landscapes for management purposes, as well as provide understanding of the spatial activities of Paleolithic to Early Bronze Age people with respect to their contemporary landscape (Passmore et al., this volume). This is more reasonable than using gridded, random squares, as has been done in many formal archaeological surveys. Dense regional concentrations of abraded surface artifacts can also be systematically studied in a spatial perspective. They may be most common in areas with a particular lithology, or at contacts between different lithologies (quarry sites), and equally so at river channel confluences, where stream gradients can change abruptly (Hosfield, 2005, this volume). The gaps in such "nonsite" distributions raise interesting questions, not just in terms of past spatial behavior, settlement expansion or retraction, and lithic provenance, but also for landscape dynamics, such as river entrenchment.

Interpretation of the UK archaeological landscape has been greatly enhanced in recent years by support from the Aggregates Levy Sustainability Fund (see Brown, 2008). This complements the once-introverted focus on site excavation with fresh spatial perspectives.

Urban Geoarchaeology

Much attention has been focused on settlement sites with architectural components, which are informative for both environmental and sociohistorical questions (Butzer, 1982, p. 83–94; Butzer, 2008; Rosen, 1986; Beach and Luzzadder-Beach, 2008). With its mix of cultural and environmental sediments, urban geoarchaeology may record natural hazards or disasters, site growth and decline, or deliberate destruction. Such deposits are sensitive to human disturbance as well as to social change. Occupation residues, artifactual fills, mudbrick residues, collapse rubbles, flood silts, or intrusive slope-soil wash can be found on house floors, in roadways or alleyside dumps, or in civic precincts (Butzer, 1981b). These may elucidate continuing or changing human activities. On the other hand, environmental insights are particularly promising in floodplain sites prone to destructive floods or channel shifts (Butzer et al., 1983), while footslope sites may be susceptible to repeated waves of soil influx (Butzer, 1981b). Larger questions of urban site formation, preservation, or erosion raise geomorphological issues of sediment accumulation, or modification and removal (Kirkby and Kirkby, 1976; Butzer, 1982, chapter 7; Rosen, 1986; Schuldenrein et al., 2004; Beach and Luzzadder-Beach, 2008), which have important implications for archaeological survey and excavation.

Unfortunately, geoarchaeological investigations carried out in urban "heritage projects," such as in York (UK) or Valencia (Spain), do not always find publication in readily visible outlets.

On the other hand, systematic urban excavations by academic teams may lack a geoarchaeological component, with some notable exceptions, such as Catalhüyük or Giza. Even today, one can see backhoes in the Mediterranean Basin removing so-called site overburden. A great deal of information is being lost or left inaccessible, suggesting the need for a special symposium on urban geoarchaeology.

Landscape Geoarchaeology and Watershed Transformation

At a larger scale, geoarchaeologists have been active in studying the Holocene evolution of small or large watersheds, in partial response to human intervention (see Needham and Macklin, 1992; Lewin et al., 1995; Brown, 1997, 2008; Howard et al., 2003). Such work is marked by a fresh attention to detail, modeling, and paleohydrology, which incorporates historical and archaeological data, and draws on palynology or tree-ring results. The result is a better understanding of the temporal and spatial parameters of climatic change or of human impacts on environmental equilibrium. However, it remains a formidable task to separate climatic and human factors, and this need is being met by increasing attention to archival chronologies and patient contextual examination (Brown, 2008; Dotterweich, 2005; Macklin et al., 2005; Benito et al., 2008). This has contemporary relevance going well beyond management issues. A diachronic approach that monitors the processes and feedbacks of "historical" change is critical to understanding contemporary, synchronic patterning, or to anticipate future contingencies. In other words, alluvial histories pose questions and provide insights in regard to global change or that elusive matter of sustainability (Butzer, 2005).

These micro- and macrothemes of site versus watershed can now facilitate a more focused analytical discussion, emphasizing the Mediterranean world with its large corpus of data. It has also attracted the interest of many international researchers.

MEDITERRANEAN LANDSCAPE HISTORY

The Debate

With the aura of Classical and earlier civilizations, the Mediterranean world has long attracted visitors from northern climes, whether scholars or travelers, barbarians or sun-worshippers. Echoing Plato and Pausanias, George Perkins Marsh (1864) fired off the opening diatribe, blaming Mediterranean people for destructive land use, whereas Ellsworth Huntington (1910) waxed nostalgic over Arcadian forests fallen victim to progressive desiccation. With the benefit of hindsight, Marsh and Huntington positioned human impact and climatic change as the polar coordinates of an environmental dialectic, even before the emergence of contemporary concerns about long-term ecology.

A new round of discourse began with publication of _The Mediterranean Valleys_ by Claudio Vita-Finzi (1969; also review by Butzer, 1969). That author claimed a single phase of Holocene alluviation, a "Younger Fill," which he considered to be of post-Roman age. It was believed to be synchronous throughout the Mediterranean world, in response to a climatic anomaly. Vita-Finzi also identified an "Older Fill" pertaining to the late Pleistocene. The ensuing debate is ably covered by the extended review of Horden and Purcell (2000, chapter 8).

The substantial corpus of research in Greece by Tjeerd Van Andel and his associates provided a more refined database. Not one, but several phases of substantial alluviation have been identified for Neolithic and Bronze Age times (Van Andel et al., 1990; Wells et al., 1990; Zangger, 1993; Jameson et al., 1994). Some of these episodes were linked to debris flows, reflecting slope failure, a more "catastrophic" process (Pope and Van Andel, 1984). Soil erosion did take place during the Classical, Roman, and later periods, but it was less dramatic and more variable. These authors favored an anthropogenic interpretation, suggesting that accelerated valley alluviation may have been preferentially linked to initial occupancy or abandonment, rather than periods of agricultural intensification. While these interpretations require more documentation, especially a local pollen record, they do not warrant identification of Van Andel as a "narrowly-culturalist" determinist (Bintliff, 2000, p. 57), whatever that may be. The issue is no longer whether human impact can have repercussions for the soil landscape, but to distinguish between the impacts of climatic perturbations and changing land use.

Sediment Facies Are Complex

During the course of intensive Quaternary and geoarchaeological studies in a half-dozen different environments of Spain and Mallorca, it has been my experience that landform evolution, and the development of alluvial and slope deposits are different in each. Key variables are elevation, relief and slope, different equilibrium thresholds, and the complexities of Cenozoic geological evolution.

Some mountain ranges were initially shaped within a medium of deep tropical soils, such as in southern Galicia (Butzer, 1967). Others were opened through the expansion of extensive erosional surfaces, endowing them with repeated knickpoints and changes of gradients, e.g., the central sierras of Spain (Gladfelter, 1971). In other cases, topographies were greatly roughed up by Pleistocene cold-climate processes or glaciers. In the Cantabrian ranges of northern Spain, alluvial formations include glaciofluvial terraces, with or without periglacial modification, that progressively change character downstream (Butzer, 1986). Cobble-bed channels may be recycled from Pleistocene units by the undercutting of older fills or reactivation of deeper channel floors (Butzer and Mateu, 1999). Massive silt/clay accumulations are derived from poorly consolidated Miocene–Pliocene basin deposits, while karstic terrain favors carbonate-impregnated fills, marls, and spring tufas (Gladfelter, 1971). Mixed-caliber valley fills may be interdigitated with Quaternary slope screes, with rubble set in a matrix of reddish soil–derived sediment (Butzer, 1964b; Butzer and Mateu, 1999). Clayey alluvia characterize limestone terrain

where weathering has dissolved clasts and sands, in contrast to the prominent bed-load alluvia and slope screes of watersheds with silicate rocks (Butzer and Mateu, 1999).

Such cases underscore the fact that one cannot lump mid- or late Holocene fills and colluvia into a single facies model, regardless of age. Geological antecedents and complex three-dimensional landscapes, coupled with Quaternary history, strongly affect facies development and variability, channel gradients, and the overarching hydraulic parameters. The architecture of sedimentary fills is correspondingly complex.

Dissimilar Patterns of Landscape Evolution

These Spanish examples are not exceptional. The mountainous northwestern half of Greece is dominated by Pleistocene features that reflect cold-climate denudation, with late Holocene detail imprinted around major historical sites. By contrast, in the southeastern half of Greece, mountain crests are bare, slope soils are thin, and the lowlands support both Holocene and Pleistocene depositional sequences. Often buried, mid-Holocene sediments on the piedmonts typically record high-energy depositional environments. Alluvium and colluvium mantling Early Roman–age urban sites may attain remarkable thicknesses of 5 m or more in places such as Eleusis or ancient Corinth, but mainly reflect low-energy transfer.

Initial observations on Cyprus suggest both differences and similarities with mainland Greece. In the mountains, the picture is comparable, but without glaciers; in the lowlands, Holocene sediment supply and volume have been small, with erosion concentrated during Late Roman times, with earlier equilibrium maintenance, despite Archaic and Classical copper-smelting and shipbuilding. However, there is evidence of renewed pedogenesis, flood silt accretion, or bed-load aggradation during the Medieval period (Butzer and Harris, 2007).

In effect, the development of alluvia and colluvia varies from one region or district to another, suggesting different progressions of slope evolution. Topography, sediment supply, climate, and land cover set distinctive equilibrium conditions in most watersheds. Feedbacks are dampened or enhanced accordingly, so that outcomes are difficult to anticipate. As a result, *no single model can be proposed for Mediterranean landscape history.* Premature regional or global teleconnections introduce unproven assumptions and ignore complexity (also Schumm, 1991). Local landscape histories, based on intensive local studies, should first be properly understood and allowed to reveal their own stories.

Difficulties of Establishing Causality

The Mediterranean world represents a nonequilibrium environment, affected by both high-magnitude climatic impulses and longer-term change. At the same time, sporadic, sustained, or intensified land use can reinforce "natural" change, or create a soil environment vulnerable to climatic perturbation. Two practical examples may illustrate the scope of the problem.

Hypothetical Case A

Assume some 4 m of soil sediment burying a former Early Roman site in a watershed with gently rolling hillsides. Scale and disproportionality of change would point to a basic land-use problem, but did colluviation actually begin before abandonment (in which case high-intensity use may have been the main culprit)? Did it only begin after desertion (in response to deteriorating terrace systems or a switch to an improvident form of pastoralism)? Was it multiphased (in part responding to renewed but nonurban cultivation two centuries later)? Did extreme precipitation events trigger one or more postabandonment events in a stressed landscape? The importance of a biological record, sufficient test trenches, tight dating controls, and comprehension of land-use histories is evident.

Hypothetical Case B

Assume 2 m of colluvium at the foot of a long, stony slope with "natural" shrub and bush cover, next to a once heavily settled valley bottom, but not in visible contact with settlement residues. Do potsherds of that occupation found in the colluvium actually date its accumulation? Did the colluvium perhaps accumulate in pulses across several millennia, both before and after occupation, in response to climatic events? Can we suppose that pastoral use of the slope before, during, or after valley settlement facilitated or "forced" soil erosion? Basic questions might be resolved by uncovering cultural interdigitations during extensive valley margin trenching (if permitted by the directing archaeologist). However, uncertainties will remain, particularly if we do not know which human actors were doing what, where, and when.

Synthesis

It is challenging to isolate climatic and land-use histories as prime suspects for waves of soil erosion in the Mediterranean world. Experimental erosion plots with different land-use types are not readily converted to watersheds, because of complex patterns of sediment storage—on slopes, floodplains, or channelways (see Butzer and Helgren, 2005; Houben, 2008). It is therefore difficult to quantify the appealing notion that climatic triggering will release the latent instability of use-stressed landscapes. Holocene stream disequilibria in mid-latitude European rivers suggest that such triggering can also be quite subtle, with cut-and-fill cycles and channel changes sometimes linked by historical evidence to high-magnitude events (Dotterweich, 2005), or amenable to tree-ring "identification" via buried timbers (Spurk et al., 2002; Zolitschka et al., 2003), and yet not apparent from coarser-grained and less-sensitive pollen diagrams.

Given such contingencies, I continue to be ambivalent about how best to interpret the interplay of climatic and human impacts in Mediterranean alluvial history. On the one hand, the higher-energy processes recorded by many mid-Holocene deposits appear to suggest climatic anomalies—commonly but not necessarily playing out on a fragile cultural landscape. On the other, late Holocene counterparts are best developed in and around major sites, where colluvial components are prominent. That would imply a response to landscape intervention, but even in heavily stressed landscapes, climatic perturbations may be necessary to trigger erosion (Butzer and Harris, 2007). Given a context of local equilibrium thresholds and vegetation change, particular settlement histories and disjunctions may therefore only influence, rather than control, the timing of erosional bursts. *No generalizing criteria have yet been devised to identify Mediterranean response to climatic inputs versus human intervention.*

This reflective discussion of Mediterranean landscape history highlights the fact that there are many ambiguities, but few certainties. Climatic pulses or anomalies, in combination with exploitative land use, may accelerate change or force an equilibrium shift, unless social adaptability and resilience dampen or arrest such processes. Long-term environmental outcomes therefore become unpredictable (see Fig. 1).

The debate that began in 1969 has been salutary, and not only because it stimulated a great deal of fresh fieldwork. With the benefit of hindsight and a more dispassionate stance, it now obliges us to (1) reexamine flawed assumptions about equilibrium ecology; (2) investigate problems at multiple scales of site, valley, and district; (3) better integrate a fine-grained geoarchaeology with a proper expertise in Quaternary studies; and (4) abandon the premise that there is a simple, deductive model for Mediterranean alluviation, slope evolution, and chronology, or for the diagnosis of climate versus anthropogenic factors.

The future of geoarchaeology lies in accepting our diversity and building on the complementary nature of researchers with unlike training and experience, whether it be in geomorphology, soils, paleobiology, archaeology, or management. We might also engage in real conversations and interact in the field, including like-minded bioscience specialists, historians, and ethnographers or cultural anthropologists. Such a cross-disciplinary discourse would facilitate a better formulation of problems and an exchange of ideas as to how to resolve them, as part of the common goal of constructing an effective environmental history.

CULTURAL AND BEHAVIORAL PERSPECTIVES ON CAUSE AND EFFECT

Human perceptions and behavior are integral to understanding cause-and-effect relationships and the impact of people on environmental history. They offer alternative readings on what is, and what is not, degradation, so as to require another look at ecological equilibrium and resilience. They clarify that sound ecological behavior has been culturally embedded since at least late prehistoric times, defined by community values, economics, and the obligations of transgenerational continuity (Butzer, 2005 herein). Such behavior is a secular ideal, rather than a theological imperative, but excessive demands on a rural population, social repression, insecurity, or the ravages of war can break community spirit and lead to ecological damage as long-term strategies are abandoned in favor of short-term survival. A grasp of the rationale behind successful or failed communities is essential for a

EQUILIBRIUM RESPONSE TO ENVIRONMENTAL VARIABILITY

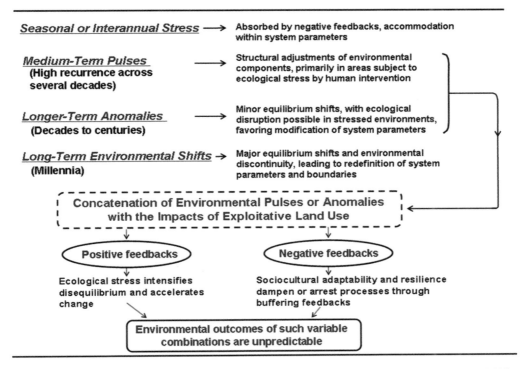

Figure 1. Equilibrium response to the recurrence, persistence, and amplitude of environmental variability. Precipitation is the major dynamic variable. The co-agency of exploitative land use will affect the feedbacks and the environmental outcome as well.

effective environmental history, and will require a deeper appreciation of human behavior, experience, and social resilience.

Cultural Preconceptions

"Degradation," as a professional evaluation, comes out of the conceptual perspective of French and British Colonial officers working in the Mediterranean during the late 1800s (for similar views to those expressed here, see Grove and Rackham, 2001). It was predicated on an incomplete appreciation of dryland ecology and a limited comprehension of traditional land-use systems. Observers were troubled by old-growth forests because they were open-spaced, and they saw mixed land-cover of woody shrubs and interspersed bushy trees as degraded (Butzer and Harris, 2007). Cultivated fields with olive groves did not match John Constable's (11 June 1776–31 March 1837) paintings of rustic harmony and were reluctantly accepted as a compromised form of nature. Indigenous farmers, alien pastoralists, or voracious goats were held responsible for the destruction of a mythical, primeval forest.

People, biota, and climate have been co-evolving for millennia (Birks et al., 1988), particularly in the Mediterranean world, so that trying to define a pre-agricultural, early or mid-Holocene datum of what is "natural" seems futile. Long pollen profiles in various countries offer proxy records of partial woodland recovery, partial reconstitution, or cultural replacement by a new array of economic hardwoods. Large-scale experimental observations show that "degraded" health of woody shrubs favors dispersal of native legumes and provides an equivalent ground cover compared to woodland (González Bernáldez, 1995). The open agropastoral landscapes of eighteenth-century Tuscany are now extensively wooded, with little or no evidence of damage. Vegetation adapts itself to the exigencies of a terrain, responding to climatic and anthropogenic pressures, and reaccommodating itself to improving conditions. Mediterranean land cover is zoned according to elevation and slope, molded to local details of roughness and substrate, within a patchwork of biotic mosaics.

These features define biotic resilience. Unless the soil mantle has been swept away, woodlands can recover, sooner rather than later, and the environment does not qualify as "destroyed." In contrast to the dichotomy of "arable" and "waste" in northwestern Europe, a typical municipal territory in the Mediterranean world embeds a threefold distinction of woodland (*monte alto*), pastoral (*monte bajo*), and cultivated domains. Depending on the changing demand for land, pastoral shrub and bush can be converted to carob and olive groves or vineyards, if not in fact dry-farm land. In the indigenous cultural perception, pastoral tracts are therefore not "degraded," but in a sort of natural fallow, which remains a productive part of a changing landscape mosaic (Butzer and Harris, 2007). This should invite "outsiders" to appreciate that there are different cultural readings of what is or is not degradation.

Furthermore, degradation and soil erosion respond to both biophysical and cultural-behavioral inputs. Since the processes and criteria will differ, this requires either cross-disciplinary experience or interactive collaboration across the disciplinary divides. What, for example, is encompassed by a concept such as land-use stress? Several social or humanistic perspectives may illustrate the explanatory possibilities of a more behavioral and inductive form of historical ecology (Butzer, 2005); they represent an extension of what Kevin Walsh (2004) has called a *cultural* geoarchaeology.

Elite Agronomic Writings

A number of legal sources, including the laws of Hammurabi, the Visigothic law code, and the Medieval Mesta, show that agropastoral activities in the wider Mediterranean world were long articulated in common law, which specified mutual agropastoral responsibilities, conflict, and cooperation (Butzer, 1988, 1994, 2005). The Roman author Varro first explained the details of small-scale, village-based transhumance of sheep, versus the long-distance, seasonal movements of animals that crossed ecozones and were controlled by squads of shepherds, working for wealthy owners of the flocks. The ecological behavior of the long-distance pastoralists was not necessarily consonant with that of the villagers engaged in local transhumance. This fact has potential applications in areas such as the Peloponnese, where uncontrolled pastoralists often represented different ethnic groups (Forbes, 2000). Yet, the seasonal presence of outside flocks has invariably had major economic significance as a source of manure. For the most part, cultivation and pastoralism have been complementary, but uncontrolled pastoralism could be destructive.

An alternative source is given by elite agronomic writings that represent early ecological perspectives and understanding (Butzer, 1993, 1994). There is a Sumerian agricultural calendar that outlines the sequential activities of the annual cycle, and probably represents a transgenerational transmission of information. Beyond some evocative images of familiar agricultural activities in the *Iliad*, Hesiod presented the annual cycle in a framework of behavioral precepts. Xenophon wrote a work for a nephew that emphasizes rational estate management, and favors improved agricultural productivity so as to stimulate general economic expansion. Theophrastus elucidated a high level of ecological comprehension and hinted at the role of common farmers in advancing cultivation practices (through crop rotation), as a matter of trial and error. Cato stands out because of his emphasis on the "good" farmer as a repository of traditional values and civic probity. The most complete treatise was written by Columella, who described soil erosion, and recommended hillside terracing and manuring, but he also supported commercial agri-

culture on large estates, which forced out small freehold farmers, as lamented by Varro and Pliny. There evidently was a protracted Roman discourse on rural problems and their underlying social and economic issues.

Islamic traditions of agronomy (ca. 930–1160 CE) can also be identified, especially in Mesopotamia and Spain. In part, its authors built on Roman and Greek experience, but went well beyond these prototypes, particularly in their comprehension of agricultural soils (Butzer, 1994). They were also engaged in agricultural expansion, in the service of a progressive elite.

These Greek, Roman, and Islamic writings were not designed to educate illiterate country people, but to explicate the intricacies of agriculture as ideally practiced in their day. In so doing, they open a window on the incremental and cumulative understanding of agroecology among rural people. The writers were cognizant of technological change as well as the human implications of intensification. A basic inference from this elite Greco-Roman discourse is that "good farming" was culturally embedded, as a civic responsibility and economic concern, rather than a philosophical or theological tenet.

Ecological Ethnohistory

In 1609, most of the residual Muslim population of Spain was expelled and their villages resettled by Christian farmers, such as in the Sierra de Espadán, north of Valencia. In this setting, Elisabeth Butzer, Juan Mateu, and I across seven seasons studied the village of Aín and some of its neighbors, based on archival history and ethnographic observation (Butzer et al., 1986). The underlying focus was on rural ecoscience, to grasp the fine grain of community decision-making and its impact on ecological behavior and the environment.

The main thrust of our findings was that sound ecological behavior is implicitly expected of each individual, and is understood to be imperative for social continuity. This can be rationalized by the strong sense of community, attachment to home, and a pride of place (Butzer, 1990, 2005). Land-use changes are made in the light of extended community discussion and with reference to community integrity, the market economy, and the responsibility to pass an undamaged resource on to future generations. Growth has been regulated by population curtailment, with out-migration considered an alternative of last resort. Trees have been explicitly cut down at a rate consonant with natural replacement. Thorny Mediterranean shrubs and brush were once burned under carefully controlled conditions; since burning is prohibited today, orchards and former pasturage are being overgrown by thorny macchia. The manure of transhumant sheep was preferred over chemical fertilizer because there were fewer pests. Slopes were terraced, and our excavations within such terraces, as well as study of valley alluvia, revealed no discernible soil erosion across four centuries; significantly, the primary stream has incised its bed because of sediment starvation.

This indigenous, rural narrative elucidates a constantly shifting repertoire of agricultural strategies in response to market opportunities, demographic growth, finite resources, and environmental problems. These in turn are predicated on values, prescribed social behavior, cumulative experience, and ongoing information exchange. This may not be an ecology palatable for idealistic modern environmentalists, but it explicates a traditional, practicable sustainability, closely tailored to a fragile Mediterranean environment.

"Good" and "Bad" Farming

As our research in Aín continued, it became clear that we were privy to an idealizing discourse that was reflective, rather than directed to us as outsiders; it sought to articulate the proper ecological behavior that was expected of the members of the community. We began to hear echoes of Cato, on the stereotypic "good farmer" and his common sense approach to ecology. That model of traditional harmony with the environment has explanatory value in its own right, and yet poor farming practices have been common in many areas for at least part of the time. Can they too be explained?

Here the Muslim experience in Aín (Butzer et al., 1986) provides a counterpoint. The district was forested and unsettled prior to the founding toward 1100 CE of a network of villages that were soon paired with small refuge castles. During the Christian (re)conquest of the Sierra de Espadán in 1242, the Muslim villagers accepted generous terms and remained in place until 1609. After a rough start with "coexistence," the area experienced population growth during the 1300s, when a number of satellite hamlets came into being.

Our record of changing ecological behavior in part derives from excavation in two preconquest castles, a postconquest hamlet (Beniali), rescue archaeology of a Muslim cemetery, and survey of a dozen other castles and abandoned hamlets. Analysis included macrobotanical remains, animal bone, snails, and soil sediments (Butzer, 2005), as well as the changing alluvial contexts of irrigation works (Butzer et al., 1986). Interpretation of the archaeology was made possible by a wealth of fragmentary and scattered archival records in Valencia and Barcelona, covering more than three centuries prior to 1609. These documents included administrative rulings, household registries, marketplace litigation, criminal cases, and general reports (Butzer et al., 1986). The resulting data composite is varied, detailed, and informative, and allows some generalizing interpretations to be made about patterns of subsistence and changing ecological behavior.

The biotic environment had not been transformed before 1363 CE. At that point, the first hamlet at Beniali was destroyed during a civil war, which was followed by a wave of soil erosion, probably as terrace walls were ruined. Reoccupation of Beniali ca. 1410 CE coincided with a decline of hardwood trees, the presence of large numbers of goats, and periodic washing of small amounts of laminated soil-derived sediment through Beniali after excessive rains. There also was torrential alluviation in the channel of the axial stream. Yet, until destruction of Beniali during a bloody uprising in 1526, the Muslim farmers planted a full array of Mediterranean crops in the valley bottom. Thereafter, the ecology deteriorated dramatically, and the uplands were treeless by 1570.

Destruction by warfare in 1363 and 1526 marked a progression to degradation, without recovery until after the expulsion in 1609. Why did these sierra villagers not bounce back? After the 1420s, there is evidence of food stress, exorbitant special taxes, increasing insecurity, and population decline. After the slaughter of 1526, the Muslims were forcibly "converted." Since forced labor was already being met with passive resistance during the mid-1400s, we infer that after 1526, the bailiffs were unable to enforce customary law in a hostile countryside, leaving the surviving woodland unprotected (Butzer, 2005).

The "captive" Muslim population then had no incentive to pursue conservationist strategies, concentrating instead on the short-term survival of their families. Community spirit and solidarity had been broken, with some adopting Christian names and surnames, others not. Socially adrift and drawn into a vicious circle of disintensification, the pace and scope of ecological damage increased. The "good farmers" of the 1340s now simply hung on and were eventually expelled without offering resistance. Conservationist land use had been rendered infeasible by extraordinary structural and economic constraints.

Ecological behavior is contextual, as the contrasting Muslim and Christian faces of Aín show. It is grounded in community experience, will, and accepted or rejected principles of common behavior. Ruinous economic demands on a rural population are counterproductive. When coupled with social repression, violence, and insecurity, they become disastrous for both economy and ecology (Fig. 2). Given such an antithesis to a "moral" economy, insecurity and warfare offer a recipe for degradation (Butzer, 2005).

Cause and effect in environmental history are ultimately about real people and living communities (Fig. 3), rather than deductive generalization. Effective study of successful or failed communities requires a certain amount of "insider" understanding of human behavior, experience, and insights, which is indispensable to evaluating ecological problems in the historical or prehistoric record. A more integrative and cross-disciplinary methodology or collaborative engagement is called for in order to better understand the cause-and-effect relationships of ecological change. This is a difficult but important charge for geoarchaeologists.

ENGAGING IN CURRENT DEBATES

A primary goal of geoarchaeology will remain an inductive and high-resolution investigation of multiscale landscape change, but more deliberate attention to cross-disciplinary issues would clarify the role of the incremental, cumulative, or "catastrophic" change that is of particular interest to environmental historians.

A host of articles and books currently proclaims "abrupt climatic change" as a prime mover of sociocultural or historical change. This new environmentalism draws from archaeological sequences on all continents to support theories for civilizational

RURAL DECISION-MAKING AND ECOLOGICAL BEHAVIOR

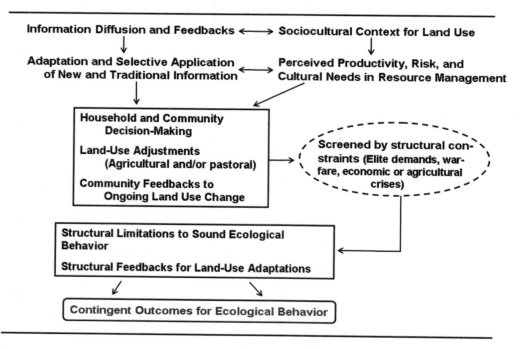

Figure 2. Rural decision-making is central to socioecological behavior. The sociocultural context includes dietary preferences, social values, intracommunity dialectics, cultural screening of priorities, as well as ritual and social restraints to innovation. In turn, local decision-making is constrained by the demands of land-owning elites and tax collectors, by warfare or insecurity, and by the growth or decline of market integration or political control.

A MODEL FOR CAUSE AND EFFECT IN ENVIRONMENTAL HISTORY

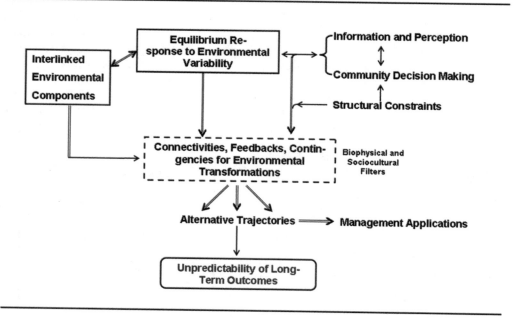

Figure 3. A simple, composite model for cause and effect in environmental history.

collapse. It can also be found as concluding applications of hard-science journal articles.

For example, the astounding title "Late Holocene drought responsible for the collapse of Old World civilizations is recorded in an Italian cave flowstone" appeared in *Geology* (Drysdale et al., 2006). Also, a deep-sea core from the Arabian Sea was claimed to identify aridification of the Near East after 2350 BCE, leading to "the formation of hierarchical societies in the overpopulated Nile Valley and Mesopotamia" (Sirocko et al., 1993, p. 324), which is incorrect on several counts. A different core from the Gulf of Oman was used to posit an abrupt climatic change ca. 2200 BCE that forced Akkadian abandonment of rain-fed agriculture in northern Mesopotamia (Cullen et al., 2000, their figure 3); this was inferred from high calcium carbonate levels as evidence of eolian dust, but it thereby reversed the criteria of Sirocko et al. (1993), and featured imprecise dating control. The common feature in these cases is the Tell Leilan "collapse" bandwagon, which itself is burdened by beginning as a story about thick volcanic ash promoting a "nuclear winter," before the tephra hypothesis was abandoned in favor of sheer aridity (see Butzer, 1997). It took science writer A. Lawler (2008) to puncture another such hypothesis, about a failure of the Indian monsoon as responsible for Indus Valley collapse (Staubwasser et al., 2003), a civilizational disaster that did not really happen. We appear to have a serious problem of reckless teleconnection, perhaps for publicity purposes, and one that seems to suggest that the peer-review system is failing repeatedly.

A different form of environmental determinism is collapse by "ecocide," when a society destroys itself by overexploiting its own resources (Diamond, 2005, p. 118). However, the arguments that support this prospect are centered on four island ecosystems. One of these is Easter Island, where Hunt (2007) showed that biotic invasion and genocide were responsible for the despoliation of Easter Island, so demolishing the case made by Diamond (2005). This pattern becomes alarming when one of the authors engaged in such "explorations" announces that "study of past cultural adaptations to persistent climate change may provide valuable perspective on possible responses of modern societies to future climate change" (deMenocal, 2001, abstract, p. 667).

Most of the more popular claims that climate has impacted history are deductive and based on data that are inadequate or misrepresented. Social resilience and adaptation are not considered, ignoring case studies of the ways in which people have confronted short- or long-term crises in the past. Such a methodology "by assertion" goes against the very grain of what anthropology stands for, and yet too few anthropological archaeologists have taken an explicit stand. Geoarchaeologists have the regional expertise to critically examine the weak factual underpinnings on which this environmentalist parade runs (Butzer, 1997; Hunt, 2007). At the very least, either local or global chronological controls are faulty, and *coincidence, even when true, does not prove causality.*

In a similar vein, anthropogenic destruction has been used to explain historical disjunction. Certainly, there is room here for serious discussion, and I am open to the possibility (e.g., Butzer,

1981b), but most diagnoses of large-scale degradation are based on incomplete, debatable, or even antiquated sources. Geoarchaeologists are among the most qualified researchers to set the record straight, but that is not always easy. The more prestigious science journals appear to prefer exuberant reviewers for best-selling books, so that there is little opportunity for effective balance.

"World-system" historians represent a special case. There are occasional claims or assumptions about degradation and its contributions to the cyclic "rise and demise" of civilizations (e.g., Chew, 2001). However, their historical interpretations may also be projected into a sober analysis of contemporary environmental issues and potential future scenarios (e.g., Chase-Dunn and Hall, 1997; Turchin, 2003). There is then reason for geoarchaeologists to engage actively with open-minded system-historians in order to communicate a more accurate and explicit environmental history, with appropriate sensitivity to system resilience. In this spirit, Figure 4 suggests a model for the systemic context of sociopolitical decline, involving both climate and degradation as potential inputs. It is unlikely that such interrelationships can be operationalized in the near future, but object-oriented simulation is now being applied to concurrently examine socioecological interactions over a broad range of such issues at various social, spatial, and temporal scales (Altaweel, 2008). Applied to Mesopotamia, the initial, stepwise results are promising.

Last but not least, there is the problem of sustainability and a sustainable global future. There is no adequate definition for this cognitive and empirical concept, which itself is being degraded by opportunistic overuse. Most of us intuitively know what is at stake, but the concept raises some uncomfortable questions. For example, can one approve of ecological modification that substitutes some of the original components and yet allows a similar or improved productivity? Are invasive taxa always bad, or can they be judged by more flexible criteria? Other issues are less ambiguous. For example, a number of well-placed individuals have claimed impending "desertification" of the Mediterranean world, leading to a generously funded European Union enterprise to assess the problem. When geoarchaeology was drawn into the effort, Grove and Rackham (2001, chapter 20) convincingly rejected the case for such desertification.

The link between geoarchaeology and sustainability is not fortuitous. Together with paleobiologists, we have the expertise to document and evaluate ten millennia of agropastoral land use or urbanism in the Mediterranean world. Nonetheless, regional productivity has not been diminished, and its coasts and cultural landscapes continue to draw artists, writers, and millions of tourists. While far from pristine, it remains uplifting. It is an endangered environment, but it has not been "destroyed" (Butzer, 2005). The Mediterranean geoarchaeological issues outlined here have become much more than an "internal debate." They are about an effective interpretation of the health of a major world ecosystem. In addition, the trajectory of Mediterranean environmental history offers a rich record of diachronic experience for reflection and prognosis. It gives testimony to both human and ecological resilience.

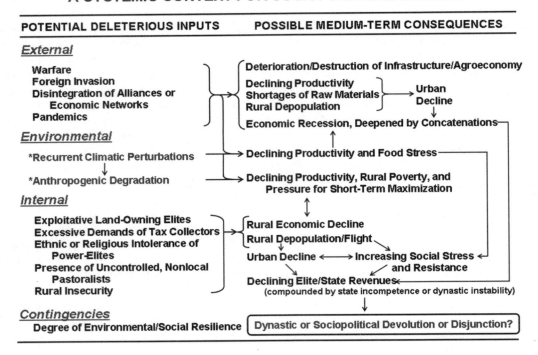

Figure 4. Sociopolitical decline can be caused by many inputs other than climatic perturbations or anthropogenic degradation (marked by *). These variables are interlinked by multiple feedbacks, as are their medium-range changes, which in this graphic representation emphasize socioeconomic problems rather than environmental history. The category of "contingencies" spans a wide range of socioecological feedbacks that help to define different forms of resilience critical to long-term outcomes.

In conclusion, this review may serve to encourage geoarchaeologists to engage more assertively in the broader academic debates of the day, not as cutters of wood for the generalizing mediators of science, but as empirical scientists, open to interdisciplinary exchange, and qualified to argue for competent and reasonable positions. We could and should play a more visible role in the emerging, multidisciplinary arena of environmental history, alongside historians and political ecologists. The popular, "new" environmental determinism about civilizational collapse in response to climatic or environmental change calls for strong voices of caution. We are qualified to monitor the ecological impacts and at least to discuss the adaptive changes central to future projections of global change and sustainability.

Those of us comfortable with the human dimensions of these issues should participate more freely in such engagements, to stake out an unimpeachable middle ground, for the benefit of upcoming generations in our academic and applied science.

ACKNOWLEDGMENTS

Several good friends over the years have contributed to my understanding of Mediterranean themes through collaboration and discussion. They include the late Juan Cuerda (Palma de Mallorca), Pascual Esteve Tomas (Aín), Elisabeth Butzer, and especially Juan Mateu (Valencia), to whom this paper is dedicated. John Bintliff provided a thoughtful critique. John Oswald converted various interactive charts into finished graphics.

REFERENCES CITED

Abbott, J.T., and Valastro, S., Jr., 1995, The Holocene alluvial records of the Chorai of Metapontum, Basilicata, and Croton, Calabria, Italy, *in* Lewin, J., Macklin, M.G., and Woodward, J.C., eds., Mediterranean Quaternary Environments: Rotterdam, Netherlands, A.A. Balkema, p. 195–206.

Altaweel, M., 2008, Investigating agricultural sustainability in northern Mesopotamia: Results produced using a socioecological modeling approach: Journal of Archaeological Science, v. 35, p. 821–835, doi:10.1016/j.jas.2007.06.012.

Beach, T., and Luzzadder-Beach, S., 2008, Geoarchaeology and plain aggradation near Kinet Höyük, Eastern Mediterranean, Turkey: Geomorphology, v. 101, p. 416–428.

Behrensmeyer, A.K., and Hill, A.P., eds., 1980, Fossils in the Making: Vertebrate Taphonomy and Paleoecology: Chicago, University of Chicago Press, 225 p.

Bell, M., 2007, Prehistoric Coastal Communities: The Mesolithic in Western Britain: York, Council for British Archaeology Research Report 149, 381 p.

Benito, G., Thornycroft, V.R., Rico, M., Sanchez-Moya, Y., and Sopena, A., 2008, Palaeoflood and floodplain records from Spain: Evidence for long-term climate variability and environmental changes: Geomorphology, v. 101, p. 68–77.

Bintliff, J., 2000, Landscape change in Classical Greece: A review, *in* Vermeulen, F., and De Dapper, M., eds., Geoarchaeology of the Landscapes of Classical Antiquity: International Colloquium Ghent 1998: Leiden, Babesch, p. 49–70.

Birks, H.H., Birks, H.J.B., Kaland, P.E., and Moe, D., eds., 1988, The Cultural Landscape: Past, Present and Future: Cambridge, UK, Cambridge University Press, 324 p.

Boardman, J., and Bell, M., 1992, Past and Present Soil Erosion: Oxford, Oxbow Books, 250 p.

Brown, A.G., 1997, Alluvial Geoarchaeology: Floodplain Archaeology and Environmental Change: Cambridge, UK, Cambridge University Press, 376 p.

Brown, A.G., 2008, Geoarchaeology, the four dimensional (4D) fluvial matrix and climatic causality: Geomorphology, v. 101, p. 278–297, doi:10.1016/j.geomorph.2008.05.021.

Butzer, K.W., 1960, Archaeology and geology in ancient Egypt: Science, v. 132, p. 1617–1624, doi:10.1126/science.132.3440.1617.

Butzer, K.W., 1961, Archäologische Fundstellen Ober- und Mittelägyptens in ihrer geologischen Landschaft: Mitteilungen, Deutsches Archäologisches Institut, Kairo, v. 17, p. 54–68.

Butzer, K.W., 1964a, Environment and Archeology: An Introduction to Pleistocene Geography: Chicago, Aldine, 524 p.

Butzer, K.W., 1964b, Pleistocene cold-climate phenomena of the island of Mallorca: Zeitschrift für Geomorphologie, v. 9, p. 7–31.

Butzer, K.W., 1967, Geomorphology and stratigraphy of the Paleolithic site of Budinho: Eiszeitalter und Gegenwart, v. 18, p. 82–103.

Butzer, K.W., 1969, Changes in the land (review of the Mediterranean valleys): Science, v. 165, p. 52–53, doi:10.1126/science.165.3888.52-a.

Butzer, K.W., 1973a, Sediments from the Acheulian site of Amanzi (Uitenhage District, South Africa): Quaternaria, v. 17, p. 299–319.

Butzer, K.W., 1973b, Geology of Nelson Bay Cave, Robberg, South Africa: South African Archaeological Bulletin, v. 28, p. 97–110, doi:10.2307/3888567.

Butzer, K.W., 1976, Early Hydraulic Civilization in Egypt: Chicago, University of Chicago Press, 134 p.

Butzer, K.W., 1981a, Cave sediments, Upper Pleistocene stratigraphy, and Mousterian facies in Cantabrian Spain: Journal of Archaeological Science, v. 8, p. 133–183, doi:10.1016/0305-4403(81)90022-4.

Butzer, K.W., 1981b, Rise and fall of Axum, Ethiopia: A geo-archaeological interpretation: American Antiquity, v. 46, p. 471–495, doi:10.2307/280596.

Butzer, K.W., 1982, Archaeology as Human Ecology: New York, Cambridge University Press, 364 p.

Butzer, K.W., 1986, Paleolithic settlement and adaptation in Cantabrian Spain: Advances in World Archaeology, v. 5, p. 201–252.

Butzer, K.W., 1988, Cattle and sheep from Old to New Spain: Annals of the Association of American Geographers, v. 78, p. 29–56, doi:10.1111/j.1467-8306.1988.tb00190.x.

Butzer, K.W., 1990, The realm of cultural-human ecology: Adaptation and change in historical perspective, *in* Turner, B.L., et al., eds., The Earth as Transformed by Human Action: New York, Cambridge University Press, p. 658–701.

Butzer, K.W., 1993, The Classical tradition of agronomic science, *in* Butzer, P.L., and Lohrmann, D., eds., Science in Western Europe and Eastern Civilization in Carolingian Times: Basel, Birkhäuser, p. 539–596.

Butzer, K.W., 1994, The Islamic tradition of agroecology: Cross-cultural experience, ideas and innovation: Ecumene: Journal of Environment, Culture and Meaning, v. 1, p. 7–50.

Butzer, K.W., 1997, Sociopolitical discontinuity in the Near East c. 2200 B.C.E.: Scenarios from Palestine and Egypt, *in* Dalfes, N., Kukla, G., and Weiss, H., eds., Third Millennium B.C. Abrupt Climatic Change and Old World Social Collapse: New York and Berlin, Springer, NATO Advanced Science Institutes Series 1: Global Environmental Change, v. 49, p. 245–295.

Butzer, K.W., 2002, Geoarchaeological implications of recent research in the Nile Delta, *in* van den Brink, E.C.M., and Levy, T.E., eds., Egypt and the Levant: Interrelations from the 4th through the Early 3rd Millennium B.C.E.: London, Leicester University Press, p. 83–97.

Butzer, K.W., 2004, Coastal eolian sands, paleosols, and Pleistocene geoarchaeology of the Southwestern Cape, South Africa: Journal of Archaeological Science, v. 31, p. 1743–1781, doi:10.1016/j.jas.2004.05.005.

Butzer, K.W., 2005, Environmental history in the Mediterranean world: Cross-disciplinary investigation of cause-and-effect for environmental degradation: Journal of Archaeological Science, v. 32, p. 1773–1800, doi:10.1016/j.jas.2005.06.001.

Butzer, K.W., 2008, Challenges for a cross-disciplinary geoarchaeology: The intersection between environmental history and geomorphology: Geomorphology, v. 101, p. 402–411, doi:10.1016/j.geomorph.2008.07.007.

Butzer, K.W., and Harris, S.E., 2007, Geoarchaeological approaches to the environmental history of Cyprus: Journal of Archaeological Science, v. 34, p. 1932–1952, doi:10.1016/j.jas.2007.01.013.

Butzer, K.W., and Helgren, D.M., 2005, Livestock, land cover, and environmental history: The Tablelands of New South Wales, Australia, 1820–1920: Annals of the Association of American Geographers, v. 95, p. 80–111, doi:10.1111/j.1467-8306.2005.00451.x.

Butzer, K.W., and Mateu, J.F., 1999, Pleistocene versus Holocene: Geomorphological change in a small but steep watershed of Mediterranean Spain, *in* Geoarqueologia i Quaternari litoral: M.P. Fumanal Memorial: Valencia, Universidad de Valencia, p. 97–111.

Butzer, K.W., Miralles, I., and Mateu, J.F., 1983, Urban geo-archaeology in Medieval Alzira (Prov. Valencia, Spain): Journal of Archaeological Science, v. 10, p. 333–349, doi:10.1016/0305-4403(83)90071-7.

Butzer, K.W., Butzer, E.K., and Mateu, J.F., 1986, Medieval Muslim communities of the Sierra de Espadán, Kingdom of Valencia: Viator: Medieval and Renaissance Studies, v. 17, p. 339–413.

Caton-Thompson, G., and Gardner, E.W., 1929, Recent work on the problem of Lake Moeris: The Geographical Journal, v. 73, p. 20–60, doi:10.2307/1782277.

Chase-Dunn, C., and Hall, T.D., 1997, Rise and Demise: Comparing World-Systems: Boulder, Colorado, Westview Press, 798 p.

Chew, S.C., 2001, World Ecological Degradation: Accumulation, Urbanization and Deforestation 3000 BC–AD 2000: Lanham, Maryland, AltaMira Press, 217 p.

Cullen, H.M., deMenocal, P.B., Hemming, S., Hemming, G., Brown, F.H., Guilderson, T., and Sirocko, F., 2000, Climate change and the collapse of the Akkadian empire: Evidence from the deep sea: Geology, v. 28, p. 379–382, doi:10.1130/0091-7613(2000)28<379:CCATCO>2.0.CO;2.

deMenocal, P.B., 2001, Cultural response to climate change during the late Holocene: Science, v. 292, p. 667–673, doi:10.1126/science.1059827.

Diamond, J., 2005, Collapse: How Societies Choose to Fail or Succeed: New York, Viking Press, 575 p.

Dotterweich, M., 2005, High-resolution reconstruction of a 1300 year old gully system in northern Bavaria, Germany: A basis for modeling long-term human-induced landscape evolution: The Holocene, v. 15, p. 994–1005, doi:10.1191/0959683605hl873ra.

Drysdale, R., Zanchetta, G., Hellstrom, J., Maas, R., Fallick, A., Pickett, M., Cartwright, I., and Piccini, L., 2006, Late Holocene drought responsible for the collapse of Old World civilizations is recorded in an Italian cave flowstone: Geology, v. 34, p. 101–104, doi:10.1130/G22103.1.

Ferring, C.R., 2001, Geoarchaeology in alluvial landscapes, *in* Goldberg, P., Holliday, V.T., and Ferring, C.R., eds., Earth Sciences and Archaeology: New York, Kluwer Academic, p. 77–106.

Forbes, H., 2000, Landscape exploitation via pastoralism: Examining the 'landscape degradation' versus sustainable economy debate in the post-Medieval Southern Argolid, *in* Halstead, P., and Frederick, C., eds., Landscape and Land Use in Postglacial Greece: Sheffield, Sheffield University Press, p. 95–109.

Fuchs, M., and Wagner, F.M., 2005, The chronostratigraphy and geoarchaeological significance of an alluvial geoarchive: Comparative OSL and AMS dating from Greece: Archaeometry, v. 47, p. 849–860, doi:10.1111/j.1475-4754.2005.00236.x.

Gladfelter, B.G., 1971, Meseta and Campiña Landforms in Central Spain: A Geomorphology of the Alto Henares Basin: University of Chicago Department of Geography Research Paper 130: Chicago, University of Chicago Press, 204 p.

Gladfelter, B.G., 1981, Developments and directions in geoarchaeology: Advances in Archaeological Method and Theory, v. 4, p. 343–364.

Goldberg, P., and Macphail, R.I., 2006, Practical and Theoretical Geoarchaeology: Oxford, Blackwell Publishing, 454 p.

Goldberg, P., Holliday, V.T., and Ferring, C.R., eds., 2001, Earth Sciences and Archaeology: New York, Kluwer Academic, 513 p.

González Bernáldez, F., 1995, Western Mediterranean land-use systems as antecedents for semiarid America, *in* Turner, B.L., Gomez Sal, A., Gonzalez Bernaldez, F., and di Castri, F., eds., Global Land Use Change: A Perspective from the Columbian Encounter: Madrid, Consejo Superior de Investigaciones Científicas, p. 131–150.

Grove, A.T., and Rackham, O., 2001, The Nature of Mediterranean Europe: An Ecological History: New Haven, Connecticut, Yale University Press, 384 p.

Helgren, D.M., 1997, Locations and landscapes of Paleolithic sites in the Semliki Rift, Zaire: Geoarchaeology: International Journal (Toronto, Ontario), v. 12, p. 337–362.

Holliday, V.T., ed., 2004, Soils in Archaeological Research: New York, Oxford University Press, 448 p.

Horden, P., and Purcell, N., 2000, The Corrupting Sea: A Study of Mediterranean History: Oxford, Blackwell Publishers, 761 p.

Hosfield, R., 2005, Individuals among palimpsest data: Fluvial landscapes in southern England, *in* Gamble, C., and Porr, M., eds., The Hominid Individual in Context: London, Routledge, p. 222–243.

Hosfield, R.T., 2011, this volume, Rolling stones: Understanding river-rolled Paleolithic artifact assemblages, *in* Brown, A.G., Basell, L.S., and Butzer, K.W., eds., Geoarchaeology, Climate Change, and Sustainability: Geological Society of America Special Paper 476, doi:10.1130/2011.2476(04).

Houben, P., 2008, Scale linkage and contingency effects of field-scale and hillslope-scale controls of long-term soil erosion: Anthropogeomorphic sediment flux in agricultural loess watersheds of southern Germany: Geomorphology, v. 101, p. 172–191, doi:10.1016/j.geomorph.2008.06.007.

Howard, A.J., Macklin, M.G., and Passmore, D.G., eds., 2003, Alluvial Archaeology in Europe: Lisse, Swets and Zeillinger, 313 p.

Hunt, T.L., 2007, Rethinking Easter Island's ecological catastrophe: Journal of Archaeological Science, v. 34, p. 485–502, doi:10.1016/j.jas.2006.10.003.

Huntington, E., 1910, The burial of Olympia: A study in climate and history: The Geographical Journal, v. 36, p. 657–686, doi:10.2307/1776838.

Jameson, M.H., Runnels, C.N., and Van Andel, T.H., 1994, A Greek Countryside: The Southern Argolid from Prehistory to the Present Day: Stanford, Stanford University Press, 654 p.

Kirkby, A., and Kirkby, M.J., 1976, Geomorphic processes and the surface survey of archaeological sites in semi-arid areas, *in* Davidson, D.A., and Shackley, M.L., eds., Geoarchaeology: Earth Science and the Past: London, Duckworth, p. 229–253.

Klein, R.G., 1987, Problems and prospects in understanding how early people exploited animals, *in* Nitecki, M.H., and Nitecki, D.V., eds., The Evolution of Human Hunting: New York, Plenum, p. 11–45.

Klein, R.G., 1989, Biological and behavioral perspectives on modern human origins in southern Africa, *in* Mellars, P., and Stringer, C., eds., The Human Revolution: Edinburgh, Edinburgh University Press, p. 529–546.

Lais, R., 1941, Über Höhlensedimente: Quartär, v. 3, p. 56–108.

Lasca, N.P., and Donahue, J., eds., 1990, Archaeological Geology of North America: Boulder, Colorado, Geological Society of America, Geology of North America, Centennial Special Volume 4, 617 p.

Laville, H., Rigaud, J.P., and Sackett, J., 1980, Rock Shelters of the Perigord: New York, Academic Press, 371 p.

Lawler, A., 2008, Indus collapse: The end or the beginning of an Asian culture?: Science, v. 320, p. 1281–1282, doi:10.1126/science.320.5881.1281.

Lewin, J., Macklin, M.G., and Woodward, J.C., eds., 1995, Mediterranean Quaternary River Environments: Rotterdam, Netherlands, A.A. Balkema, 313 p.

Limbrey, S., 1975, Soil Science and Archaeology: London, Academic Press, 384 p.

Macklin, M.G., Johnstone, E., and Lewin, J., 2005, Pervasive and long-term forcing of Holocene river instability and flooding in Great Britain by centennial-scale climate change: The Holocene, v. 15, no. 7, p. 937–943, doi:10.1191/0959683605hl867ft.

Marsh, G.P., [1864] 1965, Man and Nature, or Physical Geography as Modified by Human Action (edited by D. Lowenthal): Cambridge, Massachusetts, Harvard University Press, 472 p.

Needham, S., and Macklin, M.G., eds., 1992, Alluvial Archaeology in Britain: Oxford, Oxbow Press, 396 p.

Nocete, F., Alex, E., Nieto, J.M., Saenz, R., and Bayona, M.R., 2005, An archaeological approach to regional environmental pollution in the south-western Iberian Peninsula related to third millennium BC mining and metallurgy: Journal of Archaeological Science, v. 32, p. 1566–1576, doi:10.1016/j.jas.2005.04.012.

Pope, K.O., and Van Andel, T.H., 1984, Late Quaternary alluviation and soil formation in the Southern Argolid: Its history, causes and archaeological implications: Journal of Archaeological Science, v. 11, p. 281–306, doi:10.1016/0305-4403(84)90012-8.

Pope, M.I., and Roberts, M.B., 2011, this volume, The Valdoe: A new middle Pleistocene locality in the Boxgrove paleolandscape (West Sussex, UK), *in* Brown, A.G., Basell, L.S., and Butzer, K.W., eds., Geoarchaeology, Climate Change, and Sustainability: Geological Society of America Special Paper 476, doi:10.1130/2011.2476(02).

Rapp, G., Jr., and Gifford, J., 1985, Archaeological Geology: New Haven, Connecticut, Yale University Press, 435 p.

Rapp, G.R., Jr., and Hill, C., 2006, Geoarchaeology (revised ed.): New Haven, Connecticut, Yale University Press, 339 p.

Renfrew, C., 1976, Archaeology and the earth sciences, *in* Davidson, D.A., and Shackley, M.L., eds., Geoarchaeology: Earth Science and the Past: London, Duckworth, p. 1–5.

Ricklis, R.A., and Blum, M.D., 1997, The geoarchaeological record of Holocene sea level change and human occupation of the Texas Gulf Coast: Geoarchaeology: International Journal (Toronto, Ontario), v. 12, p. 287–314.

Rosen, A.M., 1986, Cities of Clay: The Geoarcheology of Tells: Chicago, University of Chicago Press, 167 p.

Schuldenrein, J., Wright, R.P., Mughal, M.R., and Khan, M.A., 2004, Landscapes, soils, and mound histories of the Upper Indus Valley, Pakistan: New insights on the Holocene environments near ancient Harappa: Journal of Archaeological Science, v. 31, p. 777–797, doi:10.1016/j.jas.2003.10.015.

Schumm, S., 1991, To Interpret the Earth: Ten Ways to Be Wrong: New York, Cambridge University Press, 144 p.

Sirocko, F., Sarnthen, M., Erlenkeuser, H., Lange, H., Arnold, M., and Duplessy, J.C., 1993, Century scale vents in climate over the past 24,000 years: Nature, v. 364, p. 322–324.

Spurk, M., Leuschner, H.H., Baillie, M.G.L., Briffa, K.R., and Friedrich, M., 2002, Depositional frequency of German subfossil oaks: Climatically and non-climatically induced fluctuations in the Holocene: The Holocene, v. 12, p. 707–715, doi:10.1191/0959683602hl583rp.

Staubwasser, M., Sirocko, F., Grootes, F., and Segl, M., 2003, Climate change at the 4.2 ka BP termination of the Indus valley civilization and Holocene South Asian monsoon variability: Geophysical Research Letters, v. 30, p. 1425–1428, doi:10.1029/2002GL016822.

Stein, J.K., and Farrand, W.R., eds., 2001, Archaeological Sediments in Context: Salt Lake City, University of Utah Press, 304 p

Turchin, P., 2003, Historical Dynamics: Why States Rise and Fall: Princeton, New Jersey, Princeton University Press, 254 p.

van Andel, T.H., Zangger, E., and Demitrack, A., 1990, Land use and soil erosion in prehistoric and historical Greece: Journal of Field Archaeology, v. 17, p. 379–396, doi:10.2307/530002.

Vita-Finzi, C., 1969, The Mediterranean Valleys: Geological Changes in Historical Times: Cambridge, UK, Cambridge University Press, 140 p.

Passmore, D.G., Waddington, C., van der Schriek, T., Davis, B., Tetlow, E., Smith, D., and Cotton, J., 2011, this volume, Geoarchaeology and archaeological landscapes in the River Till valley, northern England, *in* Brown, A.G., Basell, L.S., and Butzer, K.W., eds., Geoarchaeology, Climate Change, and Sustainability: Geological Society of America Special Paper 476, doi:10.1130/2011.2476(10).

Walsh, K., 2004, Caring about sediments: The role of cultural geoarchaeology in Mediterranean landscapes: Journal of Mediterranean Archaeology, v. 17, no. 2, p. 223–245, doi:10.1558/jmea.17.2.223.65539.

Waters, M.R., 1992, Principles of Geoarchaeology: A North American Perspective: Tucson, University of Arizona Press, 398 p.

Wells, B., Runnels, C., and Zangger, E., 1990, The Berbati-Limnes Archaeological Survey: Opuscula Atheniensia, v. 18, p. 207–238.

Woodward, J.C., and Goldberg, P., 2001, The sedimentary records in Mediterranean rockshelters and caves: Archives of environmental change: Geoarchaeology: International Journal (Toronto, Ontario), v. 16, p. 327–354.

Zangger, E., 1993, The Geoarchaeology of the Argolid: Berlin, German Archaeological Institute Athens, 149 p.

Zolitschka, B., Behre, K.E., and Schneider, J., 2003, Human and climatic impact on the environment as derived from colluvial, fluvial and lacustrine archives—Examples from the Bronze Age to the Migration period, Germany: Quaternary Science Reviews, v. 22, p. 81–100, doi:10.1016/S0277-3791(02)00182-8.

MANUSCRIPT ACCEPTED BY THE SOCIETY 3 AUGUST 2010

The Geological Society of America
Special Paper 476
2011

The Valdoe: A new Middle Pleistocene locality in the Boxgrove paleolandscape (West Sussex, UK)

Matthew I. Pope
Mark B. Roberts
Institute of Archaeology, University College London, 31-34 Gordon Square, London WC1H 0PY, UK

ABSTRACT

Recent excavations at the Valdoe Quarry in West Sussex have provided a new locality for the study of human activity and environment in the Middle Pleistocene. Fieldwork and analysis, funded through the Aggregates Levy Sustainability Fund, were undertaken at the Valdoe Quarry ahead of a renewed and final stage of gravel extraction at the site. Through geological mapping, sedimentary sequences entirely comparable to those at the Boxgrove Quarry, 6 km to the east, were sampled in order to determine their archaeological potential and characterize the associated paleoenvironmental conditions. This paper provides an introduction to this work ahead of detailed publication of the results. Initial results suggest that the site represents a locality within the same contemporary recessional paleolandscape as the main Boxgrove site.

INTRODUCTION

The Valdoe Quarry is located approximately midway along the line of the Westbourne-Arundel Raised Beach, mapped by the Boxgrove Project team across a 26 km stretch of the upper coastal plain of West Sussex. Previous investigations, both within and immediately adjacent to the quarry, have shown that sediments known to preserve evidence of human activity contemporary with occupation at the main Boxgrove site might be preserved within the quarry (Pope, 2004b; Roberts and Pope, 2009). If the extensions of these paleolandsurfaces were also present in the areas of planned extraction, then artifact scatters were at substantial risk of destruction. The Valdoe Assessment Survey was conceived to meet this potential threat as an exercise in determining the presence of archaeology at the site and characterizing its environmental context. The significance of lithic scatters from the site has been previously published (Pope et al., 2009); this paper provides an overview of the site in its immediate geoarchaeological context and paleogeographic setting.

CIRCUMSTANCES OF DISCOVERY

The Valdoe Quarry is situated on the northern margins of the Sussex Coastal Plain at the foot of the South Downs, 4 km northeast of Chichester and 6 km to the west of the Boxgrove Middle Pleistocene locality (SU487108, Fig. 1). From a purely topographical perspective, it therefore occupies an identical position to other key Middle Pleistocene localities associated with the Westbourne-Arundel Raised Beach. These sites include, in addition to Boxgrove: Slindon Bottom, Penfolds Pit, Manor Farm, and West Stoke (Roberts and Pope, 2009; Pope, 2001; Roberts and Pope, 2009; Woodcock, 1981).

The site was discovered when a small team from the Boxgrove Project, led by Simon Parfitt, inspected the quarry during October 1996. At the time, gravel extraction in the northern part of the quarry had largely ceased, leaving a series of silt ponds separated by 5 m baulks. No sections showing the geological sequence below the gravel were visible except in a small drainage ditch cut to the south of one of the main silt ponds. This

Pope, M.I., and Roberts, M.B., 2011, The Valdoe: A new Middle Pleistocene locality in the Boxgrove paleolandscape (West Sussex, UK), *in* Brown, A.G., Basell, L.S., and Butzer, K.W., eds., Geoarchaeology, Climate Change, and Sustainability: Geological Society of America Special Paper 476, p. 15–22, doi:10.1130/2011.2476(02). For permission to copy, contact editing@geosociety.org. © 2011 The Geological Society of America. All rights reserved.

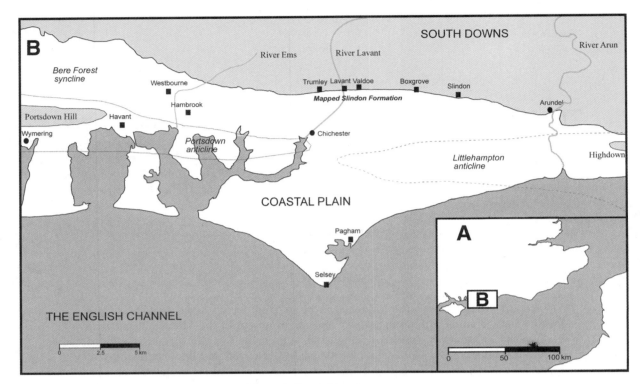

Figure 1. General location map.

section, now named Valdoe test pit 1, clearly presented a sediment sequence identical to that recorded at a number of locations at the main Boxgrove site (Fig. 2). All major sedimentary units—the Slindon Sands, The Slindon Silts, the Fe/Mn horizons, and Lower Brickearth Unit (Roberts, 1986; Roberts and Parfitt, 1999)—were seen in conformable order within the section, and the section was closely sampled for small mammal and micropaleontological remains. Further visits to the quarry by the Boxgrove Project team recorded other sand sections being exposed through continued extraction to the south of the site; however, these lay in an area where the Slindon Silts had been removed during the deposition of the solifluction gravels of the Eartham Formation (Roberts and Parfitt, 1999). No further exposure of the archaeologically significant Slindon Silts was made until the current phase of work.

During the course of the Boxgrove Raised Beach Mapping Project (RBMP) (Roberts and Pope, 2009)a series of borehole investigations was carried out close to the Valdoe Quarry in the field immediately to the west of the quarry. This field is referred to in the text as the Valdoe Field (Fig. 3). Analysis of cores recovered during this survey confirmed that, in all probability, a major portion of the quarry lay within an area formerly underlain by terrestrial and marine deposits of the Slindon Formation (Roberts and Pope, 2009). These deposits were shown, through micropaleontology and sediment composition analysis, to be broadly identical to sediments of the Boxgrove sequence. The sequence was shown to clearly include the key horizons (Units 4b, 4c, 5a, and

Figure 2. Photograph of Slindon Silts recorded at the Valdoe in 1996.

6b) that preserved in situ knapping debris, butchered fauna, and hominin remains at the original Middle Pleistocene site (Roberts and Parfitt, 1999). Now complete, the RBMP has established that this suite of deposits, preserved at both Boxgrove and Valdoe, forms only a part of an extensive, 26-km-wide preserved paleolandscape. On the basis of the RBMP work alone, it was not possible to determine whether paleolandsurfaces associated with the Westbourne-Arundel Raised Beach contained preserved artifact

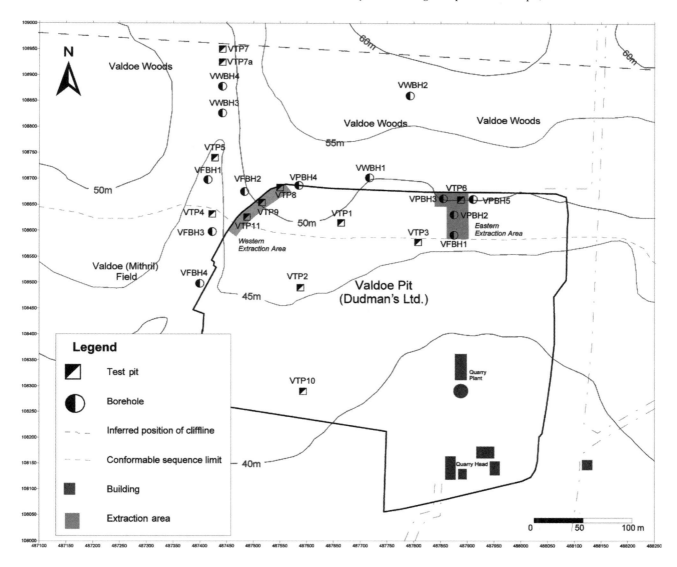

Figure 3. Valdoe Quarry Map showing extraction, test pit, and borehole locations.

scatters and butchered animal to the exceptional degree as the main Boxgrove site. Across much of this area, such signatures, if present, were shown to have been buried at great depths (up to 17 m) (Roberts and Pope, 2009; Parfitt, 1998). Opportunities to sample these land surfaces were therefore only possible within some dry valleys and through rare opportunities presented by gravel extraction.

In 2005, extraction of gravel and marine sand was set to be renewed within the northern portion of the Valdoe Quarry. This work was to cover an area of haul road toward the northern end of the site, ~250 m × 100 m in extent (Fig. 3). Quarrying, once initiated, was to proceed through mechanical extraction at a rapid pace and involved the complete removal of deposits likely to contain both in situ archaeology and paleoenvironmental material.

The renewed extraction clearly represented a potential threat to a then-undetermined archaeological record. Visits to the pit during May 2005 to assess the archaeological potential of the threatened area identified the presence of the upper part of the conformable Boxgrove sequence, showing decalcified gravel overlying calcareous chalk gravel and Brickearth Unit. The Raised Beach Mapping Project established that this sequence is invariably associated with good preservation of the underlying, archaeologically sensitive paleolandsurfaces; the calcareous nature of the lower deposits also suggested a good likelihood of preservation of mammal fauna and microfauna (Roberts and Pope, 2009; Parfitt, 1998; Whittaker, 1999). It was in response to this immediate threat that the Valdoe Assessment Survey was undertaken as a measured geoarchaeological investigation aimed at determining the presence of paleoenvironmental and artifactual evidence.

THE 2006 INVESTIGATIONS

Field work was initiated in January 2006, and the first phase was aimed at undertaking a full topographic survey and a series of boreholes across the threatened area and its immediate environs. The aim of this phase was to develop a detailed sedimentological model of the site, which, when incorporating further results from the Raised Beach Mapping Project, could be utilized to determine the exact extent of archaeologically sensitive horizons. In addition, paleoenvironmental samples were taken for assessment of potential. Guided by this work a second phase of field work was undertaken in October 2007; this work was more archaeological in nature and consisted of a series of seven test-pit excavations aimed at the recovery of artifactual material and further paleoenvironmental samples.

ENVIRONMENTAL AND SEDIMENTARY CONTEXT

The geoarchaeological investigations of the Valdoe Quarry revealed a sedimentary sequence entirely comparable to that of the wider Boxgrove paleolandscape, established both through research at the main Boxgrove site (Roberts, 1986; Roberts and Parfitt, 1999) and through the Raised Beach Mapping Project (Roberts and Pope, 2009). What needed to be determined through the Valdoe Assessment Survey was the exact nature and original distribution of these horizons and the extent to which they had been removed through gravel extraction during earlier phases of extraction. The project would also determine the presence and nature of human activity at the site and the degree to which the environmental signatures at the Valdoe were similar to those determined at other locations across the Westbourne-Arundel Raised Beach.

Figure 4 presents a correlated, composite model of the geology for two major north–south transects across the investigated locality. Across much of the site, it shows a conformable sedimentary sequence encompassing members of both the Slindon and Eartham Formations. In addition, the upper section shows the deep development of calcareous and decalcified gravels overlying the Slindon Formation through the area of the Valdoe Quarry, reflecting its situation at the foot of a downland ridge, which rises to the north of the site. The lower section shows the north-south arrangement of sediments within the Valdoe dry valley to the immediate west of the quarry. Here, fluvial and solifluction processes associated with the formation of the dry valley have effectively removed a significant extent of the solifluction gravels, leaving only 1–2 m of gravel cover over the archaeological horizons of the Slindon Formation. Critically, dry valley processes have not affected the overall degree of preservation of the underlying sediment, which was found to still be calcareous and geochemically identical to the deposit found within the main quarry area (Pope et al., 2009). As shown in these sections, six key sedimentary units of potential archaeological significance were encountered at the Valdoe. These are Unit 4b (lagoonal silts), Unit 4c (paleosol), Unit 5a (marsh deposits), Unit 5b (calcareous silts), Unit 6 (the Lower Brickearth Unit) and Unit 10 (calcareous gravels).

Archaeology of the Valdoe

In total, 115 artifacts were recovered from six of the 11 test pits investigated during the course of the assessment. Where test pits revealed fine-grained components of the sedimentary sequence, excavation was undertaken by hand in 50 mm spits (Fig. 5). All excavated artifacts were three-dimensionally recorded within each test pit, along with further information on position and orientation to assess site formation processes. The assemblage was then subjected to taphonomic, metrical, and technological analysis following procedures utilized before in the study of artifacts from the main Boxgrove site (Schick, 1987, 1992; Roberts et al., 1997; Roberts and Parfitt, 1999; Pope, 2002). These aimed at assessing site formation processes, assemblage integrity, and technological affinity and behavior in order to deliver a data set directly comparable with previous studies of material from the main Boxgrove site, subsequent investigations at Slindon, and future discoveries of artifactual material elsewhere in the Boxgrove paleolandscape.

The close similarity of the Valdoe sedimentary sequence with that previously recorded at Boxgrove and the wider extent of the Westbourne-Arundel Raised Beach provided a broad stratigraphic framework through which the archaeology could be examined. It was therefore possible, even during the initial stages of excavation, to record artifacts within the standard Boxgrove stratigraphic sequence and recognize immediate similarities between artifact scatters at the Valdoe site and those from the main Boxgrove site. Artifacts found within the surface layer of Unit 4c were fresh, lightly patinated, distributed thinly but apparently in situ across the surface of the Slindon Silts, and primarily related to later stages of biface manufacture (Fig. 6). This overall situation was characteristic for the majority of investigated localities preserving the Unit 4c horizon at Boxgrove, and yet in the case of the Valdoe, this apparent similarity had to be proved, not assumed. The analysis had to begin from first principles by determining through taphonomic analysis that we were in fact dealing with primary, in situ signatures at the Valdoe site before determining, on a technological basis, the degree of similarity between the assemblage and other scatters of low-density biface manufacturing debitage from the Boxgrove site. Addressing these issues thoroughly was central to achieving two of the major aims of the project: an accurate assessment of what had been lost in the course of gravel extraction at the Valdoe site and a correct interpretation of human behavior at the site.

Technological Summary

The Valdoe lithic assemblage is of modest size and lacks formal tools or core form, and yet it is characteristic enough for us to be confident in describing the technological affinities of the material and in making observations of the chaîne opératoire that

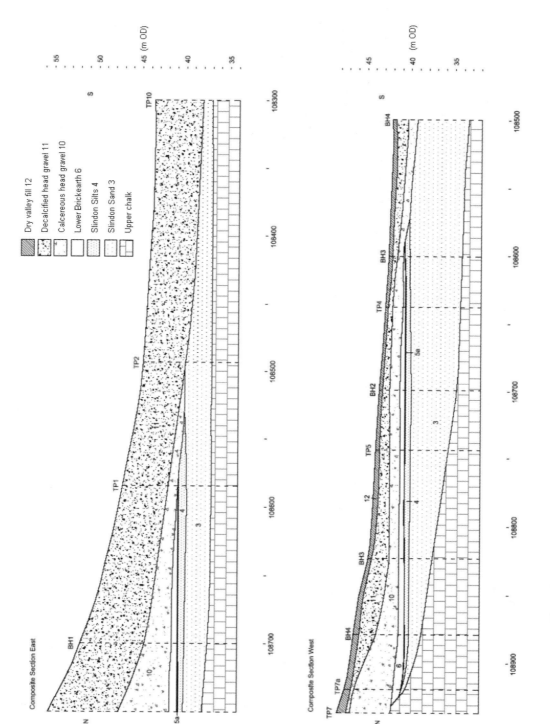

Figure 4. Two composite north-south sections of the Slindon and Eartham Formations at the Valdoe site.

Figure 5. Excavations of Unit 4c at test pit 4.

can contribute to wider discussions of tool-using behavior within the wider Boxgrove paleolandscape. The large, cortical hard-hammer flakes that constitute the primary debitage could relate equally to the initial stages of core reduction or biface manufacture; it is however clear from the smaller debitage components that virtually all reduction within the Valdoe assemblage was geared toward the manufacture of hand axes. As with Boxgrove and Slindon, the zone immediately adjacent to the Boxgrove cliff appears to contain larger proportions of primary debitage, while the open grassland of the Unit 4c paleosol contains predominantly material from the later stages of biface manufacture relating to the modification or resharpening of existing hand axes. Because material from this unit appears to be preserved in situ, it offers the potential to move from analysis of site formation processes and technology toward the integration of the Valdoe evidence into wider models of tool- and landscape-use behavior of Middle Pleistocene hominins within the wider Boxgrove paleolandscape.

CONCLUSIONS

The Valdoe Assessment Survey offered the opportunity to sample a new locale now firmly tied into the wider paleolandscape of the Westbourne-Arundel Raised Beach. As such, it offers the chance to examine the behavior of Boxgrove hominin groups outside of the confines of the Boxgrove quarry, in a part of the landscape that may offer different ecological condition and affordances. The exact differences in the ecological conditions between the Valdoe and the Boxgrove localities are now being established through a program of research. Initial findings suggest that the Valdoe was seasonally wetter, with more open vegetation and less local variation in ground conditions (Pope et al., 2009). The low-density nature of the archaeology and the apparent lack of dense activity areas might suggest that the Valdoe area presented a less attractive locale. However, biface finds

made historically within the immediate environs of the Valdoe site, notably at east Lavant (Woodcock, 1981; Wymer, 1999), suggest not only that larger sites remain preserved outside of the quarry, but that the estuary of the paleo-Lavant to the immediate west of the Valdoe site may have offered a localized preferred habitat. The estuarine area may possibly have provided a concentration of game or natural break in game movement, easy access to the wooded environments of the South Downs and a source of freshwater. It might be the case that human activity within the Valdoe area was concentrated in restricted parts of the paleolandscape to a greater degree than at Boxgrove, and differences in asymmetry in the on-site/off-site record reflect human responses to habitat heterogeneity. We intend to investigate this poorly researched part of the Boxgrove paleolandscape to test this possibility further.

It now possible to establish with little doubt that the suite of fine-grained sediments and overlying solifluction gravels recorded at the Valdoe represents the lateral extension of the Slindon and Eartham Formations recorded at Boxgrove, and that these sediments also contain both in situ and disturbed signatures of human activity, and that they exist within a behavioral chaîne opératoire directly comparable to that established for the main Boxgrove site. The talus slopes of the degraded chalk cliff at the Valdoe site continue to serve as the source of all raw material at the site and as a focus for the full range of knapping activities, from initial rough-out of biface performs to the manufacture of finished bifaces and their reworking. Within the wider paleolandscape, at both the level of Unit 4c and Unit 6, evidence for the routine transportation and modification of these tools is indicated by the low-density carpets of late-stage thinning debitage, which form a near-continuous background scatter (Roebroeks et al., 1992). Building on the multidisciplinary, geoarchaeological approach developed for the Valdoe survey, this new and potentially productive component of the ancient landscape can be brought into focus.

ACKNOWLEDGMENTS

The project staff would like to thank English Heritage for their support and guidance in putting this project together through the Aggregates Levy Sustainability Fund scheme and helping to bring it to a successful conclusion. The authors would like to extend thanks to the following people and organizations for their assistance in making the project possible and contributing to its success: Dudman Ltd. and the Goodwood Estate for allowing access to the quarry and for supplying use of equipment and resources, but especially to Neil Brundel (quarry manager) for his interest and support throughout the project; and Worthing Archaeological Society for the participation in the excavation of TP5, especially to Keith Bolton, Gil Turner, Pete Skilton, and Bob Turner for the use of their skills, demonstrating the valuable level of professional expertise to be found in British amateur archaeological societies. Thanks are also due to Darren Norris, Kevin Dearling, Kate Russell, Elinor Croxall,

Figure 6. Artifacts from the Valdoe excavations. (A) Primary and secondary flakes from the base of the cliff at TP7. (B) Biface thinning flakes from Unit 4c.

Victoria Ling, Jane Harrison, and Rob Dinnis for participation in the first season of excavation and to Simon Parfitt, Richard Preece, John Whittaker, Phil Gibbard, Megan Attree, Geoff Smith, Justin Russell, and Sharon Gerber for their assistance in postexcavation work.

REFERENCES CITED

Pope, M.I., 2001, New investigations at Slindon Bottom Palaeolithic Site, West Sussex: An interim report: Lithics, v. 22, p. 3–10.

Pope, M.I., 2002, The Significance of Biface-Rich Assemblages: An Examination of Behavioural Controls on Lithic Assemblage Formation in the Lower Palaeolithic [Ph.D. thesis]: Southampton, University of Southampton, 362 p.

Pope, M.I., 2004a, Behavioural implications of biface discard: Assemblage variability and land-use at the middle Pleistocene site of Boxgrove, *in* Lithics in Action: Lithic Studies Society Occasional Paper 24: Oxford, Oxbow Books.

Pope, M.I., 2004b, The Raised Beach Mapping Project: Archaeology International, v. 6, p. 6.

Pope, M.I., Roberts, M.B., Maxted, A., and Jones, P., 2009, Lower Palaeolithic archaeology at the Valdoe, West Sussex: Proceedings of the Prehistoric Society, v. 75, p. 56–86.

Roberts, M.B., 1986, Excavation of a Lower Palaeolithic site at Amey's Eartham Pit, Boxgrove, West Sussex: A preliminary report: Proceedings of the Prehistoric Society. v. 52, p. 215–245.

Roberts, M.B., and Parfitt, S.A., 1999, Boxgrove: A Middle Pleistocene hominid site at Eartham Quarry, Boxgrove, West Sussex: English Heritage Archaeological Report 17, 565 p.

Roberts, M.B., and Pope, M.I., 2009, The archaeological and sedimentary records from Boxgrove and Slindon, *in* Briant, R.M., Bates, M.R., Hosfield, R.T., and Wenban-Smith, F.F., eds., The Quaternary of the Solent Basin and West Sussex Raised Beaches: London, Quaternary Research Association Field Guide, p. 96–122.

Roberts, M.B., Parfitt, S.A., Pope, M.I., and Wenban-Smith, F.F., 1997, Boxgrove, West Sussex: Rescue excavations of a Lower Palaeolithic landsurface (Boxgrove Project B, 1989–91): Proceedings of the Prehistoric Society, v. 63, p. 303–358.

Roebroeks, W., De Loecker, D., and Hennekens, P., 1992, 'A veil of stones': On the interpretation of an early Palaeolithic low-density scatter at Maastricht Belvedere (The Netherlands): Analecta Praehistorica Leidensia, v. 25, p. 1–16.

Schick, K., 1987, Modeling the formation of Early Stone Age artifact concentrations: Journal of Human Evolution, v. 16, p. 789–807, doi:10.1016/0047-2484(87)90024-8.

Schick, K., 1992, Geoarchaeological analysis of an Acheulean site at Kalambo Falls, Zambia: Geoarchaeology: International Journal (Toronto, Ontario), v. 7, p. 1–26.

Woodcock, A., 1981, The Lower and Middle Palaeolithic Periods in Sussex: British Archaeological Report 94, 418 p.

Wymer, J.J., 1999, The Lower Palaeolithic Occupation of Britain: Salisbury, UK, Wessex Archaeology (with English Heritage), 2 vols., 234 p.

Manuscript Accepted by the Society 3 August 2010

The Geological Society of America
Special Paper 476
2011

The geoarchaeology of Paleolithic rivers of southwest Britain

Laura S. Basell*
Antony G. Brown*
*Paleoenvironmental Laboratory University of Southampton (PLUS), School of Geography, Highfields Campus,
University of Southampton, Southampton SO17 1BJ, UK*

Robert T. Hosfield*
*Department of Archaeology, School of Human & Environmental Sciences, University of Reading, Whiteknights, Reading,
RG6 6AB, UK*

Phillip S. Toms*
Department of Natural and Social Sciences, University of Gloucestershire, Cheltenham, GL50 4AZ, UK

ABSTRACT

In Britain, the majority of Lower and Middle Paleolithic archaeological finds come from river terrace deposits. The impressive "staircase" terrace sequences of southeast England, and research facilitated by aggregate extraction have provided a considerable body of knowledge about the terrace chronology and associated archaeology in that area. Such research has been essential in considering rates of uplift, climatic cycles, archaeological chronologies, and the landscapes in which hominins lived. It has also promoted the view that southeast England was a major hominin route into Britain. By contrast, the terrace deposits of the southwest have been little studied. The Palaeolithic Rivers of South West Britain (PRoSWEB) project employed a range of geoarchaeological methodologies to address similar questions at different scales, focusing on the rivers Exe, Axe, Otter, and the paleo-Doniford, all of which were located south of the maximum Pleistocene glacial limit (marine oxygen isotope stage [MIS] 4–2). Preliminary analysis of the fieldwork results suggests that although the evolution of these catchments is complex, most conform to a standard staircase-type model, with the exception of the Axe, and, to a lesser extent, the paleo-Doniford, which are anomalous. Although the terrace deposits are less extensive than in southeast Britain, differentiation between terraces does exist, and new dates show that some of these terraces are of great antiquity (MIS 10+). The project also reexamined the distribution of artifacts in the region and confirms the distributional bias to the river valleys, and particularly the rivers draining southward to the paleo–Channel River system. This distribution is consistent with a model of periodic occupation of the British peninsula

---

*E-mails: L.S.Basell@soton.ac.uk; Tony.Brown@soton.ac.uk; r.hosfield@rdg.ac.uk; ptoms@glos.ac.uk.

Basell, L.S., Brown, A.G., Hosfield, R.T., and Toms, P.S., 2011, The geoarchaeology of Paleolithic rivers of southwest Britain, *in* Brown, A.G., Basell, L.S., and Butzer, K.W., eds., Geoarchaeology, Climate Change, and Sustainability: Geological Society of America Special Paper 476, p. 23–36, doi:10.1130/2011.2476(03).

along and up the major river valleys from the paleo–Channel River corridor. These data have a direct impact on our understanding of the paleolandscapes of the southwest region, and therefore our interpretations of the Paleolithic occupation of the edge of the continental landmass.

ARCHAEOLOGICAL CONTEXT: PALEOLITHIC ARCHAEOLOGY IN SOUTHWEST ENGLAND

Over the last few years, Paleolithic archaeology has been revitalized, and our knowledge of the chronology and ecology of hominin presence in the British Isles has greatly improved. This is partly part due to large research projects such as the Stage Three Project (van Andel and Davies, 2004), Ancient Human Occupation of Britain Project (AHOB), and Environmental Factors in the Chronology of Human Evolution and Dispersal program (EFCHED). The increase in activity and importance of Paleolithic archaeology, which started with discoveries and excavation at Boxgrove (Roberts and Parfitt, 1999), has continued with important discoveries at Lynford (Lord, 2002; Boismier et al., 2003; Schreve, 2006), Happisburgh, and Pakefield (Parfitt et al., 2005, 2010), the last of which pushed back the first hominin presence in the UK to around 700,000 yr B.P. (marine oxygen isotope stage [MIS] 17 or 19). All of these sites are in southeast England. The only site of comparative importance in the southwestern peninsula is Kent's Cavern, where recent studies have suggested a hominin presence before MIS 10, and possibly as early as MIS 13 (Proctor et al., 2005). Roe's 1981 summary distribution of Lower and Middle Paleolithic find spots in England (Fig. 1) reveals a marked increase in density toward the southeast of England. This pattern remains today, and closer examination reveals that the find distribution is strongly related to the geomorphology of the Thames, the Great Ouse–Breckland (Cambridge region), and Solent Rivers, where the majority of finds are located in the terrace gravels of these rivers. An undoubted bias in this distribution is due to the presence of abundant flint, derived from the Cretaceous chalk, in southeast England, and it is only recently that other rock types, such as quartzites, have been recognized as having been used to any significant extent (Howard et al., 2007).

The archaeological records from Kent's Cavern, other cave sites in Devon and North Somerset, and even the Scilly Isles, which today lie 26 miles (42 km) off Land's End, as well as almost every southwest river valley (Hosfield et al., 2008), indicate some hominin presence at various times during the Pleistocene. It could be argued that the lower find densities in the southwest are related to a lower frequency of visitation or habitation by hominins, but this is not straightforward for two reasons. First, as Wymer (1999) pointed out, the vast majority of Paleolithic finds in the British Isles come from river terrace gravels, and more specifically their quarrying, largely by hand, in the nineteenth century for building aggregate. This has long been disproportionately distributed in the UK due to a combination of demand, driven by the population growth of the southeast region, and a lack of alter-

native hard rock supplies (Brown, this volume; Brown, 2009). The second factor is the geotectonic character of southern England. Although most of southern England was located beyond the Pleistocene glacial maximum, the terrestrial preservation of the Paleolithic landscapes is systematically biased east to west. This is due to a combination of long-term tectonic change, with relative subsidence in the southeast and uplift in the southwest, and a contrast between soft rocks in the southeast and hard rocks in the southwest. So today, in the Thames Basin and North Sea, there is almost an entire Pleistocene lowland landscape from lowland interfluves (watershed divides) to the shallow sea; in the Solent Basin (central south coast), the middle to lowland reaches are still preserved, as are some interfluves, although much of the former catchment (including the river valley itself) is drowned. Further west, only the upper parts of the Paleolithic catchments are visible, but they have been significantly eroded. This long-term trend, which is supported by both thermal exhumation modeling using appetite-fission track dating (Chen et al., 1996; Hillis et al., 2008) and by marine cores, is the result of a complex interplay of forces, including subsidence of the North Sea Basin and continued tectonic deformation operating along reactivated Variscan and Alpine structures and possibly magmatic underplating (cf. Brodie and White, 1994; Westaway, 2010).

All three catchment areas, the Thames, Solent, and southwest rivers drain into the Channel River and west to the Atlantic, but there is a decreasing proportion of each catchment above sea level. It is generally supposed (but minimally explored) that the principal routes of migration and locations of hominin activity were along river valleys (e.g., Ashton et al., 2006). If this is the case, the restricted visibility of paleocatchments today has obvious implications for the present-day patterning of Paleolithic sites. Indeed, it can be hypothesized that the *average state* in the later quarter of the Pleistocene (post–MIS 12) was a relatively open, cool to warm, temperate environment dominated by the Rhine, Thames, and Channel Rivers and their tributaries (Gupta et al., 2007). In this wider context, the southern English record is clearly important, and an understanding of its geotectonic situation suggests two possible research strategies for the southwest. First, archaeological evaluation and survey of the continental shelf off the peninsula, and second, concentrated study of both the archaeological and environmental records preserved in the terrace sequences that do occur in the region. The former approach, although extremely difficult, is being undertaken under the ALSF Marine Programme (Ward, this volume), while the latter approach is taken by the Palaeolithic Rivers of South West England (PRoSWEB) project, the results of which are summarized in this paper.

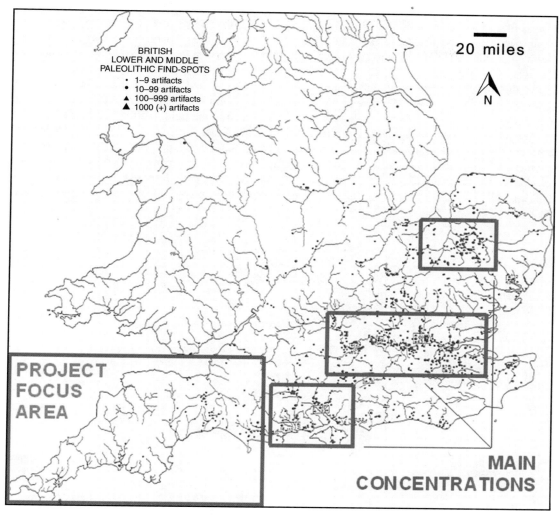

Figure 1. The distribution of Paleolithic material in England and Wales from Roe (1981), with the Palaeolithic Rivers of South West Britain (PRoSWEB) project study area and main lithic macroconcentrations (see text).

GEOMORPHOLOGICAL CONTEXT AND STUDY SITES

The rivers examined as part of PRoSWEB varied in size, geological setting, and regional geomorphology. The Doniford River is a small headwater stream draining a structural valley between the Exmoor Massif and the Quantock Hills. It drains into the proto–Severn River, which is not part of the Rhine–Thames–Channel River system, and it drains to the west across the continental shelf directly into the North Atlantic. It would therefore always have been necessary to access the area by traversing the spine of the southwest peninsula, or the interfluve from the Thames or Solent systems. The remaining study rivers, the Exe, Otter, and Axe would have all drained directly into the Channel River during the Pleistocene. The Exe has an altitudinally separated stack of eight terrace levels ranging over ~100 m of relative altitude. The Otter has a similar geomorphic sequence,

with 10 terraces ranging over ~60 m of relative altitude (altitude above modern floodplain). The Axe, however, contains only one principal terrace, which ranges over a height of only 18–20 m in relative altitude. From their alignment, it is likely that all three valleys are headwaters of the proto-Exe, which drained south approximately following the line of the Sticklepath-Lustleigh fault zone into the western Channel River at the Hurd Deep (Antoine et al., 2003). The anomalous sequence of the Axe valley, which is due to local factors and probably related to mid-Pleistocene capture (Gallois, 2006), is of great geoarchaeological importance in relation to both the temporal and spatial pattern of Paleolithic artifacts in the region.

METHODOLOGY

PRoSWEB was a three-phase project. Phase I was a desk-based assessment of all catchments in the southwest, which aimed to ascertain the areas that would be most useful in clarifying the Paleolithic hominin occupation and landscape evolution of the region. Once the main catchments were chosen, accessible and suitable locations for fieldwork were then identified through a combination of literature review, overlaying the distributions of Paleolithic find spots from the Sites and Monuments Records Offices of Devon, Dorset, Somerset, and Cornwall with the British Geological Survey (BGS) 1:50,000 maps of the region (within an ArcGIS and Access database), and ground-truthing. There is currently no commercial aggregate quarrying into any of the gravel terraces, and there are few natural exposures. The exception to this is the Axe valley, where sections are still visible in some old workings and in the active quarry at Chard Junction. Due to the lack of large terrace exposures, the study utilized borehole records, occasional natural and artificial exposures, and machine-cut trenches.

Phases 2 and 3 of the project were dominated by fieldwork, analysis, and modeling. Large areas of all the catchments were examined in the field, but focused fieldwork was undertaken in nine main locations shown in Figure 2. Identification of suitable locations for fieldwork was partly determined by accessibility, landowners' permissions, and land use (crop cover, crop harvesting, livestock, etc.). Exposed sections and machine-cut trenches were sedimentologically logged and photographed. They were

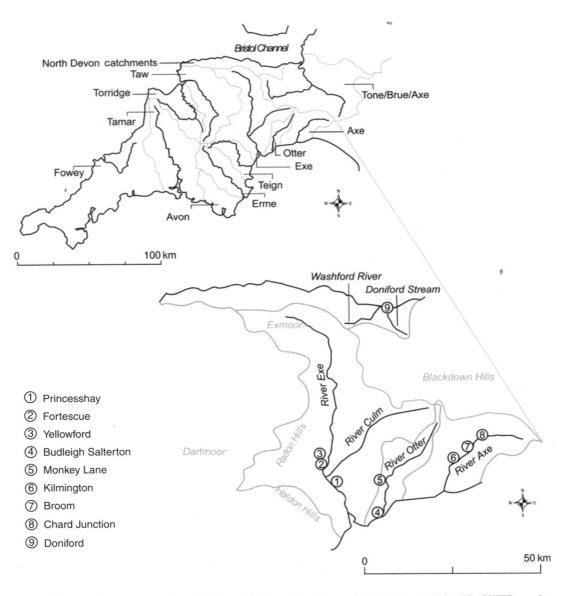

Figure 2. The catchments investigated during the Palaeolithic Rivers of South West Britain (PRoSWEB) project and the main sites discussed in the text.

sampled for dating and environmental studies where appropriate and surveyed using a differential global positioning system (DGPS). Clast analysis was undertaken where possible in order to determine clast shape, dip, and orientation using standard procedures (Jones et al., 1999), and GeoOrient software was used to generate stereographic plots. The area around each exposure or excavated trench was geomorphologically mapped in most cases in order to demarcate the terrace fragment more clearly than was available from the geological map. The methods applied to each site and summary data are shown in Table 1. Sedimentological logging and clast analysis was applied to all sites with the exception of Broom, where work had been conducted previously (Shakesby and Stephens, 1984) and is ongoing (Toms et al., 2005; Hosfield and Chambers, 2009; Hosfield et al., 2011). A limited amount of ground-penetrating radar work was done at two sites in order to attempt to clarify gravel depth and extent. This will not be discussed in detail here, and further information can be found in Hosfield et al. (2007).

Interferometric synthetic aperture radar (IfSAR) and orthorectified aerial photographic data were purchased for the River Axe. The IfSAR data included both digital terrain (ground surface) and digital surface (includes vegetation, buildings, etc.) data. These data were manipulated within ArcGIS, allowing models to be created over which the aerial photographs, find spots, fieldwork sites and geological data could be draped. The vertical resolution of the digital terrain model (DTM) and digital surface model (DSM) was 5 m. This was then viewed in three-dimensions (3-D) within ArcScene, vertically exaggerated, rotated, and shaded from different angles. At Doniford, similar DTMs at a coarser resolution were obtained through Digimap, which is available to subscribing universities through academic licensing, and modeled using the same methods. Higher-resolution, but far less extensive modeling was achieved for Monkey Lane using x-y-z data generated from a DGPS survey of the terrace fragment on which fieldwork was conducted.

All terrace deposits investigated were entirely decalcified due to the acidic nature of the majority of the lithologies making up the catchments and the antiquity of the deposits. No shell or bone was encountered, and no organic sediments suitable for biocorrelation were found. Therefore, optically stimulated luminescence (OSL) was the only means of dating possible. For the OSL dating, samples were collected in daylight from sections using opaque plastic tubing (150 × 45 mm) forced into each face or carved as lithified blocks (75 × 75 × 50 mm). In addition, one nonconventional sample (Fortescue Farm, GL06035), located within a clast-supported unit, was collected in daylight, but as a large aggregated mass (500 × 500 × 250 mm), and it was protected from light by opaque sheeting. In order to attain an intrinsic metric of reliability, where possible, multiple samples were obtained from stratigraphically equivalent units targeting positions likely divergent in dosimetry on the basis of textural differences. A measure of γ dose rate was made in situ using an EG&G μNomad portable NaI gamma spectrometer. To preclude optical erosion of the datable signal prior to measurement, all

samples were prepared under controlled laboratory illumination provided by Encapsulite RB-10 (red) filters. Following segregation of material potentially exposed to light during sampling, fine sand–sized quartz was isolated by performing acid and alkaline digestion (10% HCl, 15% H_2O_2) to attain removal of carbonate and organic components, a further acid digestion in HF (40%, 60 min) to etch the outer 10–15 μm layer affected by α radiation and degrade each samples' feldspar content, and then 10% HCl was added to remove acid-soluble fluorides. Each sample was resieved, and quartz was isolated from the remaining heavy mineral fraction using a sodium polytungstate density separation at 2.68 g/cm^3. Equivalent dose (D_e) values were acquired using a Riso TL-DA-15 irradiation-stimulation-detection system (Markey et al., 1997; Bøtter-Jensen et al., 1999) and single-aliquot regenerative-dose protocol (Murray and Wintle, 2000, 2003). Optimal thermal treatment was evaluated from measures of D_e and dose recovery preheat dependence. Dose rate (D_r) values were estimated through a combination of in situ gamma spectrometry (γ D_r), neutron activation analysis (β D_r), and geographical position and overburden thickness (cosmic D_r; Prescott and Hutton, 1994). Disequilibrium in the U-series was monitored by means of laboratory-based gamma spectrometry using an Ortec GEM-S high-purity Ge coaxial detector system.

RESULTS

During phase I, the majority of open (noncave) Paleolithic artifact find spots in the southwest were identified as being in the counties of Dorset, Devon, and Somerset. BGS mapping shows some significant areas of river terraces in the region, most notably in the catchments of the Exe, Axe, Otter, Taw, and Tone (Fig. 2). However, there was considerable variability in the degree of terrace definition and differentiation within single catchments across the geological maps. This was due to differences in the date and quality of mapping of the superficial ("drift") deposits; on some of the older sheets, for example, terraces had not been mapped separately from solifluction ("head") deposits. The most extensive and well-mapped terrace sequences with archaeological associations (discussed later herein) were in the Exe and the Otter. Preliminary examination of the borehole logs and literature review suggested that some of the terrace deposits were relatively thick (3 m+) and vertically separated by bedrock (altitudinal separation), with overlapping terraces at lower elevations. In addition, Scrivener (1984) and Edwards and Scrivener (1999) had suggested a difference in the form of the upper terraces (higher than terrace 6) for the Exe being draped over the landscape rather than altitudinally separated, and ground truthing suggested similar differences in terrace form for the Otter and the paleo-Doniford, but not for the Axe.

Little detailed information was available on the precise age of the terraces. Kidson (1962) attempted some correlation between the sequences of the Exe and Otter on an altitudinal basis, but chronometric dates were lacking with three exceptions. Fyfe et al. (2004) and Bennett (2005), and Bennett et al. (this

TABLE 1. SUMMARY OF THE GEOARCHAEOLOGICAL METHODS USED AT PROSWEB SITES

CATCHMENT	SITE	TERRACE NUMBER	EXPOSURE TYPE	PROSWEB OSL DATING	PROSWEB SEDIMENTOLOGICAL LOGGING	PALEOLITHIC ARCHAEOLOGICAL FINDS KNOWN FROM PRECISE LOCATION	CLAST ANALYSIS	GROUND-PENETRATING RADAR	GEOMORPHOLOGICAL MAPPING/ DIFFERENTIAL GPS/IfSAR MODELING	GRAVEL EXPOSURE THICKNESS (m)	CRYOTURBATION FEATURES	CHANNEL FEATURES	BEDDING AND SAND LENSES
Exe	Fortescue	4	Natural exposure	Y	Y	N	Y	N	N	3.7–4	Y	Y	Y
Exe	Princesshay	6	Archaeological excavation due to development	Y	Y	N	N	N	N	1.1	Y	N	Y
Exe	Yellowford	6	Mechanically excavated 20 m trench	Y	Y	N	Y	Y	N	3.05–3.15	Y	N	Y
Otter	Monkey Lane	7	Mechanically excavated 20 m trench	Y	Y	N	Y	Y	Y	1.4	N	Y	Y
Otter	Budleigh Salterton	2	Natural exposure	Y	Y	N	Y	N	N	2.5	N	N	Y
Axe	Kilmington	U	Former extraction area	Y	Y	Y	Y	N	Y	9–14	Y	Y	Y
Axe	Chard Junction	U	Commercial aggregate extraction	Y	Y	Y	Y	N	Y	14	Y	Y	Y
Axe	Broom Pit	U	Former extraction area	N	N	Y	N	Y	Y	~8	Y	N?	Y
Doniford	Doniford	2	Natural shoreline exposure	Y	Y	Y	N	N	Y	~6	Y	Y	Y

Note: OSL—optically stimulated luminescence; PRoSWEB—Palaeolithic Rivers of South West England project; IfSAR—interferometric synthetic aperture radar.

volume) produced dates on the floodplain and lower terraces of the Exe using radiocarbon and OSL methods, respectively, and work conducted at Broom on the Axe using OSL (Toms et al., 2005) gave some indication of the antiquity of the "Middle Beds" and "Upper Gravels" at this important Paleolithic site. In addition, the largely undifferentiated terrace deposits (BGS mapping) of the Axe were well known to have yielded large quantities of Paleolithic bifaces (Evans, 1872; Calkin and Green, 1949; Stephens, 1977; Green, 1988; Marshall, 2001; Hosfield and Chambers, 2003). By contrast, direct associations of Paleolithic artifacts with river terrace deposits elsewhere in the southwest were less frequent, but bifaces had been found in terrace 5 of the Exe (e.g., the Magdelen Street biface; Pickard, 1933–1936) and terrace 5 of the Otter (e.g., the Wiggaton biface; Smith, 1933–1936), and further bifaces were known from the lower terraces of these fluvial sequences. Occasional artifacts have been found in association with terraces of other rivers, but these have been infrequent. The only other site where more than one Paleolithic artifact had been found within gravel deposits was at Doniford, near Watchet (Gilbertson and Mottershead, 1975). Here, "a most stupendous accumulation of gravel" (Mackintosh *in* Date, 1887, p. 51–52), which is still visible in the seashore cliff, had yielded Lower Paleolithic, Upper Paleolithic, and Mesolithic artifacts, as well as mammoth teeth and tusk (Wedlake, 1950, 1973; Norman, 1978). Examination of the geographic information system (GIS) database also showed that single lithics were commonly found in the lower parts of valley slopes but off, or not in direct association with, mapped gravel terraces. An example is the cluster of single bifaces found in the Halberton area near Tiverton. These were found in a shallow valley near extensive tracts of undifferentiated gravels along the River Lowman. Other examples in similar physiographic settings have been found at Thorverton and to the east of Exeter Airport (Basell, 2008, personal observation), and all appear to relate to areas of former gravel extent that has been subsequently eroded away. These studies, in combination with ground-truthing and the memoirs of the BGS, demonstrated that there was indeed a concentration of lithics within the major valleys and that the best chance of establishing a reliable chronology would be in the terrace deposits of the rivers Exe, Otter, Axe, and Doniford.

Detailed presentations of fieldwork results and analyses conducted in phases II and III of PRoSWEB for each catchment are beyond the scope of this paper, and are published elsewhere, or are in preparation (Hosfield et al., 2006a, 2006b, 2007; Toms et al., 2008; Brown et al., 2010; Basell et al., 2011). Instead, we present here examples of the ways in which the geoarchaeological data were used, an overview of the results, and some of the problems encountered.

First, at most of the sites, sedimentological logging revealed deposits to have been affected by cryoturbation. Several types of cryoturbation features were recorded, including ice wedge casts (although these were infrequent), frost cracks, heave structures, involutions, flame structures, and congelifracted clasts. The combination of these features indicates both periglacial conditions

(ice wedge casts) and seasonally frozen ground (frost cracks) and water-release phenomena indicating the melting of saturated regolith (Ballantyne and Harris, 1994). For example, the deposits at Yellowford Farm were affected to a depth of 2.3 m, indicating repeated cryoturbation episodes probably through several periglacial cycles. Here, clast analysis was used to demonstrate cryoturbation in different units (Fig. 3). The large section at Doniford also revealed several episodes of cryoturbation. The fieldwork sites of the Otter by contrast did not show such features, but this is probably due to the small size of the exposure at Budleigh Salterton and disturbance in the upper part of the section by tree roots. At Monkey Lane, also on the Otter (Fig. 2), the gravels were found to be truncated, and there was evidence of tree throws, so cryoturbation features in the upper part of the deposit are likely to have been lost. However, a large block of presumably ice-rafted Mercia Mudstone (Upper Keuper Marl) was discovered within the gravels, which must have come from the westward-facing scarp face of the Blackdown Hills, ~2 km to the east.

Second, terrace deposits were generally found to be of considerable, though varied, thickness. At two sites, Princesshay and Monkey Lane, the deposits were significantly truncated. Monkey Lane is high, forms an interfluve, and historically the site has undergone significant soil erosion, to the extent that it has necessitated a change in land management patterns (Colleton Estate, 2008, personal commun.). Princesshay, by contrast, lies in the heart of Exeter, and anthropogenic activity in the area from Roman times through to the present day has been high. Indeed, the principal exposure examined was in a feature interpreted by Exeter Archaeology as a medieval night-soil pit. It is likely that this anthropogenic activity has truncated the deposits. However, there is also some evidence from Princesshay to suggest that the gravels varied in thickness across the site, so an alternative interpretation is that the main section examined was simply a thin spread of gravel at the margins of a larger channel feature. Further discussion was presented by Brown et al. (2010). Scrivener (1984) and Edwards and Scrivener (1999) have argued that the highest terraces in the Exe draped over the landscape, a feature possibly associated with glacial outwash or once much thicker deposits with an inset or cut-and-fill form, which have since been heavily eroded. Some support for the latter hypothesis comes from the occurrence of sarsens, both within the upper terrace gravels and on the interfluves in the Middle Exe just above the remaining patches of higher gravel terraces. Sarsens are large blocks (up to 1 m+ maximum axis) of silica-cemented sandstone that are generally believed to be of Tertiary age (Paleogene–Neogene) and that may have been derived from Tertiary deposits that capped the Haldon, Radon, and Blackdown Hills. Trenches excavated also demonstrated that the middle and lower terrace gravels in both the Exe and Otter River valleys were deeper than expected. The gravels at Doniford were remarkably deep (~6 m) in relation to the misfit (cf. shrunken) Doniford stream that flows out at Doniford today. This indicates that the gravels must relate to a much larger river (referred to here as the paleo–Doniford River) previously draining parts of northeast Exmoor and the

Figure 3. Typical periglacial features from Kilmington and Doniford: (A) cryoturbation feature at Kilmington, which disrupts an overlying sand lens, (B) cryoturbation involution at Doniford, and (C and D) congelifracted clasts at Doniford. The white card in B, C, and D is 9 cm long, and scale divisions in A and D are 1 cm.

western slopes of the Quantock Hills. Unusually thick accumulations of gravel were also recorded at all fieldwork sites in the Axe valley, supporting previous work conducted in the area (e.g., Green, 1988). Terrace gravel exposures recorded at Kilmington and Chard Junction (both undifferentiated terrace gravels) were ~14 m in depth, although, like the Doniford, the Axe valley sites exhibited significant vertical and horizontal sedimentological variability. It should also be noted that the thickness of terrace gravel at Chard is known to be in the region of 23 m.

Third, at several sites, it was possible to identify fluvial bedding and channels and, through clast analysis, to identify paleoflow directions. Overall, in the Axe Valley sites, there was more evidence of cryoturbation in the upper units, and more bedding structures in the lower units. At all sites where clast analysis was

undertaken, these directions did not differ dramatically from the existing valley direction. The lack of channels at sites such as Budleigh Salterton is probably related to the small size of the exposure. By contrast, at Chard Junction and Doniford, large channels several meters across, but generally under 1 m deep, were identified.

Fourth, examination of the clast lithologies showed that in all cases, clasts were locally derived and did not differ significantly from the bedrock types present in each of the studied catchments. At Yellowford Farm, for example, it could be demonstrated through clast analysis that the paleoriver was high energy, braided and transported material derived predominantly from Exmoor. Proportions of each lithology did, however, change between units at some sites.

Finally, clast analysis and sedimentological analyses showed a general trend of increasing roundedness and decreasing size from the upper to the lower terraces. In addition to traditional logging and clast analysis techniques, ground-penetrating radar (GPR) was employed at two sites, and the results were presented by Hosfield et al. (2007). A test run was conducted at Broom in the Axe valley, while at Monkey Lane the base of gravels was detected, as well as variations within them. This showed a bipartite structural division of the interfluve gravels, with the lower unit corresponding to thinner gravels on an adjacent slope. In combination with the DGPS survey results, which were then modeled within ArcScene as discussed already, these variations are interpreted as indicating a compound terrace within the Monkey Lane site.

Terrace form, the degree of altitudinal separation between terraces, and degree of terrace pairing were examined through geomorphological mapping in the field, the use of DGPS, and Digimap and IfSAR data manipulated within ArcGIS (ArcScene), as illustrated in Figure 4. This analysis showed greater complexity in terrace form than could be seen from the geological mapping, even when the BGS 1:10,000 maps or field slips were examined. Geomorphological features could be brought out through manipulation using shading and vertical exaggeration, facilitating targeted examination in the field. The 5 m resolution of the IfSAR data proved better than the coarser-resolution Digimap data, although the use of DGPS survey data to model the Monkey Lane site suggests that light detection and ranging (LiDAR) data at a 1 m resolution would be an even more powerful tool for ongoing work, as has been shown by Howard et al. (2008). Generally, the lower terraces (<4) of the Exe and Otter Rivers are cut into each other, and above them, there is a classic staircase sequence in the catchments of the Exe and Otter (Fig. 5) but not the paleo-Doniford and the Axe, which both contain stacked sequences. Some of the terraces mapped and numbered as a single unit were shown to be more complex and are interpreted as compound terraces, as is also the case in the staircases of the River Thames (Bridgland, 1994; Brown, 2009). Both the paleo-Doniford and the Axe revealed only one relatively low terrace, but of unusual thickness and compound (containing more than one sedimentary member). In the case of the paleo-Doniford, the catchment is very small (under 50 km²), and a maximum height exists for any higher terraces set by the height of the interfluve with the Tone valley to the south. In the case of the river Axe, it is postulated that the cause maybe the capture of a significant part of its catchment area in the mid- to late Pleistocene. This geomorphic history almost certainly has affected the occurrence of bifaces, since in stacked sequences most of the past floodplain remains in situ, with less wholesale reworking. This may be part of the explanation of the high and localized concentrations of lithics in this valley.

Dates were obtained from all sites, allowing the construction of the first terrace-based chronology for the region. The most likely marine isotope attributions for all the sites are summarized in Table 2, following the results presented by Toms et al. (2008).

Several causes of unreliable dates were identified, although in most of the region, the quartz appeared not to have retained an earlier OSL signal and was fully bleached, and environmental dose rates were intermediate. However, problems were encountered with high environmental dose rates in one area (Thorverton area). Several dates, and particularly shallower dates, also appeared far too young, most likely due to the incorporation of younger material into the gravels by cryoturbation.

DISCUSSION AND CONCLUSIONS

The aims of the research reported here was fundamentally archaeological, and the fieldwork was effective largely based on the initial desk-based assessment and literature review. The integration of extant geological, archaeological, and geomorphological data allowed us to identify the most promising areas for fieldwork. Catchments were chosen because of (1) a direct association between artifacts and terraces, (2) an extensive sequence of terraces and locations where some preliminary work had been undertaken already, and (3) although few, some previous dating, providing a useful starting point and comparison for any new dates obtained.

The sedimentology, geomorphology, and clast analyses have allowed us to compare the Exe and the Otter with classic staircase sequences further east, such as the Thames and the Solent. The presence of compound terraces within these sequences demonstrates the necessity of a geoarchaeological approach. The presence of compound terraces has implications for both the chronological sequence and for the preservation of artifacts. Because of the erosion and downcutting between periods of deposition inherent within the cyclic staircase model (sensu Bridgland, 2000, 2006), a significant proportion of lithics from one floodplain must be reworked into the subsequent lower floodplain deposit suite. There is therefore a strong element of a cascading system, which might be expected to favor the downstream distribution of artifacts. In stacked systems, this element is greatly reduced, and while there may be localized reworking due to bank erosion and floods, less artifact dispersal and more frequent areas of localized high artifact density would be expected. This may also favor the co-occurrence of abraded and nonabraded lithics as has been noted at Broom (Hosfield and Chambers, 2004). Work on the data generated by the project is ongoing; new fieldwork and geostatistical modeling of these processes are being continued, particularly at Chard Junction quarry (Brown and Basell, 2008). It is anticipated that modeling work within ArcGIS on the Axe sequence will provide a much clearer understanding of why concentrations of artifacts exist in specific locations, and illuminate the archaeological implications of different geomorphological and tectonic processes. In addition, LiDAR data have been purchased for specific areas of the Exe and Doniford, in order to examine more closely the geomorphology of terrace fragments in these catchments at high vertical resolution (1 m), and to develop idealized 3-D models of terrace sequences in these locations.

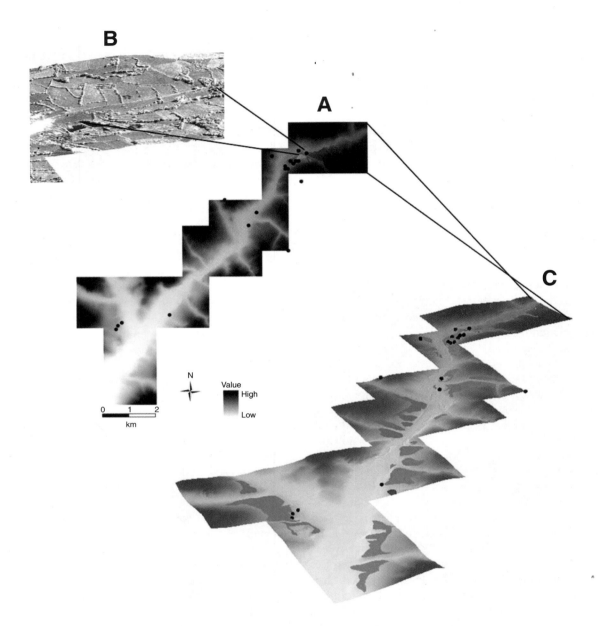

Figure 4. Some examples of basic modeling within ArcGIS for the Axe Valley. (A) Interferometric synthetic aperture radar (IfSAR) digital terrain model (DTM) of the Axe valley, displayed in two dimensions (2-D) within ArcMap, overlain with open (noncave) Paleolithic find spots (black dots) as recorded in the Historic Environment Records for Somerset, Dorset, and Devon Counties. High is 161.1 m; low is 9.5 m altitude. (B) IfSAR digital surface model draped with orthorectified aerial photograph of the Axe valley and Paleolithic find spots as for A, modeled in three dimensions (3-D) within ArcScene. Subject: Close-up of the Chard Junction area. No vertical exaggeration or illumination. (C) IfSAR DTM of the Axe valley modeled in 3-D within ArcScene, and draped with terrace deposits (solid monotone gray) extracted from British Geological Survey (BGS) mapping and Paleolithic find spots (black dots), as for A. Vertical exaggeration is 1.5, illumination azimuth is 321.6°, illumination altitude is 30°, and contrast is 75%. Image has been tilted and rotated to display topography. IfSAR data were purchased from Bluesky under license to L.S. Basell. Superficial geological deposit data were purchased from BGS under license to L.S. Basell. License numbers 2005/089 and 2006/005.

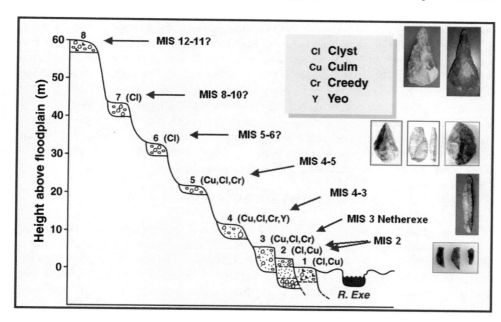

Figure 5. A generalized and provisional terrace staircase from the Exe valley with representative lithics. MIS—marine isotope stages. The inset photographs are, from top to bottom, examples of Lower Paleolithic bifaces, Lower or Middle Paleolithic bifaces, Upper Paleolithic blades, and Mesolithic flakes.

TABLE 2. SUMMARY OF THE PRoSWEB DATING, PLACING TERRACES INTO THE MOST PROBABLE MARINE OXYGEN ISOTOPE STAGE BASED UPON OPTICALLY STIMULATED LUMINESCENCE DATING

Site	Sample	Terrace	Present drainage	Approximate MIS
Doniford	1	U	Doniford	3
Doniford	2	U	Doniford	3
Doniford	3	U	Doniford	3 to 4
Doniford	4	U	Doniford	3 to 4
Yellowford	1	6	Exe	2 (cryoturbated)
Yellowford	2	6	Exe	2 (cryoturbated)
Washfield	1	3	Exe	3
Five Fords	1	3	Clum (Exe)	3
Princesshay	1	6	Exe	3 (cryoturbated)
Princesshay	2	6	Exe	3 (cryoturbated)
Fortescue	1	4	Exe	3 to 4
Yellowford	3	6	Exe	5a to 3 (cryoturbated)
Budleigh Salterton	1	2	Otter	4 to 5a
Monkey Lane	1	7	Otter	5c to 5d (cryoturbated)
Budleigh Salterton	2	2	Otter	5b to 5d
Monkey Lane	2	7	Otter	5d to 6 (cryoturbated)
Monkey Lane	3	7	Otter	6 to 7 (cryoturbated)
Chard	1	U	Axe	5c to 5d
Chard	2	U	Axe	5b to 5d
Kilmington	1	U	Axe	6
Chard	3	U	Axe	6
Kilmington	2	U	Axe	6 to 7
Kilmington	3	U	Axe	8
Broom	1	U	Axe	8
Chard	4	U	Axe	8
Chard	5	U	Axe	8 to 9
Kilmington	4	U	Axe	8 to 9
Chard	6	U	Axe	9 to 11

Note: For detail of the individual dates, see Toms et al. (2008). Shaded rows were not generated as part of Palaeolithic Rivers of South-West Britain (PRoSWEB) project. See text for details.

OSL dating has been used to provide a chronology for a number of fluvial geoarchaeological sites in Europe, but where it has been found to contradict other methods, it has received some criticism, as discussed in Briant et al. (2006). In the sites discussed here, no alternative method was possible. The dates achieved displayed internal consistency, with the exception of the highest terraces of the Exe and the Otter, where the dates were almost certainly too young. Because the quartz in the region appears suitable and dose rates are generally low to intermediate (with notable exceptions), the method has the potential to provide relatively long chronologies, and further work is planned at different sites with the anticipation that more accurate dates should be achievable.

Although not yet as old as the record at Kent's Cavern, the open-air record of hominin occupation of southwest Britain now dates well into the Lower Paleolithic (Period I sensu Wymer, 1999). The reanalysis of the gross distribution of bifaces in the region, along with observations at particular sites of the association of bifaces with remnants of terraces, or their residual nature, supports the contention that the southern-draining valleys were the principal routeways of hominin occupation of the southwestern massif, with another routeway being from the Thames Valley along the Avon to the Severn Valley, or estuary, as it is today. Given the lack of gravel quarrying in the southwest region and the subsequent discovery of Lower Paleolithic bifaces in at least one of the sites studied by the project (Chard Junction; Brown and Basell, 2008), it is almost certain that the distribution revealed in Figure 1 is an underestimate of the co-association of bifaces with river valley floors and tributaries. This raises the question, why did hominins move along river valleys? Little attention has been paid to this, with the exception of a paper dealing specifically with MIS 11 (Ashton et al., 2006).

Differences in landscape use and adaptation among the Lower, Middle, and Upper Paleolithic, and at shorter time scales, are obviously likely, and for the Lower and Middle Paleolithic, a more detailed understanding of vegetation cover through environmental analyses and modeling will help to clarify the argument. More broadly, however, some advantages of moving along river valleys are evident, for example, (1) close proximity to a relatively safe (i.e., nonstagnant) supply of water; (2) the opportunity to employ ambush hunting of game coming to drink; (3) the occurrence of fish, shellfish, crustaceans and nutritious and relatively easily obtainable riparian and aquatic plants (a scarce resource in closed canopy woodland); and (4) the existence of a natural routeway that can be marked and retraced. This last advantage is the most difficult to investigate, but it may be the most important as a part of hominins' opportunistic adaptive behavior, which was itself part of the emergence of extended intelligence (Clark, 1997). There are of course potential disadvantages, such as the very occasional danger posed by floods and problems of crossing rivers. However, the shallower nature of most Pleistocene braided and anastomosing channel systems reduces both of these dangers in comparison with the Holocene environment. The major disadvantage would be the lack of good vantage points over the landscape for both strategic and ambush hunting, thus explaining the importance of gorge sites, such as Kent's Cavern, where geomorphology would have facilitated such activities. While there is a danger of falsely dichotomizing Pleistocene landscapes into inhabited valleys and unoccupied intervening uplands, both the lithic record and resource considerations (both positive and negative) increasingly suggest that this may be the case in areas of high relief, such as southwest Britain, and it may be of more marginal importance in the large lowlands of the northern European seaboard, such as in southeast Britain.

ACKNOWLEDGMENTS

This chapter is based upon research carried out with funding from the Aggregates Levy Sustainability Fund administered by English Heritage (PNUM 3847). We must thank many individuals and institutions for their help, including: J. Bennett, C. Carey, R. Gallois, F. Griffith, S. Hounsell, C. Norman, E. Robinson, R. Taylor, the British Geological Survey Regional Office, Exeter and Devon County Council (Environment Department), Dorset County Council HER (Historic Environments Record) Officers, and Somerset County Council HER Officers. We must also express particular thanks to Exeter Archaeology for their records and observations at Princesshay, B. Morris, and also the landowners who kindly gave us permission to work on their lands.

REFERENCES CITED

Antoine, P., Coutard, J.-P., Gibbard, P., Hallegouet, B., Lautridou, J.-P., and Ozouf, J.-C., 2003, The Pleistocene rivers of the English Channel region: Journal of Quaternary Science, v. 18, p. 227–243, doi:10.1002/jqs.762.

Ashton, N., Lewis, S.G., Parfitt, S., and White, M., 2006, Riparian landscapes and human habitat preferences during the Hoxnian (MIS 11) Interglacial: Journal of Quaternary Science, v. 21, p. 497–505, doi:10.1002/jqs.1032.

Ballantyne, C.K., and Harris, C., 1994, The Periglaciation of Great Britain: Cambridge, UK, Cambridge University Press, 330 p.

Basell, L.S., Brown, A.G., and Toms, P.S., 2011, The Quaternary of the Exe Valley and Adjoining Areas. Field Guide: London, Quaternary Research Association.

Bennett, J.A., 2005, Late Pleistocene and Holocene Fluvial Geomorphology of the River Exe, Devon, UK [Ph.D. thesis]: Exeter, University of Exeter, 265 p.

Bennett, J.A., Brown, A.G., Schwenninger, J.-L., and Rhodes, E.J., 2011, this volume, Holocene channel changes and geoarchaeology of the Exe River, Devon, UK, and the floodplain paradox, *in* Brown, A.G., Basell, L.S., and Butzer, K.W., eds., Geoarchaeology, Climate Change, and Sustainability: Geological Society of America Special Paper 476, doi:10.1130/2011.2476(11).

Boismier, W.A., Schreve, D.A., White, M.J., Robertson, D.A., Stuart, A.J., Etienne, S., Andrews, J., Coope, G.R., Field, M.H., Green, F.M.L., Keen, D.H., Lewis, S.G., French, C., Rhodes, E., Schwenninger, J.-L., Tovey, K., Donahue, R.E., Richards, M.P., and O'Connor, S., 2003, A Middle Palaeolithic site at Lynford Quarry, Mundford, Norfolk: Interim statement: Proceedings of the Prehistoric Society, v. 69, p. 315–324.

Bøtter-Jensen, L., Mejdahl, V., and Murray, A.S., 1999, New light on OSL: Quaternary Science Reviews, v. 18, p. 303–309, doi:10.1016/S0277-3791(98)00063-8.

Briant, R.M., Bates, M.R., Schwenninger, J.-L., and Wenban-Smith, F., 2006, An optically stimulated luminescence dated middle to late Pleistocene fluvial sequence from the western Solent Basin, southern England: Journal of Quaternary Science, v. 21, p. 507–523, doi:10.1002/jqs.1035.

Bridgland, D.R., 1994, Quaternary of the Thames: Geological Conservation Review Series Volume 7: Nature Conservation Committee: London, Chapman and Hall, 441 p.

Bridgland, D.R., 2000, River terrace systems in north-west Europe: An archive of environmental change, uplift and early human occupation: Quaternary Science Reviews, v. 19, p. 1293–1303, doi:10.1016/S0277-3791(99)00095-5.

Bridgland, D.R., 2006, The Middle and Upper Pleistocene sequence in the Lower Thames: A record of Milankovitch climatic fluctuation and early human occupation of southern Britain: Henry Stopes Memorial Lecture: Proceedings of the Geologists' Association, v. 117, p. 281–305.

Brodie, J., and White, N., 1994, Sedimentary basin inversion caused by igneous underplating: Geology, v. 22, p. 147–150, doi:10.1130/0091-7613(1994)022<0147:SBICBI>2.3.CO;2.

Brown, A.G., 2009, The Environment and Aggregate Related Archaeology: Heritage Publishing and Marketing/Oxbow Books, 220 p.

Brown, A.G., 2011, this volume, Aggregate-related archaeology in England in a changing environment, *in* Brown, A.G., Basell, L.S., and Butzer, K.W., eds., Geoarchaeology, Climate Change, and Sustainability: Geological Society of America Special Paper 476, doi:10.1130/2011.2476(14).

Brown, A.G., and Basell, L.S., 2008, Two new bifaces from the Axe Valley, Chard Junction: PAST, v. 60, p. 1–3.

Brown, A.G., Basell, L.S., Toms, P.S., Bennett, J., Hosfield, R.T., and Scrivener, R.C., 2010, Late Pleistocene evolution of the Exe Valley. A chronstratigraphic model of terrace formation and its implications for palaeolithic archaeology: Quaternary Science Reviews, v. 29, p. 897–912.

Calkin, J.B., and Green, J.F.N., 1949, Palaeoliths and terraces near Bournemouth: Proceedings of the Prehistoric Society, v. 15, p. 21–37.

Chen, Y., Zentili, M.A., Clark, A.H., Grist, A.M., and Willis-Richards, J., 1996, Geochronological evidence for post-Variscan cooling and uplift of the Carnmellis granite, SW England: Journal of the Geological Society of London, v. 153, p. 191–195, doi:10.1144/gsjgs.153.2.0191.

Clark, A., 1997, Being There: Putting Brain, Body and World Together: Cambridge, Massachusetts, MIT Press, 269 p.

Edwards, R.A., and Scrivener, R.C., 1999, Geology of the Country around Exeter: Memoir of the British Geological Survey, Sheet 325 (England and Wales), 183 p.

Evans, J., 1872, The Ancient Stone Implements, Weapons and Ornaments of Great Britain: London, Longmans, 672 p.

Fyfe, R.M., Brown, A.G., and Coles, B.J., 2004, Vegetational change and human activity in the Exe valley, Devon, UK: Proceedings of the Prehistoric Society, v. 69, p. 161–182.

Gallois, R.W., 2006, The evolution of the rivers of east Devon and south Somerset, UK: Geoscience in South-West England, v. 11, p. 205–213.

Gilbertson, D.D., and Mottershead, D.N., 1975, The Quaternary deposits at Doniford, west Somerset: Field Studies, v. 4, p. 117–129.

Green, C.P., 1988, The Palaeolithic site at Broom, Dorset, 1932–41: From the record of C.E. Bean, Esq., F.S.A.: Proceedings of the Geologists' Association, v. 99, p. 173–180.

Gupta, S., Collier, J.S., Palmer-Felgate, A., and Potter, G., 2007, Catastrophic flooding origin of shelf valley systems in the English Channel: Nature, v. 448, p. 342–345, doi:10.1038/nature06018.

Hillis, R.R., Holford, S.P., Green, P.F., Gatliff, R.W., Stoker, M.S., Thomson, K., Turner, J.P., Underhill, J.R., and Williams, G.A., 2008, Cenozoic exhumation of the southern British Isles: Geology, v. 36, p. 371–374, doi:10.1130/G24699A.1.

Hosfield, R.T., and Chambers, J.C., 2003, Recent research at the Broom Lower Palaeolithic site: Antiquity, v. 77, no. 297, 421 p.

Hosfield, R.T., and Chambers, J.C., 2009, Genuine diversity? The Broom biface assemblage: Proceedings of the Prehistoric Society, v. 75, p. 65–100.

Hosfield, R.T., Brown, A.G., Basell, L.S., and Hounsell, S., 2006a, Beyond the caves: The Palaeolithic rivers of South-West Britain: Geoscience in South-West England, v. 11, p. 183–190.

Hosfield, R.T., Brown, A.G., Basell, L.S., Hounsell, S., Toms, P., and Young, R., 2006b, The Palaeolithic Rivers of South-West Britain. Phases I & II. Report for English Heritage (PNUM 3847): London, English Heritage Archive Report.

Hosfield, R.T., Chambers, J.C., and Toms, P., 2007, The Archaeological Potential of Secondary Contexts: English Heritage ALSF Project Report (Project No. 3361): London, English Heritage Archive Report, 195 p.

Hosfield, R.T., Straker, V., Gardiner, P., Brown, A.G., Davies, P., Fyfe, R., Jones, J., and Tinsley, H., 2008, Palaeolithic and Mesolithic, *in* Webster,

C.J., ed., The Archaeology of South West England. South West Archaeological Research Framework Resource Assessment Agenda: Taunton, Somerset County Council, p. 23–62.

Hosfield, R.T., Green, C.P., Toms, P., Scourse, J., Scaife, R., and Chambers, J.C., 2011, The Middle Pleistocene deposits and archaeology at Broom, *in* Basell, L.S., Brown, A.G., and Toms, P.S., eds., The Quaternary of the Exe Valley and Adjoining Areas. Field Guide: London, Quaternary Research Association (in press).

Howard, A.J., Bridgland, D., Knight, D., McNabb, J., Rose, J., Shreve, D., Westaway, R., and White, T.S., 2007, The British Pleistocene fluvial archive: East Midlands drainage evolution and human occupation in the context of the British and NW European record: Quaternary Science Reviews, v. 26, p. 2724–2737, doi:10.1016/j.quascirev.2007.06.029.

Howard, A.J., Brown, A.G., Carey, C.J., Challis, K., Cooper, L.P., Kincey, M., and Toms, P., 2008, Archaeological resource modelling in temperate river valleys: A case study from the Trent Valley, UK: Antiquity, v. 82, p. 1040–1054.

Jones, A.P., Tucker, M.E., and Hart, J., eds., 1999, The Description and Interpretation of Quaternary Stratigraphic Field Sections: Quaternary Research Association Technical Guide No. 7: London, Quaternary Research Association, 291 p.

Kidson, C., 1962, Denudation chronology of the River Exe: Transactions of the Institute of British Geographers, v. 31, p. 43–66.

Lord, J., 2002, A flint knapper's foreword to Lynford: Lithics, v. 23, p. 60–70.

Mackintosh, D., 1867, Pholas-borings, Denudation, and Deposition in S.E. Devon: Geological Magazine, v. 4, p. 295–299.

Markey, B.G., Bøtter-Jensen, L., and Duller, G.A.T., 1997, A new flexible system for measuring thermally and optically stimulated luminescence: Radiation Measurements, v. 27, p. 83–89, doi:10.1016/S1350-4487(96)00126-6.

Marshall, G.D., 2001, The Broom pits: A review of research and a pilot study of two Acheulian biface assemblages, *in* Wenban-Smith, F., and Hosfield, R.T., eds., Palaeolithic Archaeology of the Solent River: Lithic Studies Society Occasional Paper 7: London, Lithic Studies Society, p. 77–84.

Murray, A.S., and Wintle, A.G., 2000, Luminescence dating of quartz using an improved single-aliquot regenerative-dose protocol: Radiation Measurements, v. 32, p. 57–73, doi:10.1016/S1350-4487(99)00253-X.

Murray, A.S., and Wintle, A.G., 2003, The single aliquot regenerative dose protocol: Potential for improvements in reliability: Radiation Measurements, v. 37, p. 377–381, doi:10.1016/S1350-4487(03)00053-2.

Norman, C., 1978, Two flint artefacts: Proceedings of the Somerset Archaeology and Natural History Society, v. 122, p. 157–158.

Parfitt, S.A., Barendregt, R.W., Breda, M., Candy, I., Collins, M.J., Coope, G.R., Durbridge, P., Field, M.H., Lee, J.R., Lister, A.M., Mutch, R., Penkman, K.E.H., Preece, R.C., Rose, J., Stringer, C.B., Symmons, R., Whittaker, J.E., Wymer, J.J., and Stuart, A.J., 2005, The earliest record of human activity in northern Europe: Nature, v. 438, p. 1008–1012, doi:10.1038/nature04227.

Parfitt, S.A., Ashton, N.M., Lewis, S.G., Abel, R., Coope, G.R., Field, M.H., Gale, R., Hoare, P.G., Larkin, N.R., Lewis, M.D., Karloukovski, V., Maher, B.A., Peglar, S.M., Preece, R.C., Whittaker, J.E., and Stringer, C.B., 2010, Early Pleistocene human occupation at the edge of the boreal zone in northern Europe: Nature, v. 466, p. 229–233.

Pickard, R., 1933–1936, Stone implements of Devon: Proceedings of the Devon Archaeological Exploration Society, v. 2, p. 206–212.

Prescott, J.R., and Hutton, J.T., 1994, Cosmic ray contributions to dose rates for luminescence and ESR dating: Large depths and long-term time variations: Radiation Measurements, v. 23, p. 497–500.

Proctor, C.J., Berridge, P.J., Bishop, M.J., Richards, D.A., and Smart, P.L., 2005, Age of middle Pleistocene fauna and lower Palaeolithic industries from Kent's Cavern, Devon: Quaternary Science Reviews, v. 24, p. 1243–1252, doi:10.1016/j.quascirev.2004.07.022.

Roberts, M.B., and Parfitt, S.A., 1999, Boxgrove: A Middle Pleistocene Hominid Site at Eartham Quarry, Boxgrove, West Sussex: London, English Heritage, 456 p.

Roe, D.A., 1964, The British Lower and Middle Palaeolithic: Some problems, methods of study and preliminary results: Proceedings of the Prehistoric Society, v. 30, p. 245–267.

Roe, D., 1981, The Lower and Middle Palaeolithic Periods in Britain: London, Routledge, 340 p.

Schreve, D.C., 2006, The taphonomy of a Middle Devensian (MIS 3) vertebrate assemblage from Lynford, Norfolk, UK, and its implications for Middle

Palaeolithic subsistence strategies: Journal of Quaternary Science, v. 21, p. 543–556, doi:10.1002/jqs.1036.

Scrivener, R.C., 1984, Geological notes and local details for 1:10,000 sheets: Sheet SX 99 SW (Exeter): British Geological Survey, 48 p.

Shakesby, R.A., and Stephens, N., 1984, The Pleistocene gravels of the Axe Valley, Devon: Report of the Transactions of the Devon Association for the Advancement for Science, v. 116, p. 77–88.

Smith, R.A., 1933–1936, Stone implements of Devon: Proceedings of the Devon Archaeological Exploration Society, v. 2, p. 241–243.

Stephens, N., 1977, The Axe Valley, *in* Mottishead, D.N., ed., INQUA Congress Guidebook for Excursions A6 and C6. South-West England: Geo Abstracts, Norwich, p. 24–29.

Toms, P.S., Hosfield, R.T., Chambers, J.C., Green, C.P. and Marshall, P., 2005, Optical Dating of the Broom Palaeolithic Sites, Devon and Dorset: English Heritage Centre for Archaeological Dating Report 16/2005.

Toms, P.S., Brown, A.G., Basell, L.S., and Hosfield, R.T., 2008, Palaeolithic Rivers of South-West Britain: Optically Stimulated Luminescence Dating of Residual Deposits of the Proto-Axe, Exe, Otter, and Doniford: English Heritage Centre for Archaeological Dating Report 2/2008, 47 p.

van Andel, T.H., and Davies, W., 2004, Neanderthals and Modern Humans in the European Landscape during the Last Glaciation: Archaeological Results of the Stage 3 Project: Cambridge, McDonald Institute for Archaeological Research, 265 p.

Wedlake, A.L., 1950, Mammoth remains and Pleistocene implements found on the west Somerset coast: Proceedings of the Somerset Archaeology and Natural History Society, v. 95, p. 167–168.

Wedlake, A.L., 1973, The origins of Watchet, *in* A History of Watchet: Dulverton, The Exmoor Press, 145 p.

Wedlake, A.L., and Wedlake, D.J., 1963, Some paleoliths from the Doniford Gravels on the coast of west Somerset: Proceedings of the Somerset Archaeology and Natural History Society, v. 107, p. 93–100.

Westaway, R., 2010, Cenozoic uplift of southwest England: Journal of Quaternary Science, v. 25, p. 419–432.

Wymer, J., 1999, The Lower Palaeolithic Occupation of Britain, Volumes 1 and 2: London, Wessex Archaeology and English Heritage, 234 p.

MANUSCRIPT ACCEPTED BY THE SOCIETY 3 AUGUST 2010

The Geological Society of America
Special Paper 476
2011

Rolling stones: Understanding river-rolled Paleolithic artifact assemblages

Robert T. Hosfield*

Department of Archaeology, School of Human & Environmental Sciences, University of Reading, Whiteknights, Reading, RG6 6AB, UK

ABSTRACT

Key geoarchaeological factors are explored with reference to the formation and potential preservation and/or loss of early Paleolithic artifact assemblages within Pleistocene fluvial deposits. The importance of these assemblages concerns the uniquely long-term perspectives that they offer to the study of early hominin occupation histories and landscape use. The factors explored (river type, bedrock type, the chronology and cycles of fluvial activity, and confluence activity) build upon the previous work of D.R. Bridgland, and A.J. Howard and M.G. Macklin with regard to terrace formation, preservation, and other fluvial activity. Particular emphasis is placed upon short-term fluvial activity (the context for assemblage formation) and the long-term potential for preservation and erosion of fluvial terraces and their archaeological contents. Case study examples are presented for the Solent River and the River Axe on the British south coast, exploring geoarchaeological issues within the context of understanding assemblage taphonomy and hominin behavior at local and regional scales. The paper concludes by assessing the potential and limitations of the approaches outlined.

INTRODUCTION

The Lower and Middle Paleolithic archaeology of northern Europe is characterized by occasional, well-preserved in situ sites such as Boxgrove (Roberts and Parfitt, 1998), Harnham (Whittaker et al., 2004), and Soucy (Lhomme, 2007), and large numbers of derived assemblages, occurring in secondary context within river terrace gravel and sand deposits (e.g., for the UK generally and the Thames Valley specifically—Wymer, 1968, 1999; McNabb, 2007; Bridgland, 1994; for northern France—Tuffreau and Antoine, 1995; for northern and central Germany—Bosinski, 1995; Mania, 1995; for a European perspective—Bridgland et al., 2006). These latter assemblages provide valuable and uniquely long-term perspectives on Pleistocene hominin occupa-

tion histories and land use. However, the interpretation of these assemblages, and in particular any evaluation of their spatial and chronological integrity, is dependent not only upon the physical condition of the artifacts themselves, but also on the nature of the fluvial environment and local depositional conditions.

The potential importance of these assemblages has a long history of recognition, as have models for their interpretation. Wymer (1968, his figures 5 and 6) provided a schematic model of the development of a river floodplain and terrace complex over a glacial-interglacial cycle. The model highlighted the potential burial, reworking, and intermixing of a series of hypothetical lithic industries, discarded at different times and locations across the floodplain, in response to flooding events, depositional episodes, and channel cutting and filling. More recently, the value of river terrace artifacts for the understanding of early hominin archaeology, both in the UK and other areas of the globe, has

*r.hosfield@rdg.ac.uk

Hosfield, R.T., 2011, Rolling stones: Understanding river-rolled Paleolithic artifact assemblages, *in* Brown, A.G., Basell, L.S., and Butzer, K.W., eds., Geoarchaeology, Climate Change, and Sustainability: Geological Society of America Special Paper 476, p. 37–52, doi:10.1130/2011.2476(04). For permission to copy, contact editing@geosociety.org. © 2011 The Geological Society of America. All rights reserved.

been re-highlighted (Gamble, 1996; Bridgland, 2000; Ashton and Lewis, 2002; Bridgland et al., 2006; Hosfield, 2007; Howard et al., 2007; Mishra et al., 2007; Ashton and Hosfield, 2010). This paper contributes to this recent focus by exploring geoarchaeological models and methods appropriate to the analysis and interpretation of these data at both site-level and regional scales.

The paper builds upon two key studies by Bridgland (1985) and Howard and Macklin (1999), which respectively explored the impact of different bedrock types upon river terrace formation and preservation, and the contrasting nature of fluvial activity in upland, lowland, and estuarine settings. This paper suggests a series of key factors (river type, bedrock, the chronology of fluvial activity, and depositional processes at confluences) that influence both short-term fluvial activity (the context in which stone artifacts become entrained within channel and floodplain sediments) and the long-term formation, preservation, and erosion of river terraces and their artifact contents.

Short examples are presented from the United Kingdom's Pleistocene rivers, including (1) the north-bank tributaries of the now-extinct Solent River, where heavily abraded lithic artifacts have been recovered in large concentrations from the terraces of the Test and Avon rivers (Hosfield, 2001; Ashton and Hosfield, 2010); and (2) the river Axe, where a predominantly lightly abraded lithic assemblage occurs within the fluvial sequence at Broom (Hosfield and Chambers, 2009). In both of these examples emphasis is given to understanding the nature and chronology of river development and the local/regional geological controls, their impacts upon the interpretation of these assemblages, and the nature of hominin land-use behavior in the surrounding environs.

FOCUSING ON RIVER TERRACE ARTIFACTS

The value of Pleistocene river terraces and their Paleolithic artifact assemblages is highlighted by Ashton and Lewis' (2002) modeling of the United Kingdom's Middle Thames' archaeology and interpretations of population and settlement history, the timing of the English Channel breach, and changing hominin landscape preferences during the early Middle Paleolithic (see also Ashton and Hosfield, 2010). Such approaches have clear potential for Pleistocene terraces with artifact assemblages in many other regions of the Paleolithic world. However, the artifact density–based model took no account of potential vertical reworking (i.e., from higher terraces into lower deposits). Given the observed pattern (declining values from the older to the younger terraces) and Ashton and Lewis' (2002) interpretation (reducing population sizes through time), the vertical reworking issue was not fundamentally problematic *in this case*, as any vertical reworking would only reduce the magnitude rather than the trend in artifact density per terrace through time. However, for this type of approach to be applicable elsewhere, an acknowledgment of derivation would be a key requirement, especially if artifact numbers were found to increase from the higher to the lower terraces (cf. Ashton and Hosfield, 2010).

A second factor highlighting the importance of geoarchaeological understanding of assemblage formation concerns a recent reappearance of the deployment of earlier Paleolithic artifacts as chronological markers. Examples from the UK include Westaway et al.'s (2006) use of the twisted ovate hand axe as a marine oxygen isotope stage (MIS) 11/10 indicator within their geochronological modeling of the Solent River terraces, Bridgland's (1996, 2001) highlighting of the first appearance of Levallois artifacts as an indicator of MIS 9/8 for both the Thames and the Solent River, and Wenban-Smith's (2004) recent suggestion that ficron and cleaver forms may indicate a late Acheulean (MIS 8?) stage in the UK. It should be emphasized that all of these studies are robust, in particular the "first appearance" age indicators for Levallois artifacts in the Thames (although the proportion of twisted ovate hand axes [15%] highlighted by Westaway et al. [2006] falls below the range originally presented by White [1998; White and Schreve, 2000] for a twisted ovate–dominated assemblage). However, there is potential here for geochronological confusion in *future* studies where the presence or absence of particular artifacts is taken as a dating indicator without due consideration for the degree of derivation and reworking that they may have undergone.

A final factor concerns the potential importance of artifact reworking for understanding key research questions, in particular apparent gaps in hominin presence. For example, the recent work at Pakefield on the United Kingdom's East Anglian coast (Parfitt et al., 2005) has extended the British Lower Paleolithic chronology back to ca. 700–750 ka[1], after which there is an apparently substantial "quiet" period prior to the first major occupation in MIS 13 (typified at Boxgrove, for example). While this patterning may be genuine, a sample of the rich pre-Anglian (Bridgland et al., 1995; Lee et al., 2004; Westaway, 2009; but cf. Gibbard et al., 2009) hand-axe assemblage at Warren Hill shows considerable evidence of wear and abrasion (Solomon, 1933; Roe, 1981, p. 111–116; Bridgland et al., 1995, p. 59–61; Wymer, 1999, p. 140 and figure 51) and may consist at least partly of artifacts derived from older deposits and land surfaces, potentially closer in age to the earlier Pakefield finds. Analysis of assemblage formation offers one means of assessing such possibilities.

KEY QUESTIONS

Analysis of derived artifact assemblages should focus upon two central issues:

1. What combinations of processes, for example, hominin/human behavior and glacial or fluvial action, have formed the artifact assemblage at this particular location? In the specific case of river terraces, this is particularly important when archaeologists are dealing with a "significant" concentration of artifacts ("significance" is often partially defined by the size of the

---

[1]Since the completion of this paper, the beginning of the British Lower Palaeolithic has been further pushed back to beyond 0.78 Ma due to the discoveries at the Happisburgh 3 site (Parfitt et al., 2010).

assemblage relative to the extant local or regional archaeological record), since such concentrations are sometimes viewed as potential indicators of a local hominin/human presence (Wessex Archaeology, 1993, p. 12, for example).

2. How long was the interval between the artifacts' discard upon the contemporary land surface, and their "final" accumulation within the sedimentary deposit? This is especially important for early Paleolithic lithic artifact assemblages within river terraces, since the date (e.g., based on optically stimulated luminescence [OSL] or amino acid racemization) for the deposit provides the only artifact typology–independent chronology for the material. Key factors influencing the length of the interval include the timing and nature of the fluvial activity cycle, subaerial erosion and transport processes (e.g., solifluction), and the scope for vertical reworking of artifacts between terrace landforms.

ARTIFACT CONCENTRATIONS: WHERE AND WHY?

The answer to why artifact assemblages occur at certain locations, and not others, within Pleistocene river landscapes is a combination of hominin landscape preferences and behaviors (including artifact discard) and fluvial processes. In order to access hominin behavior, it is therefore necessary to evaluate the nature and the impact of the local/regional fluvial system with respect to the formation of any particular assemblage.

There has been extensive experimental archaeological research regarding the transportation and/or physical modification of lithic artifacts within fluvial systems, both in the UK and abroad (Shackley, 1974; Schick, 1986, 1987; Petraglia and Nash, 1987; Harding et al., 1987; Isaac, 1989; Macklin, 1995; Hosfield and Chambers, 2005; Chambers, 2005). This research has utilized both laboratory techniques (flume and tumbling mill equipment) and field-based experiments to explore spatial patterning associated with the fluvial dispersal of artifacts, and the damage (arête abrasion, edge microflaking) sustained by the artifacts. One of the limitations of such work, however, concerns the difficulties in replicating the likely conditions characteristic of high-energy Pleistocene rivers, and therefore in modifying experimental artifacts to the degrees seen in the archaeological record (Chambers, 2005, p. 32; Brown, 1997, p. 96).

An alternative approach to identifying and modeling the formation of artifact concentrations highlights the factors of concentration and condition, particularly on those occasions where dense concentrations of heavily modified (fluvially abraded) artifacts occur. It has been argued that large artifact concentrations within a fluvial setting are likely to have only been transported short distances, as otherwise greater size sorting and wider dispersal of the material would be expected (Wessex Archaeology, 1993, p. 12), and yet the UK record includes a number of instances (e.g., Wood Green and Dunbridge on the north-bank tributaries of the Solent River [Hosfield, 2001; Ashton and Hosfield, 2010], Grovelands Pit in the Middle Thames [Wymer, 1968, p. 152–158], and Warren Hill, in the valley of the Lark but associated with the now-extinct Bytham River [Solomon, 1933;

Bridgland et al., 1995; Rose et al., 1996; Wymer, 1999, figure 51; but cf. Gibbard et al., 2009]) where dense artifact concentrations do contain a significant percentage of heavily abraded specimens. Although extensive abrasion is at least a *partial* indicator of long transport distances (it is certainly not a direct correlate), the questions of how these assemblages form, and why at those particular locations, remain.

Fluvial evidence (Best and Bristow, 1993; Schumm, 2005) suggests that two groups of local and regional processes (direct and indirect) play important roles in supporting the repeated deposition of transported artifacts in particular locations, generating localized concentrations of material from a range of source areas (i.e., both near- and far-traveled specimens).

Bedrock and Alluvial Sediment Conditions

The impact of bedrock and alluvium sediments upon fluvial behavior and morphology (including valley and channel widths and the ability of the river to shift laterally) has been widely recognized. Schumm (2005, p. 97–103), for example, emphasized the influences of the presence and type of bedrock (e.g., resistant or soft), the presence of resistant alluvium in river terraces and alluvial fans, colluvium (e.g., debris flows), and glacial outwash. From a Pleistocene perspective, Bridgland (1985) highlighted the specific impact of bedrock upon fluvial terrace formation and preservation at a regional scale for the Thames in the UK (Fig. 1), while Wymer (1968, p. 28) also discussed this issue at a local scale with respect to the outcropping of hard, resistant rocks. Wymer noted that local bedrock features can promote the preservation of terrace deposits where an outcrop of resistant rock constricts the river, thus protecting those terraces that form immediately downstream of it.

Bridgland (1985, p. 31) noted that major staircase terrace sequences in the Thames were confined to areas of clayey bedrock, with sandy bedrock tending to be associated with sporadic but equal preservation of terraces on both sides of the valley, while terraces were largely absent in areas of chalk bedrock (similar patterns were also observed for the Solent River basin in the southern UK by Allen and Gibbard, 1993, p. 520–521). Bridgland emphasized both the relative resistance to erosion of the bedrock type (particularly in the case of chalk) and the permeability of the bedrock, because rivers flowing over clay appear to move off their most recently deposited sands and gravels and erode into the bedrock on the opposite valley side during downcutting phases, encouraging lateral migration of the river. In contrast, rivers flowing on chalk appear to remain entrenched in one position, cutting into their own valley floor deposits when downcutting occurs.

Bridgland (1985, p. 29–30) further indicated that contrasting patterns of terrace preservation between areas of Tertiary clay (terrace staircases on one side of the valley) and unconsolidated sands (sporadic terraces on both sides of the valley) can also be linked to the erosion-resistant nature of highly permeable sedimentary rocks (e.g., unconsolidated sands and gravels), which

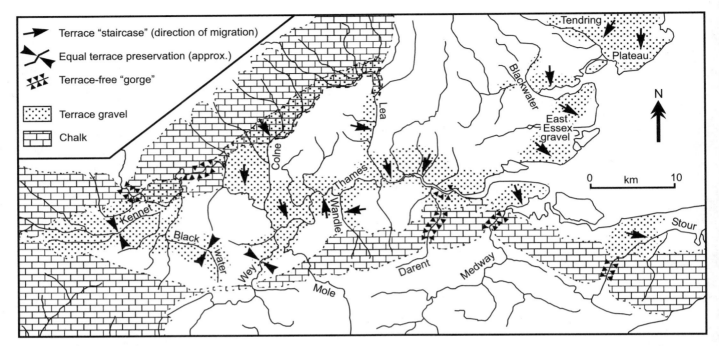

Figure 1. Variable fluvial terrace preservation in the Thames Basin (Bridgland, 1985, his figure 1). London is at ~51°N latitude, 0° longitude.

occurs because their permeability inhibits surface runoff. After initial unidirectional migration (e.g., to the south), clay-bedrock rivers are largely prevented from remigrating north by the presence and resistance of permeable terrace sands and gravels overlying the softer clays on that side of the valley (even when incision takes the channel below the level of the terrace deposits, the clay bedrock "bluff" at the terrace edge is likely to be rapidly covered by slumped and soliflucted sands and gravels, which will continue to impede erosion of the northern valley side). The river therefore tends to always migrate in the same direction (e.g., southwards in this example), producing extensive terrace staircases on one side of the valley. For sandy-bedrock rivers, there is little difference between the bedrock and the aggraded materials, so fluvial migration is bidirectional, and sporadic terrace preservation occurs on both sides of the valley (Fig. 1).

These processes emphasize that while artifacts may initially be deposited in a wide range of fluvial settings, local- and regional-scale bedrock factors are likely to limit the number of locations with long-term terrace preservation potential. Subsequent erosion of vulnerable floodplain sediments is therefore likely to concentrate derived artifacts into a smaller set of terrace deposits (see the example for the Solent River tributaries described herein).

Alluvial Fans and River Confluences

The impacts of main channel–tributary confluences upon sedimentary behavior are well documented (e.g., Best, 1986,

1987, 1988; Robert, 2003, p. 157–168; Fig. 2), with bed and/or channel forms arising from the changes and/or differences in channel flow and sediment load between the tributary and the main channel (e.g., Brown, 1997, his Table 1.1). While the specific location and type of sediment bars at channel confluences will vary according to planform geometry (Robert, 2003, p. 162), there is a common presence of sediment accumulation zones along channel confluences. A factor of particular interest is Mosher and Martini's (2002, p. 229) observation that only the coarsest fraction of sediment was stored in the bars formed at the confluence of two sub-Arctic Canadian rivers (the finer fractions were transported downstream). Best (1988, p. 492) observed coarser material and reduced sediment movement at the mouth of a confluence channel, which was thought to reflect the influence of the lower-velocity flows in the stagnation zone combined with the effect of greater flow depth to particle size ratios. Since the most commonly recovered early Paleolithic artifacts (Acheulean hand axes) from river terrace deposits are relatively large clasts in size (cobbles, after Friedman and Sanders' [1978] classification), the processes observed by Mosher and Martini (2002) and Best (1988) favor the preferential deposition of entrained artifacts within the confluence zone. Such deposits would be vulnerable to subsequent flooding and reworking; nonetheless, Mosher and Martini (2002, p. 230) suggested that the diagnostic side bar features (forming in the alternating zones of flow separation and characterized in their study by sandy gravels ranging from pebbles to small boulders) can be readily preserved in the geological record (although their river-confluence origin can only

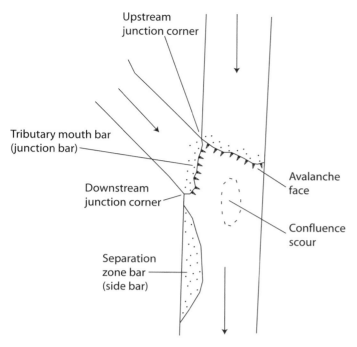

Figure 2. Schematic bed morphology and depositional features at asymmetric stream confluences (modified from Mosher and Martini, 2002, their figure 17).

be recognized in the context of associated stratigraphical units). Best (1988, p. 494–495) also emphasized a series of characteristic features that can aid the identification of ancient confluence sediments, including large foreset slopes and cross-sets (up to several meters in height for large rivers), and complex bedding surfaces with both normal and parallel dipping to the dominant paleoflow direction and abrupt grain-size changes (the separation zone bar deposits).

A review of the Lower and Middle Paleolithic archaeology associated with major UK Pleistocene fluvial systems (Gibbard, 1985, 1994; Allen and Gibbard, 1993; Bridgland, 1994; Wymer, 1999) highlights a series of earlier Paleolithic assemblages (partially or wholly abraded) located in the vicinity (less than 1 km distant, with the exception of West Drayton) of confluences: at Milford Hill (Salisbury), where the Bourne joins the Avon (Wymer, 1999, p. 108–109 and Map 29), at the meeting of the Dun and the Test (Wymer, 1999, p. 109, and Map 28), at the inferred paleoconfluence of the Colne and the Thames in the vicinity of West Drayton (Wymer, 1999, p. 62 and Map 8), the joining of the Cherwell and the Thames (Wymer, 1999, p. 46–47 and Map 4), and the confluence of the Chess and the Gade with the Colne (Wymer, 1999, p. 90, and Map 18; Table 1). These confluences were principally identified on the basis of geographical location rather than sedimentary records, due to the nature of the historical quarrying that exposed the deposits and the archaeology and that resulted in limited documentary records. Similar associations are also evident in the northern French Lower Paleolithic record, including the Carpentier quarry at Abbeville

(located on the right bank of the Somme, at the confluence with its small tributary, the Scardon), and the sites at Saint-Acheul, on the left bank of the Somme at its confluence with the Avre (Tuffreau and Antoine, 1995, p. 148 and 150). While it is clear from Ashmore (1993) that there is a wide range of distinctive sedimentary processes associated with (braided stream anabranch) confluences, including bar complex erosion and destruction, the evidence from the Paleolithic geoarchaeological record suggests that fluvial confluences and their immediate downstream reaches are probable contributory factors in assemblage formation at the *micro* scale (much of the extant discussions of confluences with regard to Lower and Middle Paleolithic artifact distributions, for example in Wymer [1999, p. 46–48], have concerned the attractions to hominins of confluences' facilitation of communication and movement, and therefore emphasize a different role of confluences at the *local* and *regional* scales).

A second set of processes contributing to the clustered deposition of transported artifacts includes the formation of sedimentary alluvial fans, in particular, their tendency to trap the majority of the coarse sediment (potentially including larger lithic artifacts) delivered from mountain/upland catchments as stream competence and carrying capacity are effectively reduced by the increased flow area (French, 1987, p. 32; Harvey et al., 2005, p. 1). Although much of the focus on these landforms has concerned the arid landscapes of the American Southwest, Harvey et al. (2005) emphasized the fact that alluvial fans occur in all climatic environments, combine a range of depositional processes (e.g., debris flows and sheet and channelized fluvial activity: see also Mather, 1999, p. 77–79), and range widely in scale (from small debris cones to megafans). With specific reference to the Pleistocene, Lewis et al. (2006) observed these processes at Latton in the United Kingdom's Thames Valley, where the sedimentology and geometry of the gravels are consistent with a low-angled alluvial fan. They suggested that the fan formed as a consequence of the high-gradient River Churn depositing its sediment onto the low-gradient floodplain of the main Thames valley.

There are examples of artifact concentrations associated with alluvial-fan deposits, including the UK's Lower Paleolithic assemblage from the Wallingford fan gravels (although recovered from a series of pits, Roe [1968, p. 22] noted that the artifacts all originate from the fan deposit: 11.3 km [7 mi] long and between 1.6 km [1 mi] and 6.4 km [4 mi] wide). The gravels accumulated by a mixture of solifluction and fluvial deposition (Horton et al., 1981, p. 246–247), leading Wymer (1999, p. 175–176) to suggest that the paleoliths must have been derived off the slopes or crest of the Chilterns' chalk escarpment.

Example 1: Local Concentrations

The River Axe valley in southwest England (Fig. 3) shows persistent evidence for the role of river confluences in focusing sediment deposition: notable concentrations are associated with the Yarty/Axe confluence (between Axminster and Kilmington), the Blackwater/Axe confluence (at Broom; Green, 1988, p. 180),

TABLE 1. SELECTED MAIN-CHANNEL AND TRIBUTARY CONFLUENCES AND ASSOCIATED LOWER AND MIDDLE PALEOLITHIC ASSEMBLAGES FROM THE UNITED KINGDOM

Main river	Tributaries	Confluence	Key sites	Artifact condition(s)	References
Avon	Bourne	". . . this, again, is a classic example of rich accumulations of discarded palaeoliths at the confluence of rivers in chalk country." (Wymer, 1999, p. 108–109)	New Godolphin School, Milford Hill, Foley's Pit	Includes "very heavily abraded material" (after Shackley, 1974)	Hosfield (1999, p. 185–193); Wymer (1999, p. 108–109 and Map 29)
Test	Dun	"A small tributary stream flowing from the west here [the Dun] joins the Test . . . immediately [to the] south . . . the ground rapidly rises . . . it is here the gravel is quarried." (Dale, 1918, p. 21)	Dunbridge	Includes "very heavily abraded material" (after Shackley, 1974)	Dale (1918, p. 20–22); Hosfield (1999, p. 185–193); Wymer (1999, Map 28)
Colne	Chess, Gade	"The gravel pits at Croxley Green, between the Chess and the Gade . . . Mill End, situated below the confluence of the Chess . . ." (Sherlock and Noble 1922, p. 43–44); ". . . the only prolific sites exist at Rickmansworth and Croxley Green, where the Colne receives the Chess and the Gade." (Wymer, 1999, p. 47)	Rickmansworth (Long Valley Wood, Croxley Green, and Mill End)	~98% (Croxley Green) and 80% (Mill End) nonsharp/mint artifacts (Wymer 1968, p. 247 and 249), and mixtures of "simple" and "refined" technologies (Wymer, 1999, p. 90)	Sherlock and Noble (1922, p. 44); Wymer (1968, p. 246–249; 1999, p. 90 and Map 18)
Thames	Cherwell	". . . this [the confluence of the tributary with the main river] could account for the rich Acheulean sites of Wolvercote and Iffley . . ." (Wymer, 1999, p. 46)	Iffley (Cornish's Pit)	No artifacts in "sharp or mint condition" (Wymer 1968, p. 92), and "an *omnium gatherum* of all the debris that ever rolled in the Thames valley." (Arkell, 1947, p. 220)	Arkell (1947, p. 220–221); Wymer (1968, p. 91–92; 1999, p. 46–47 and Map 4)
Thames	Colne	". . . there is a prolific spread of hand-axes in the Yiewsley–West Drayton area . . . where the Colne would have met the Thames . . ." (Wymer, 1999, p. 47)	Hillingdon, Yiewsley (Sabey's and Eastwood's Pits) and West Drayton	~89% nonsharp/mint artifacts in the non-Levallois component (Wymer, 1968, p. 258)	Wymer (1968, p. 255–259; 1999, p. 47, 62 and Map 8)

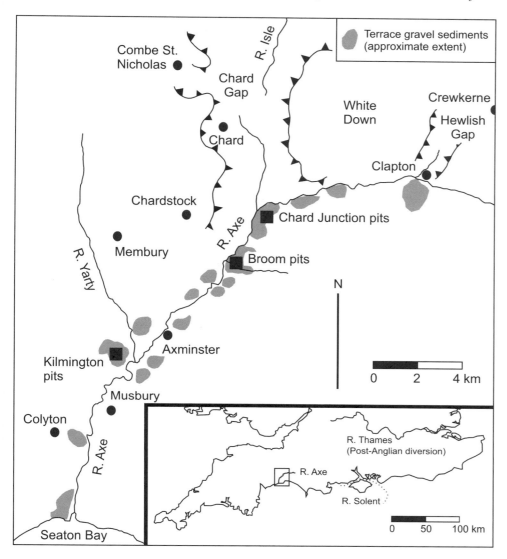

Figure 3. Fluvial deposits in the Axe valley, southwest England (after Shakesby and Stephens, 1984, their figure 1). Reproduced with the permission of The Devonshire Association. R.—River. Rectangle in map at bottom shows placement of top figure.

and a further confluence at Chard Junction (Shakesby and Stephens, 1984, their figure 1; Campbell et al., 1998, p. 309, and their figure 9.10; British Geological Survey, 2005). While not all of these locations have yielded major artifact concentrations (this is reliant both upon hominin activity, either in the vicinity of the deposit or further upstream, and archaeological discoveries), the Axe valley's (and the UK's southwest region's) major Lower Paleolithic assemblage is located at one of these confluences: the fluvial deposits at Broom (Hosfield, 2005; Hosfield and Chambers, 2009).

Full descriptions of the Broom sediments can be found in Campbell et al. (1998, p. 307–318), with additional site information in Shakesby and Stephens (1984), Green (1988), and Hosfield and Chambers (2009). In summary, the Broom sediments consist of a tripartite deposit with fine-grained clays and silts (the Middle Beds) sandwiched between coarser fluvial materials (the Upper and Lower Gravels). The three units suggest two phases of periglacial braided stream activity, depositing the Upper and Lower Gravels, interrupted by temperate climate floodplain deposition of the fine-grained sediments. The 1930s field notes of the principal artifact collector at Broom (Hosfield, 2009), combined with Moir (1936), indicate that for those artifacts where provenance data were available, the majority were associated with the Middle Beds (Hosfield and Chambers, 2009, p. 88–89). Analysis of the physical condition of a large sample of the Broom hand axes (*n* = 977; Hosfield and Chambers, 2009) indicates that while the majority (89%) bore only limited evidence of fluvial transport and derivation (although none of them was interpreted as being "unrolled" and in situ), a small proportion (11%) was more heavily abraded. The deposition of these latter specimens, probably further-traveled, within the Broom fluvial sediments, and the overall concentration of locally reworked artifacts, is best explained by the local conditions created by the confluence of the Axe and the Blackwater.

From the perspective of hominin behavioral models, the Broom data indicate a combination of concentrated artifact discard in the near vicinity (presumably reflecting the attractions of the local landscape, e.g., animals, water sources, crossing points) and wider-ranging activity and discard across the Axe valley landscape, followed by artifact reworking and redeposition at Broom.

Example 2: Regional Reworking

The north-bank tributaries of the now-extinct Solent River system on the UK's south coast indicate the role of bedrock conditions and river confluences in concentrating sedimentation and archaeological material. The impact of bedrock conditions is most evident for the Hampshire/Wiltshire Avon and the Hampshire Test, which flow over Upper Chalk bedrock in their upper reaches, before shifting onto Tertiary sands and clays as they approach Christchurch Bay and Southampton Water, respectively (Fig. 4).

Major artifact assemblages are associated with both the Avon and the Test, at Wood Green (~500 artifacts) and Dunbridge (~1000 artifacts), respectively (Fig. 4). Visual and metrical analysis of small artifact samples from both locations (Hosfield, 1999, p. 125) indicated a significant proportion of very heavily abraded (after Shackley, 1974) specimens (80% at Dunbridge and 100%

at Wood Green), suggestive of extensive transportation. The question of why the artifacts had not been more extensively dispersed and size-sorted is answered by the location of the two assemblages immediately downstream of the bedrock transition from the harder chalk to softer Tertiary sediments. Following Bridgland (1985) and Allen and Gibbard (1993), it is proposed that there *was* repeated artifact deposition, re-erosion and dispersal along the steeper gradient chalk stream stretches of the rivers (explaining the artifacts' physical conditions) as floodplain sediments were repeatedly lain down and reworked within the constraints of the relatively narrow, steep-sided valleys (there are only limited terrace remnants evident today). By contrast, the deposition of the reworked artifacts within the floodplain sediments at Wood Green and Dunbridge (probably also influenced in the latter case by the confluence of the Test and the Dun: Fig. 4) was the "final act," with offloading of the gravel and its archaeological contents by the rivers as they reached the lower gradients of the Tertiary bedrock (Ashton and Hosfield, 2010). Critically, those sediments were subsequently preserved as fluvial terraces due to the rivers migrating away from the deposits, across their wider, Tertiary floodplains (which retain extensive terrace deposits to the present, and are attractive to modern aggregates companies, thus exposing the gravels to "hand-axe hunters" and developing a further explanatory factor behind the concentration and distribution of artifacts in the archaeological record; Ashton and Hosfield, 2010).

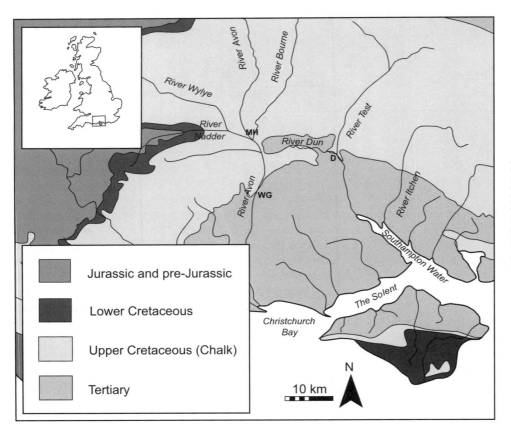

Figure 4. Pre-Quaternary bedrock in the Solent River landscape and key Lower Paleolithic assemblages and localities. D—Dunbridge; MH—Milford Hill (Salisbury); WG—Wood Green. Figure is after Ashton and Hosfield (2010, their figure 1), reproduced with permission of Wiley-Blackwell. Salisbury is at ~51°N latitude, 2°W longitude.

With regard to hominin landscape behavior and suggestions of concentrated activity and discard in the vicinity of Wood Green and Dunbridge, the data suggest that this was not entirely the case, but rather that hominin artifact discard was at least partly focused further upstream, in the chalk landscapes of Salisbury Plain and the North Downs (although it is likely that the rich gravels in the chalk-Tertiary boundary areas were attractive raw material sources to hominins, and that the less heavily abraded specimens *were* locally discarded; Ashton and Hosfield, 2010). Similar patterns are evident for the extensive fluvial deposits underlying Salisbury, relating to the confluences of the Avon with the Bourne to the east and the Nadder and Wylye to the west (Fig. 4). Sampling of the Salisbury artifacts in the area of Milford Hill between the Bourne and the Avon revealed extensive abrasion (90% of 78 sampled artifacts are classified after Shackley [1974] as very heavily abraded: Hosfield, 1999, p. 188–190), strongly suggesting that they have been fluvially transported downstream and that various locations upstream of Salisbury may also have been a target for hominin activity (in addition to the Salisbury environs that Wymer [1999, p. 113] interpreted as a key focus of hominin activity, with groups attracted to the confluence of four rivers, and the facility of movement in different directions that it provided with respect to the river valleys and the chalk downland). The potential time-depth of the reworking of the artifacts as they were transported through the chalk stream landscapes may well span several marine isotope stages (following Bridgland's [2000] climatic cycle-driven models of fluvial terrace formation), thus challenging assumptions of relatively large, "short"-lived (on MIS time scales) occupations, and raising the possibilities of more sporadic, lower-level hominin presences over longer time spans.

Hominin Influences

The previous discussions emphasize the role of geological and fluvial factors in concentrating Paleolithic artifacts. Such factors are of course modifying rather than constructing the archaeological signatures. Fluvial environments would have been strongly attractive to hominins, as permanent water sources, sources of game (e.g., as at Swanscombe, Clacton, and Soucy—Singer et al., 1973; Conway et al., 1996; McNabb, 2007; Lhomme, 2007), crossing places via sand and gravel bars, and sources of raw materials for knapping (e.g., as at Barnham—Ashton et al., 1998). Artifacts would therefore have habitually accumulated on channel margins and floodplains. It is not the intention of the paper to downplay those factors, rather to highlight that nonbehavioral factors also play a role in spatially structuring the record, particularly where a wide range of heterogeneous artifact conditions is evident within the assemblage.

INTERVALS IN TIME?

A second challenge when examining fluvial terrace archaeology concerns the duration of the time interval between the discarding of artifacts by hominins and their deposition within the dated sediments from which they are recovered. In some instances, these intervals may be relatively brief in Pleistocene terms (e.g., a few centuries or millennia). At Broom, for example, OSL dating of two of the three principal sedimentary units indicated probable sub–MIS stage intervals between the deposition of the Middle Beds and the Upper Gravels, while the presence and fresh condition of flakes alongside the hand axes in the Middle Beds suggested that these artifacts were discarded during a late MIS 9–early MIS 8 substage, broadly contemporaneous with the formation of the Middle Beds (Toms et al., 2005; Hosfield and Chambers, 2009). However, where the temporal intervals between discard and deposition are extensive (e.g., artifacts discarded in one MIS being reworked into the deposits of a later MIS), this has clear implications for the use of river terrace artifacts as a basis for settlement models (Ashton and Lewis, 2002; Ashton and Hosfield, 2010), for the use of diagnostic artifacts as chronological indicators, and for the relevance (with respect to the artifacts) of any paleoenvironmental evidence recovered from the deposits.

Assessments of these intervals are neither straightforward nor achievable at a high resolution, reflecting the currently undatable nature of the lithic artifacts and the large error ranges associated with fluvial sediment dating techniques (e.g., OSL). Nonetheless, evaluation of the probability of a shorter (e.g., sub–MIS) or longer (e.g., multiple MIS) interval duration is possible through a range of data relating to the artifacts, their local sedimentary setting, and the regional fluvial context, all of which should (where possible) be considered in combination.

Timing of Landform and Deposit Formation

Wymer (1968, 1999) and Bridgland (1994) documented numerous instances in the United Kingdom in which Lower or Middle Paleolithic artifact assemblages from the fluvial terraces of the River Thames and its tributaries are found in association with the bedrock surface and/or basal fluvial deposits (e.g., at Botany Chalk Pit and Esso Pit, Purfleet—Bridgland, 1994, p. 218–228; Cannoncourt Farm Pit, Furze Platt—Wymer, 1968, p. 221; Bridgland, 1994, p. 149–157; Cornish's Pit, Iffley—Wymer, 1968, p. 91; Globe Pit [Geological Conservation Review Site], Little Thurrock—Bridgland, 1994, p. 228–237; Gravelly Guy Pit, Oxfordshire—Hardaker, 2001, p. 186; Grovelands Pit, Reading—Wymer, 1968, p. 155; Highlands Farm Pit, Rotherfield Peppard—Wymer, 1968, p. 191–194; Bridgland, 1994, p. 141–145; Pearson's Pit, Dartford Heath—Bridgland, 1994, p. 189; and Wolvercote Brick Pit, Oxfordshire—Wymer, 1968, p. 88; Table 2). Interpretation of this stratigraphic patterning and its possible significance is aided by Bridgland's models (e.g., 2000) of terrace formation, originally developed for the River Thames and linked to the glacial-interglacial cycles, uplift, and other climatic fluctuations of the Pleistocene. A factor of particular relevance is Bridgland's association between the principal downcutting events (the abandonment of a higher/older floodplain and the formation of a new/lower floodplain) and the warming limb

TABLE 2. SELECTED LOWER AND MIDDLE PALEOLITHIC ASSEMBLAGES FROM BASAL DEPOSITS AND/OR BEDROCK
SURFACES IN THE UNITED KINGDOM

Site	Description	Reference
Dartford Heath (Pearson's Pit)	"Dewey (1959; unpublished, cited in Bridgland, 1994) clearly reported that some of Mr. Pearson's personal collection of hand-axes had been derived from the lowest part of the gravel…"	Bridgland (1994, p. 189)
Furze Platt (Cannoncourt Farm Pit)	"One large primary flake in near-mint condition lay on the chalk, and a few dozen primary and finishing flakes in sharp or slightly rolled condition were in the [up to 18 in.] gravel . . ." (JJW); "Treacher (1904) later described only 2.5 m of gravel at the site, the lowest 0.5 m yielding artefacts . . ." (DRB)	Wymer (1968, p. 221); Bridgland (1994, p. 150)
Stanton Harcourt (Gravelly Guy Pit)	". . . those recovered by MacRae from the base of the Stage 6 gravels in the pit . . ."	Hardaker (2001, p. 186)
Reading (Grovelands Pit)	". . . faunal remains . . . in association with flakes and hand-axes, in sand about 2 ft. from the base of the gravel . . . Both the faunal remains and the majority of the artefacts appear to have come from the lower part of the gravel . . ."	Wymer (1968, p. 155)
Harpsden (Highlands Farm Pit)	". . . crude flakes and cores in a rolled condition . . . [occurred] throughout the deposit for the most part between six inches and two feet above the chalk at the base . . ."	Wymer (1968, p. 191)
Iffley (Cornish's Pit)	". . . some of the implements are reported as coming from the surface of underlying Oxford Clay."	Wymer (1968, p. 91)
Little Thurrock (Globe Pit Geological Conservation Review Site)	". . . the Clactonian artefacts that occur in the gravel underlying the interglacial beds. This gravel . . . is presumed to represent the pre-interglacial aggradational phase (phase 2) . . ."	Bridgland (1994, p. 236)
Purfleet (Botany Chalk Pit and Esso Pit)	"The gravel immediately adjacent to this rising bank of Chalk contains one of the richest concentrations of worked flint in the British Palaeolithic . . ."; "The [Esso Pit] section proved to be rich in Palaeolithic artefacts [from the sandy gravel immediately overlying the Chalk] . . . with minimal disturbance of in situ material."	Bridgland (1994, p. 220–221 and figure 4.19)
Wolvercote (Brick Pit)	"Calcareous gravel. The Oxford Clay beneath is pot-holed and these holes are filled with gravel containing bones and artefacts."	Wymer (1968, p. 88)

(the glacial-interglacial transition) of the climatic cycle (where two downcutting episodes per cycle have been proposed, such as for the Solent River [Bridgland, 2001], the major incision event is still linked to the warming limb). Following this incision, the basal deposits are also assigned to the warming limb of the climatic cycle (i.e., Bridgland's phase 2 aggradation, demonstrated, for example, by the Swanscombe basal gravels; Bridgland, 1994, p. 196). Limited fine-grained deposition (during the fully temperate interglacial: phase 3) and a major aggradation on the cooling limb (phase 5) complete the cycle.

A key difficulty concerns the challenge in identifying and distinguishing sediments as either phase 2/warming limb deposits or phase 5/cooling limb deposits in the absence of intervening (phase 3) interglacial sediments, and consequently ease of interpretation varies by site (see discussions in Bridgland, 1994). It is also important to note that even within single systems, there is regional variability in the cycle: Bridgland et al. (2004) noted, for example, that in the Lower Thames, a basal cold-climate gravel

aggradation precedes interglacial sediments (as at the Globe Pit GCR [Global Conservation Review] site, Little Thurrock; Table 2), while in the Upper Thames (and also in the Severn–Avon), it is suggested that downcutting was immediately followed by deposition under interglacial conditions (as with the Stanton Harcourt Channel; Bridgland, 1994, p. 66). While these variations have clear implications for the contemporary climatic regimes, the overall principle of the warming limb incision as an important stratigraphic marker holds.

Based on these climatically driven cycles of fluvial activity, two alternative interpretations are proposed for the age of discard of artifacts occurring upon bedrock surfaces at the base of fluvial terrace sequences, or within the basal deposits burying those surfaces:

1. They are broadly contemporaneous with the formation of the basal deposits, and therefore with either the warming limb of the cycle (e.g., MIS 10/9, 8/7 etc., in the case of Bridgland's post-incision phase 2 aggradation) or with

the early part of the cooling limb (e.g., MIS 9/8, 7/6 etc., in the case of Bridgland's major phase 5 aggradation).

2. They are derived from higher and older floodplain (terrace) deposits, which were incised and eroded as part of the downcutting event, and then subsequently reworked as basal floodplain deposits. Such artifacts would therefore be at least one MIS older, e.g., probably dating to the full interglacial (e.g., MIS 11, 9, etc.) or the cooling limb (e.g., MIS 11/10, 9/8, etc.) of the *previous* cycle (with which Bridgland associates the principal aggradation events of his fluvial model).

The remaining problem therefore concerns the method with which to evaluate the contrasting interpretations of the time interval between the artifacts' discard and deposition. Alongside the position of the artifacts within the basal deposits, their *état physique* (e.g., the arête abrasion and edge microflaking) is of significance. Following the terminologies of Wymer (1968), Shackley (1974), and Ashton (1998), the presence of "mint," "sharp," or "fresh" material would appear to favor an assemblage for which discard was broadly contemporaneous with the formation of the basal deposits (e.g., the Clactonian material at Globe Pit; Bridgland, 1994, p. 236), as opposed to one reworked from a previous terrace level. However, four short examples indicate the variety of interpretations that have been applied:

1. At Cannoncourt Farm Pit in the Middle Thames Valley (Wymer, 1968, p. 221), material has been recovered that is both sharp *and* is reported to have been recovered from the bedrock surface: "The large proportion of sharp and near-mint hand-axes, some known to have been found on the chalk, strongly suggests a site which has, in part at least, been disturbed only slightly by the gravel which now lies over it" (Wymer, 1968, p. 221).

This would appear to suggest an assemblage discarded at a time broadly contemporary with the formation of the gravel deposit. In this case, however, the position of the deposit within the climatic cycle is uncertain in the absence of interglacial terrace sediments (phase 3), with Bridgland (1994, p. 157) noting that the Lynch Hill gravels at Cannoncourt Farm might represent either the warming limb (phase 2) or the cooling limb (phase 5) aggradations.

2. At the site of McIlroy's Pit, Reading, in the Middle Thames Valley, the "near mint" condition of a series of hand axes, combined with the field notes of a local collector, suggested to Wymer (1968, p. 150) that the artifacts lay "virtually *in situ* on a buried surface of Reading Clay", predating but probably broadly contemporary with the deposition of the Lynch Hill Terrace (MIS 10/9/8) gravel. Unfortunately, the absence of intervening interglacial sediments again means it is uncertain whether these are the warming limb (basal Lynch Hill) or cooling limb (major Lynch Hill aggradation) deposits.

3. At the Gravelly Guy pit in the Upper Thames (Hardaker, 2001; Scott and Buckingham, 2001), although the majority of the artifacts were described as "fresh" (Scott and Buckingham, 2001, p. 210), their position at the very base of cold-climate MIS 6 (Stanton Harcourt) gravels, sometimes at the junction with the Oxford Clay, and their association with characteristic MIS 7 fauna led to their interpretation as predating the gravels that buried them (Scott and Buckingham, 2001, p. 211). In this instance, the regional archaeological and environmental contexts, in particular the severe cold of MIS 6 and the apparent absence of humans from the UK between MIS 6 and late MIS 4 (Sutcliffe, 1995; Currant and Jacobi, 2001; Ashton, 2002), was an important additional factor in the reworking interpretation (although MacRae [1990] had previously suggested the possibility that the artifacts might have been discarded during an interstadial associated with the deposition of the "cold gravels").

4. Similar reworking interpretations have been suggested at other pits in the Upper Thames, in this case containing Devensian (Late Pleistocene) deposits. The majority of the artifacts at Cassington Pit were recovered from the coarse basal gravels lying directly upon the Oxford Clay (Hardaker, 2001, p. 191), and the gravels and other deposits (facies associations A and B) were dated to MIS 5 (Maddy et al., 1998). Although the adherence of Oxford Clay on a number of the artifacts might have suggested an assemblage contemporary with the exposure of the bedrock (through the cutting of the channel and floodplain), this would have implied an early Devensian, cold-climate human presence, in contradiction with the evidence both from the artifacts' technology and from the rest of the UK at this time (Sutcliffe, 1995; Currant and Jacobi, 2001; Ashton, 2002). This led Hardaker (2001) to conclude that the artifacts, predominantly rolled, were significantly derived from older land surfaces (probably at least as old as MIS 7) prior to their deposition.

In summary, the evidence from stratigraphic position within terrace sequences is frequently ambiguous with regard to the interval between artifact discard and deposition, and generalized statements are inappropriate. While artifact condition and other criteria (e.g., the presence of bedrock traces) are useful, it is always necessary to assess both these specific local conditions and the wider Pleistocene context (e.g., the inferred climatic conditions associated with the formation of the deposits, the position of the deposits within the climatic cycle, and the overall patterning of hominin presence and absence in the regional archaeological record), as in the latter two examples presented here.

Finally, it is emphasized that although many Pleistocene fluvial sequences do not conform to the Bridgland (2000) model described previously (in the Somme, for example, interglacial sediments occur at the top of the terrace formations, with cold-climate gravels beneath, perhaps suggesting that incision occurred in response to climate cooling; Bridgland et al. 2004), the overall impression is that all Pleistocene terrace systems do form in synchrony with climatic cycles, albeit at varying scales (e.g., glacial-interglacial versus megacycles; Bridgland, 2000). The principles outlined here would therefore be translatable to different systems, with local terrace stratigraphy providing information as to the possible depositional histories of artifacts.

Artifact Condition

Artifact condition can give a broad indication as to the likely degree of chronological reworking to which the material has been subject: contrast, for example, the condition of the artifacts from the lower gravels at Highlands Farm Pit (rolled Clactonian-type artifacts and generally less-rolled hand axes; Bridgland, 1994, p. 193), and the basal gravels (sharp Clactonian-type material) at the Purfleet Esso and Botany Chalk pits (Bridgland, 1994, p. 218–228). Similarly, analysis of hand-axe condition (after Ashton, 1998) from five terraces in the Solent River strongly supported an interpretation of significant vertical and chronological reworking, as the proportions of very rolled material increased in the lower terraces (Ashton and Hosfield, 2010). However analysis of an artifact's state of abrasion may be misleading because its condition (e.g., heavily abraded specimens) can reflect extensive lateral reworking along river valleys over very short periods, perhaps decadal or even annual. This is illustrated by Schmidt and Ergenzinger's (1992; Schmidt, 1994) tracer experiments on Lainbach River, southern Bavaria. During extreme floods (with a recurrence interval in excess of 100 yr) in the summer of 1990, magnetic tracers were transported up to at least 300–350 m downstream, and Schmidt (1994, p. 124) suggested that a greater number of the tracers (only ~25% were retrieved) had probably been transported out of the surveyed reach. A radio-tracer pebble, for example, moved over 800 m during a single flood in August 1988, through cumulative transport steps and non-movement intervals (Schmidt and Ergenzinger, 1992, p. 159). Nonetheless, there are three further measurable traits for assessing the probable scale (sub-MIS or spanning MIS) of any time intervals between discard and deposition.

River Type

Howard and Macklin (1999, their Tables 1–3) emphasized the differential geomorphological behavior and preservation potential (including terraces) of fluvial systems from source to mouth. Factors of particular interest are the contrasts between terrace preservation and sediment reworking in the upland and lowland zones:

- In uplands, long-term terrace preservation can be prevented, especially in narrow valleys, and high-magnitude flooding is capable of flushing the sedimentary fills from the valleys.
- In lowlands, river-system stability and the dominance of vertical accretion processes can result in the burial and preservation of archaeological materials.

The *general* scope for artifact reworking and the scale of probable time intervals are therefore likely to vary (and decrease) markedly between upland and lowland fluvial systems (Fig. 5): Where well-preserved, long terrace flights are present (e.g., as in the lower River Thames valley [Bridgland, 1994] and the lower reaches of the Solent River [Allen and Gibbard, 1993]), the potential for artifact derivation across multiple terrace levels

and oxygen isotope stages should be reduced (but cf. Ashton and Hosfield, 2010).

Bedrock Conditions

Within a particular river zone (e.g., the lowland zone of the Thames Basin), bedrock, and therefore terrace preservation, can vary markedly, ranging from terrace flights or "staircases" on clays and sands to terrace-free "gorges" on chalk (Bridgland, 1985; Fig. 1). Bedrock variability will therefore influence the scope for artifact reworking over relatively short and long time scales (e.g., sub-MIS and multiple MIS).

Alluvial Fans

Alluvial fans can rework and bring into close proximity sediments (and archaeology) of markedly different ages (this is particularly exacerbated by the presence of a braided zone featuring unstable channels and potentially multiple flow paths; French, 1987, p. 20). Gábris and Nagy (2005, p. 61) observed that on the Sajó-Hernád fan (associated with the Sajó and Hernád Rivers on the margins of the Carpathian Basin), sedimentary activity varied between glacial and interglacial stages. During the former, only fine sediments were transported onto the fan, with sands and gravels deposited in the Sajó valley as terrace sediments. In the interglacial stages, the gravel and sand terraces were eroded, and the coarser material was remobilized, transported, and deposited on the fan. Moreover, the fan displays clear evidence for multiple fluvial phases (dating between the Last Glacial Maximum and the Subboreal Holocene), including lateral erosion and incision episodes resulting in the reworking of sediments.

Lewis et al.'s (2006, p. 203) work in the Upper Thames at Latton documented a complex series of depositional and erosional events spanning MIS 7 to MIS 2, with MIS 7 and MIS 4 to MIS 2 age sediments occurring within a narrow altitudinal range and superimposed within the same sedimentary succession. They suggested that this could be related to the dynamics of the alluvial fan at Latton, with periodic switching of the main channel from one part of the fan to another, expressed as a series of cut-and-fill sequences (i.e., channel incision and infilling). They contrasted the resulting sedimentary pattern against the models of chronologically distinct large-scale terrace aggradations and incision episodes driven by major glacial-interglacial climatic fluctuations and crustal uplift, which have been applied to the Thames as a whole (Bridgland, 1994; Maddy et al., 2001). They concluded by suggesting that an alluvial-fan system interpretation at Latton has implications for the timing of gravel emplacement in the Upper Thames, the significance of deposit and terrace distribution and altitude, and the overall sediment dynamics of the Upper Thames. From the artifact assemblage perspective of this paper, an alluvial-fan environment may also enhance the potential for significant chronological reworking of archaeology, with artifacts of substantially differing ages brought into close proximity through channel infilling and incision.

A) Upland river system with poorly preserved terrace landforms and deposits

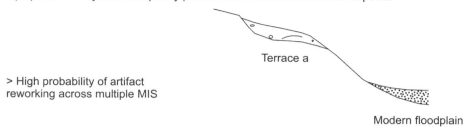

Terrace a

> High probability of artifact
reworking across multiple MIS

Modern floodplain

B) Lowland river system with well-preserved terrace landforms and deposits

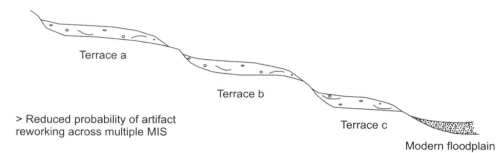

Terrace a

Terrace b

> Reduced probability of artifact
reworking across multiple MIS

Terrace c

Modern floodplain

Figure 5. Contrasting reworking models
for upland and lowland zone rivers (after Howard and Macklin, 1999). MIS—
Marine oxygen isotope stage.

POTENTIAL AND LIMITATIONS

The described approaches to interpreting and understanding Paleolithic artifact assemblages from fluvial terraces have clear potential and benefits, but also limitations. The potential and benefits include:

1. An understanding of the patterns in chronological reworking of artifacts can inform debates concerning broad-scale patterns, e.g., "absence of evidence or evidence or absence" from particular fluvial landscapes and/or regions at particular time periods (e.g., the absence of hominins from the UK between MIS 6 and MIS 4).
2. Assessments of patterns in assemblage location can assist in contextualizing hominin landscape activity (e.g., Wymer's [1999, p. 113] model of hominin focus in and around the Salisbury river confluences).
3. Modeling of artifact condition can support the classification of samples as homogeneous or heterogeneous, and in the latter case assist in the broad division of material groups. This can potentially permit robust patterns in artifact typology and technology to be explored (e.g., the discussion of the fresh and worn hand-axe groups from Warren Hill presented by Roe [1981] and Bridgland et al. [1995]).
4. Overall, modeling of spatial and chronological artifact reworking can assist in identifying appropriate data sets for particular research questions and/or appropriate questions for particular data sets (for example, avoiding fluvial terrace sequences with severe vertical reworking when exploring demographic, settlement or techno-typological patterns through time).

All of these points are therefore central to a fuller understanding of a fluvial artifact record that dominates much of the earlier Paleolithic (e.g., Bridgland et al., 2006; Mishra et al., 2007). Nonetheless, the approaches described here also have clear limitations:

1. It is not realistic to model artifact transportation and reworking in anything other than broad terms, such as "within a single MIS," "derivation from sources adjacent to the findspots" (cf. Hosfield, 2001). This does not invalidate the approaches described here, however; it simply emphasizes the importance of explicitly identifying appropriately scaled questions (Gamble, 1996; Hosfield, 2007).
2. Analysis of data sets can appear as simple exercises in deconstruction, i.e., "we cannot discuss hominin behaviours because the assemblages are reworked." Two points are highlighted in response. First, it is important to refrain from asking inappropriate questions of data sets, rather than ignoring the structural realities of the data. This has previously been effectively demonstrated by Stern (1993, p. 202 and 207) for the east African early Pleistocene record, where she concluded that a series of archaeological materials could only be considered to be contemporaneous within the boundaries of the Lower Okote Member (up to 8 m of channel and floodplain deposits) and that there was a serious mismatch between the structure of the archaeological record and the interpretive models being applied to it. Second, acknowledgment of the data's structure will always lead to new questions, albeit at scales and resolutions that may not previously have been considered (e.g., the Ashton and Lewis [2002] and Ashton

and Hosfield [2010] MIS-scale settlement models for the Middle Thames and Solent River catchments).

CONCLUSIONS

The realities of much of the Paleolithic archaeological record associated with fluvial terraces concern artifact reworking and taphonomic influences upon assemblage formation and location. From the perspective of various behavioral questions (e.g., settlement histories and land use), assessment of these realities is a key requirement. This paper has proposed a number of lines of evidence and approaches for evaluating artifact reworking and assemblage formation, including artifact condition, river type (including the presence of confluences and alluvial fans), bedrock type, and the cyclical chronology of fluvial activity.

While the approaches described here emphasize relative and/or low-resolution measures (e.g., intra- or inter-MIS time scales for reworking), such measures are appropriate for the nature of the archaeological and sedimentary records. In placing a requirement upon archaeologists to frame suitably scaled questions, this paper therefore highlights the geoarchaeological realities of a widespread and valuable strand of Paleolithic data.

ACKNOWLEDGMENTS

Much of the work reported here was funded by English Heritage through the Aggregates Levy Sustainability Fund (project no. 3361), and their support is gratefully acknowledged. The ideas in this paper were originally presented at the Geoarchaeology 06 conference (Exeter University, UK, September 2006). Other work was funded by an Arts and Humanities Research Board studentship and a British Academy Postdoctoral Fellowship. Thanks also go to Martin Bell and Jennifer Heathcote for their comments on earlier drafts of this paper, and to the three anonymous referees for their many helpful comments.

REFERENCES CITED

Allen, L.G., and Gibbard, P.L., 1993, Pleistocene evolution of the Solent River of southern England: Quaternary Science Reviews, v. 12, p. 503–528, doi:10.1016/0277-3791(93)90067-V.

Arkell, W.J., 1947, The Geology of Oxford: Oxford, Clarendon Press, 267 p.

Ashmore, P., 1993, Anabranch confluence kinetics and sedimentation processes in gravel-braided streams, in Best, J.L., and Bristow, C.S., eds., Braided Rivers: Geological Society of London Special Publication 75, p. 129–146.

Ashton, N.M., 1998, The taphonomy of the flint assemblages, in Ashton, N.M., Lewis, S.G., and Parfitt, S.A., eds., Excavations at the Lower Palaeolithic Site at East Farm, Barnham, Suffolk 1989–94: London, British Museum Occasional Paper 125, p. 183–204.

Ashton, N.M., 2002, Absence of humans in Britain during the last interglacial (oxygen isotope stage 5e), in Roebroeks, W., and Tuffreau, A., eds., Le Dernier Interglaciaire et les Occupations Humaines du Paléolithique Moyen: Lille, Publications du Centre d'études et de recherches préhistoriques, p. 93–103.

Ashton, N., and Hosfield, R., 2010, Mapping the human record in the British early Palaeolithic: Evidence from the Solent River system: Journal of Quaternary Science, v. 25, no. 5, p. 737–753, doi: 10.1002/jqs.1350.

Ashton, N., and Lewis, S., 2002, Deserted Britain: Declining populations in the British late middle Pleistocene: Antiquity, v. 76, p. 388–396.

Ashton, N.M., Lewis, S.G., and Parfitt, S.A., eds., 1998, Excavations at the Lower Palaeolithic Site at East Farm, Barnham, Suffolk 1989–94: London, British Museum Occasional Paper 125, 305 p.

Best, J.L., 1986, The morphology of river channel confluences: Progress in Physical Geography, v. 10, p. 157–174, doi:10.1177/030913338601000201.

Best, J.L., 1987, Flow dynamics at river channel confluences: Implications for sediment transport and bed morphology, in Ethridge, F.G., Flores, R.M., and Harvey, M.D., eds., Recent Developments in Fluvial Sedimentology: Contributions from the Third International Fluvial Sedimentology Conference: Society of Economic Paleontologists and Mineralogists Special Publication 39, p. 27–35.

Best, J.L., 1988, Sediment transport and bed morphology at river channel confluences: Sedimentology, v. 35, p. 481–498, doi:10.1111/j.1365-3091.1988.tb00999.x.

Best, J.L., and Bristow, C.S., eds., 1993, Braided Rivers: Geological Society of London Special Publication 75, 419 p.

Bosinski, G., 1995, The earliest occupation of Europe: Western central Europe, in Roebroeks, W., and van Kolfschoten, T., eds., The Earliest Occupation of Europe: Proceedings of the European Science Foundation Workshop at Tautavel (France) 1993: Leiden, Leiden University Press, p. 103–128.

Bridgland, D.R., 1985, Uniclinal shifting: A speculative reappraisal based on terrace distribution in the London Basin: Quaternary Newsletter, v. 47, p. 26–33.

Bridgland, D.R., 1994, Quaternary of the Thames: London, Chapman and Hall, Geological Conservation Review Series 7, 441 p.

Bridgland, D.R., 1996, Quaternary river terrace deposits as a framework for the Lower Palaeolithic record, in Gamble, C.S., and Lawson, A.J., eds., The English Palaeolithic Reviewed: Salisbury, Wessex Archaeology Ltd., p. 23–39.

Bridgland, D.R., 2000, River terrace systems in north-west Europe: An archive of environmental change, uplift and early human occupation: Quaternary Science Reviews, v. 19, p. 1293–1303, doi:10.1016/S0277-3791 (99)00095-5.

Bridgland, D.R., 2001, The Pleistocene evolution and Palaeolithic occupation of the Solent River, in Wenban-Smith, F.F., and Hosfield, R.T., eds., Palaeolithic Archaeology of the Solent River: Lithic Studies Society Occasional Paper 7, p. 15–25.

Bridgland, D.R., Lewis, S.G., and Wymer, J.J., 1995, Middle Pleistocene stratigraphy and archaeology around Mildenhall and Icklingham, Suffolk: Report on the Geologists' Association Field Meeting, 27 June 1992: Proceedings of the Geologists' Association, v. 106, p. 57–69.

Bridgland, D.R., Maddy, D., and Bates, M., 2004, River terrace sequences: Templates for Quaternary geochronology and marine-terrestrial correlation: Journal of Quaternary Science, v. 19, no. 2, p. 203–218, doi:10.1002/jqs.819.

Bridgland, D.R., Antoine, P., Limondin-Lozouet, N., Santisteban, J.I., Westaway, R., and White, M., 2006, The Palaeolithic occupation of Europe as revealed by evidence from the rivers: Data from IGCP 449: Journal of Quaternary Science, v. 21, no. 5, p. 437–455, doi:10.1002/jqs.1042.

British Geological Survey, 2005, Sidmouth, England and Wales Sheet 326 and Part of 340: Solid & Drift Geology: Keyworth, Nottingham, British Geological Survey, scale 1:50,000.

Brown, A.G., 1997, Fluvial Geoarchaeology: Floodplain Archaeology and Environmental Change: Cambridge, UK, Cambridge University Press, 377 p.

Campbell, S., Hunt, C.O., Scourse, J.D., Keen, D.H., and Stephens, N., 1998, The Quaternary of South-West England: London, Chapman and Hall, Geological Conservation Review Series 14, 439 p.

Chambers, J.C., 2005, River gravels and handaxes: New experiments in site formation, stone tool transportation and transformation, in Fansa, M., ed., Experimentelle Archäologie in Europa, Bilanz 2004, Heft 3: Oldenburg, Isensee Verlag, p. 25–41.

Conway, B., McNabb, J., and Ashton, N., eds., 1996, Excavations at Barnfield Pit, Swanscombe, 1968–72: London, British Museum Occasional Paper 94, 266 p.

Currant, A., and Jacobi, R., 2001, A formal mammalian biostratigraphy for the late Pleistocene of Britain: Quaternary Science Reviews, v. 20, p. 1707–1716, doi:10.1016/S0277-3791(01)00035-X.

Dale, W., 1918, Report as Local Secretary for Hampshire: Proceedings of the Society of Antiquaries, second series, v. 30, p. 20–32.

French, R.H., 1987, Hydraulic Processes on Alluvial Fans: Amsterdam, Elsevier, 244 p.

Friedman, G.M., and Sanders, J.B., 1978, Principles of Sedimentology: New York, Wiley & Sons, 792 p.

Gábris, G., and Nagy, B., 2005, Climate and tectonically-controlled river style changes on the Sajó-Hernád alluvial fan (Hungary), *in* Harvey, A.M., Mather, A.E., and Stokes, M., eds., Alluvial Fans: Geomorphology, Sedimentology, Dynamics: Geological Society of London Special Publication 251, p. 61–67.

Gamble, C.S., 1996, Hominid behaviour in the middle Pleistocene: An English perspective, *in* Gamble, C.S., and Lawson, A., eds., The English Palaeolithic Reviewed: Salisbury, Wessex Archaeology Ltd., p. 61–71.

Gibbard, P.L., 1985, The Pleistocene History of the Middle Thames Valley: Cambridge, UK, Cambridge University Press, 155 p.

Gibbard, P.L., 1994, The Pleistocene History of the Lower Thames Valley: Cambridge, UK, Cambridge University Press, 229 p.

Gibbard, P.L., Pasanen, A.H., West, R.G., Lunkka, J.P., Boreham, S., Cohen, K.M., and Rolfe, C., 2009, Late middle Pleistocene glaciation in East Anglia, England: Boreas, v. 38, p. 504–528, doi:10.1111/j.1502-3885.2009.00087.x.

Green, C.P., 1988, The Palaeolithic site at Broom, Dorset, 1932–41: From the record of C.E. Bean, Esq., F.S.A.: Proceedings of the Geologists' Association, v. 99, p. 173–180.

Hardaker, T., 2001, New Lower Palaeolithic finds from the Upper Thames, *in* Milliken, S., and Cook, J., eds., A Very Remote Period Indeed: Papers on the Palaeolithic Presented to Derek Roe: Oxford, Oxbow Books, p. 180–198.

Harding, P., Gibbard, P.L., Lewin, J., Macklin, M.G., and Moss, E.H., 1987, The transport and abrasion of flint handaxes in a gravel-bed river, *in* Sieveking, G. de G., and Newcomer, M.H., eds., The Human Uses of Flint and Chert: Proceedings of the Fourth International Flint Symposium Held at Brighton Polytechnic, 15 October April 1983: Cambridge, UK, Cambridge University Press, p. 115–126.

Harvey, A.M., Mather, A.E., and Stokes, M., 2005, Alluvial fans: Geomorphology, sedimentology, dynamics—Introduction. A review of alluvial fan research, *in* Harvey, A.M., Mather, A.E., and Stokes, M., eds., Alluvial Fans: Geomorphology, Sedimentology, Dynamics: Geological Society of London Special Publication 251, p. 1–7.

Horton, A., Worssam, B.C., Whittow, J.B., Holyoak, D.T., and Worsley, P., 1981, The Wallingford fan gravel: Royal Society of London Philosophical Transactions, ser. B, v. 293(1064), p. 215–255.

Hosfield, R.T., 1999, The Palaeolithic of the Hampshire Basin: A Regional Model of Hominid Behaviour during the Middle Pleistocene: British Archaeological Reports British Series 286, 162 p.

Hosfield, R.T., 2001, The Lower Palaeolithic of the Solent: Site formation and interpretive frameworks, *in* Wenban-Smith, F.F., and Hosfield, R.T., eds., Palaeolithic Archaeology of the Solent River: Lithic Studies Society Occasional Paper 7, p. 85–97.

Hosfield, R.T., 2005, Individuals among palimpsest data: Fluvial landscapes in southern England, *in* Gamble, C.S., and Porr, M., eds., The Hominid Individual in Context: Archaeological Investigations of Lower and Middle Palaeolithic Landscapes, Locales and Artefacts: Abingdon, Routledge (Taylor & Francis), p. 220–243.

Hosfield, R.T., 2007, Terrestrial implications for the maritime geoarchaeological resource: A view from the Lower Palaeolithic: Journal of Maritime Archaeology, v. 2, no. 1, p. 4–23, doi:10.1007/s11457-007-9013-7.

Hosfield, R.T., 2009, The unsung heroes, *in* Hosfield, R., Wenban-Smith, F.F., and Pope, M., eds., Great Prehistorians: 150 Years of Palaeolithic Research, 1859–2009 (Special Volume 30 of Lithics: The Journal of the Lithic Studies Society): London, Lithic Studies Society, p. 185–200.

Hosfield, R.T., and Chambers, J.C., 2005, River gravels and flakes: New experiments in site formation, stone tool transportation and transformation, *in* Fansa, M., ed., Experimentelle Archäologie in Europa, Bilanz 2004, Heft 3: Oldenburg, Isensee Verlag, p. 57–74.

Hosfield, R.T., and Chambers, J.C., 2009, Genuine diversity? The Broom biface assemblage: Proceedings of the Prehistoric Society, v. 75, p. 65–100.

Howard, A.J., and Macklin, M.G., 1999, A generic morphological approach to archaeological interpretation and prospection in British river valleys: A guide for archaeologists investigating Holocene landscapes: Antiquity, v. 73, p. 527–541.

Howard, A.J., Bridgland, D., Knight, D., McNabb, J., Rose, J., Schreve, D., Westaway, R., White, M.J., and White, T.S., 2007, The British Pleistocene fluvial archive: East Midlands drainage evolution and human occupation in the context of the British and NW European record: Quaternary Science Reviews, v. 26, no. 22–24, p. 2724–2737, doi:10.1016/j.quascirev.2007.06.029.

Isaac, G.L., 1989, Towards the interpretation of occupation debris: Some experiments and observations, *in* Isaac, B., ed., The Archaeology of Human Origins: Papers by Glynn Isaac: Cambridge, UK, Cambridge University Press, p. 191–205.

Lee, J.R., Rose, J., Hamblin, R.J.O., and Moorlock, B.S.P., 2004, Dating the earliest lowland glaciation of eastern England: A pre–MIS 12 early middle Pleistocene Happisburgh glaciation: Quaternary Science Reviews, v. 23, p. 1551–1566, doi:10.1016/j.quascirev.2004.02.002.

Lewis, S.G., Maddy, D., Buckingham, C.M., Coope, G.R., Field, M.H., Keen, D.H., Pike, A.G.W., Roe, D.A., Scaife, R.G., and Scott, K., 2006, Pleistocene fluvial sediments, palaeontology and archaeology of the upper River Thames at Latton, Wiltshire, England: Journal of Quaternary Science, v. 21, no. 2, p. 181–205, doi:10.1002/jqs.958.

Lhomme, V., 2007, Tools, space and behaviour in the Lower Palaeolithic: Discoveries at Soucy in the Paris Basin: Antiquity, v. 81, p. 536–554.

Macklin, M.G., 1995, Archaeology and the river environment of Britain: A prospective review, *in* Barham, A.J., and MacPhail, R.I., eds., Archaeological Sediments and Soils: Analysis, Interpretation and Management: London, Institute of Archaeology, p. 205–220.

MacRae, R.J., 1990, New finds and old problems in the Lower Palaeolithic of the Upper Thames Valley: Lithics: Newsletter of the Lithic Studies Society, v. 11, p. 3–15.

Maddy, D., Lewis, S.G., Scaife, R.G., Bowen, D.Q., Coope, G.R., Green, C.P., Hardaker, T., Keen, D.H., Rees-Jones, J., Parfitt, S., and Scott, K., 1998, The Upper Pleistocene deposits at Cassington, near Oxford, England: Journal of Quaternary Science, v. 13, no. 3, p. 205–231, doi:10.1002/(SICI)1099-1417(199805/06)13:3<205::AID-JQS357>3.0.CO;2-N.

Maddy, D., Bridgland, D.R., and Westaway, R., 2001, Uplift-driven valley incision and climate-controlled river terrace development in the Thames Valley, UK: Quaternary International, v. 79, p. 23–36, doi:10.1016/S1040-6182(00)00120-8.

Mania, D., 1995, The earliest occupation of Europe: The Elbe–Saale region (Germany), *in* Roebroeks, W., and van Kolfschoten, T., eds., The Earliest Occupation of Europe: Proceedings of the European Science Foundation Workshop at Tautavel (France) 1993: Leiden, the Netherlands, Leiden University Press, p. 85–101.

Mather, A.E., 1999, Alluvial fans: A case study from the Sorbas Basin, southeast Spain, *in* Jones, A.P., Tucker, M.E., and Hart, J.K., eds., The Description and Analysis of Quaternary Stratigraphic Field Sections: Quaternary Research Association Technical Guide 7, p. 77–109.

McNabb, J., 2007, The British Lower Palaeolithic: Stones in Contention: London, Routledge, 448 p.

Mishra, S., White, M.J., Beaumont, P., Antoine, P., Bridgland, D.R., Limondin-Lozouet, N., Santisteban, J.I., Schreve, D.C., Shaw, A.D., Wenban-Smith, F.F., Westaway, R.W.C., and White, T.S., 2007, Fluvial deposits as an archive of early human activity: Quaternary Science Reviews, v. 26, no. 22–24, p. 2996–3016, doi:10.1016/j.quascirev.2007.06.035.

Moir, J.R., 1936, Ancient man in Devon: Proceedings of the Devon Archaeological Exploration Society, v. 2, p. 264–275.

Mosher, S.-J., and Martini, I.P., 2002, Coarse-grained flood bars formed at the confluence of two subarctic rivers affected by hydroelectric dams, Ontario, Canada, *in* Martini, I.P., Baker, V.R., and Garzón, G., eds., Flood and Megaflood Processes and Deposits: Recent and Ancient Examples: International Association of Sedimentologists Special Publication 132, p. 213–231.

Parfitt, S.A., Barendregt, R.W., Breda, M., Candy, I., Collins, M.J., Coope, R.G., Durbridge, P., Field, M.H., Lee, J.R., Lister, A.M., Mutch, R., Penkman, K.E.H., Preece, R.C., Rose, J., Stringer, C.B., Symmons, R., Whittaker, J.E., Wymer, J.J., and Stuart, A.J., 2005, The earliest record of human activity in northern Europe: Nature, v. 438, p. 1008–1012, doi:10.1038/nature04227.

Parfitt, S.A., Ashton, N.M., Lewis, S.G., Abel, R.L., Coope, G.R., Field, M.H., Gale, R., Hoare, P.G., Larkin, N.R., Lewis, M.D., Karloukovski, V., Maher, B.A., Peglar, S.M., Preece, R.C., Whittaker, J.E., and Stringer, C.B., 2010, Early Pleistocene human occupation at the edge of the boreal zone in northwest Europe: Nature, v. 466, p. 229–233.

Petraglia, M.D., and Nash, D.T., 1987, The impact of fluvial processes on experimental sites, *in* Nash, D.T., and Petraglia, M.D., eds., Natural Formation Processes and the Archaeological Record: British Archaeological Reports International Series 352, p. 108–130.

Robert, A., 2003, River Processes: An Introduction to Fluvial Dynamics: London, Arnold, 224 p.

Roberts, M.B., and Parfitt, S.A., 1998, Boxgrove: A Middle Pleistocene Hominid Site at Eartham Quarry, Boxgrove, West Sussex: London, English Heritage, 456 p.

Roe, D.A., 1968, British Lower and Middle Palaeolithic handaxe groups: Proceedings of the Prehistoric Society, v. 34, p. 1–82.

Roe, D.A., 1981, The Lower and Middle Palaeolithic Periods in Britain: London, Routledge & Kegan Paul Ltd., 324 p.

Rose, J., Allen, P., Green, C.P., Hey, R.W., Lewis, S.G., Sinclair, J.M., and Whiteman, C.A., 1996, The Kesgrave and Bytham sands and gravels of East Anglia: Quaternary Newsletter, v. 79, p. 10–25.

Schick, K.D., 1986, Stone Age Sites in the Making: Experiments in the Formation and Transformation of Archaeological Occurrences: British Archaeological Reports, International Series 319, 313 p.

Schick, K.D., 1987, Experimentally-disturbed criteria for assessing hydrologic disturbance of archaeological sites, *in* Nash, D.T., and Petraglia, M.D., eds., Natural Formation Processes and the Archaeological Record: British Archaeological Reports International Series 352, p. 86–107.

Schmidt, K.-H., 1994, River channel adjustment and sediment budget in response to a catastrophic flood event (Lainbach catchment, southern Bavaria), *in* Ergenzinger, P., and Schmidt, K.-H., eds., Dynamics and Geomorphology of Mountain Rivers: Berlin, Springer-Verlag, p. 109–127.

Schmidt, K.-H., and Ergenzinger, P., 1992, Bedload entrainment, travel lengths, step lengths, rest periods—Studied with passive (iron, magnetic) and active (radio) tracer techniques: Earth Surface Processes and Landforms, v. 17, p. 147–165, doi:10.1002/esp.3290170204.

Schumm, S.A., 2005, River Variability and Complexity: Cambridge, UK, Cambridge University Press, 220 p.

Scott, K., and Buckingham, C.M., 2001, A river runs through it: A decade of research at Stanton Harcourt, *in* Milliken, S., and Cook, J., eds., A Very Remote Period Indeed: Papers on the Palaeolithic Presented to Derek Roe: Oxford, Oxbow Books, p. 207–213.

Shackley, M.L., 1974, Stream abrasion of flint implements: Nature, v. 248, p. 501–502, doi:10.1038/248501a0.

Shakesby, R.A., and Stephens, N., 1984, The Pleistocene gravels of the Axe Valley, Devon: Report of the Transactions of the Devon Association for the Advancement of Science, v. 116, p. 77–88.

Sherlock, R.L., and Noble, A.H., 1922, The Geology of the Country around Beaconsfield: Memoirs of the Geological Society, England and Wales Sheet 255, 59 p.

Singer, R., Wymer, J., Gladfelter, B.G., and Wolff, R.G., 1973, Excavation of the Clactonian industry at the golf course, Clacton-on-Sea, Essex: Proceedings of the Prehistoric Society, v. 39, p. 6–74.

Solomon, J.D., 1933, The implementiferous gravels of Warren Hill: The Journal of the Royal Anthropological Institute, v. 63, p. 101–110.

Stern, N., 1993, The structure of the Lower Pleistocene archaeological record: Current Anthropology, v. 34, no. 3, p. 201–224, doi:10.1086/204164.

Sutcliffe, A.J., 1995, Insularity of the British Isles 250,000–30,000 years ago: The mammalian, including human, evidence, *in* Preece, R.C., ed., Island Britain: A Quaternary Perspective: Geological Society of London Special Publication 96, p. 127–140.

Toms, P., Hosfield, R.T., Chambers, J.C., Green, C.P., and Marshall, P., 2005, Optical dating of the Broom Palaeolithic sites, Devon & Dorset: London, English Heritage, Centre for Archaeology Report 16/2005, 50 p.

Treacher, L., 1904, On the occurrence of stone implements in the Thames Valley between Reading and Maidenhead: Man, v. 10, p. 17–19.

Tuffreau, A., and Antoine, P., 1995, The earliest occupation of Europe: Continental northwestern Europe, *in* Roebroeks, W., and van Kolfschoten, T., eds., The Earliest Occupation of Europe: Proceedings of the European Science Foundation Workshop at Tautavel (France) 1993: Leiden, the Netherlands, Leiden University Press, p. 147–163.

Wenban-Smith, F.F., 2004, Handaxe typology and Lower Palaeolithic cultural development: Ficrons, cleavers and two giant handaxes from Cuxton: Lithics: The Journal of the Lithic Studies Society, v. 25, p. 11–21.

Wessex Archaeology, 1993, The Southern Rivers Palaeolithic Project Report No. 2. 1992–1993. The South West and South of the Thames: Salisbury, Wessex Archaeology & English Heritage.

Westaway, R., 2009, Quaternary vertical crustal motion and drainage evolution in East Anglia and adjoining parts of southern England: Chronology of the Ingham River terrace deposits: Boreas, v. 38, p. 261–284, doi:10.1111/j.1502-3885.2008.00068.x.

Westaway, R., Bridgland, D.R., and White, M.J., 2006, The Quaternary uplift history of central southern England: Evidence from the terraces of the Solent River system and nearby raised beaches: Quaternary Science Reviews, v. 25, p. 2212–2250, doi:10.1016/j.quascirev.2005.06.005.

White, M.J., 1998, Twisted ovate bifaces in the British Lower Palaeolithic: Some observations and implications, *in* Ashton, N., Healy, F., and Pettitt, P., eds., Stone Age Archaeology: Essays in Honour of John Wymer: Oxford, Oxbow (Monograph 102), and Lithic Studies Society Occasional Paper 6, p. 98–104.

White, M.J., and Schreve, D.C., 2000, Island Britain–peninsula Britain: Palaeogeography, colonisation and the Lower Palaeolithic settlement of the British Isles: Proceedings of the Prehistoric Society, v. 66, p. 1–28.

Whittaker, K., Beasley, M., Bates, M.R., and Wenban-Smith, F.F., 2004, The Lost Valley: British Archaeology, v. 74, p. 22–27.

Wymer, J.J., 1968, Lower Palaeolithic Archaeology in Britain, as Represented by the Thames Valley: London, John Baker, 429 p.

Wymer, J.J., 1999, The Lower Palaeolithic Occupation of Britain: Salisbury, Wessex Archaeology & English Heritage, 234 p.

MANUSCRIPT ACCEPTED BY THE SOCIETY 3 AUGUST 2010

The Geological Society of America
Special Paper 476
2011

Mapping the landform assemblages and archaeological record of the Lower Khuzestan plain (SW Iran) using remote-sensing and GIS techniques

Laëtitia Dupin*

Geological Survey of Belgium, rue Jenner, 13, 1000 Brussels, Belgium

ABSTRACT

The semiarid plain of Lower Khuzestan, SW Iran, is drained by three active rivers: Karun, Karkheh, and Jarrahi. In this study, the history of this apparently homogeneous topographic landscape was investigated for the first time in detail through surficial geology and archaeological mapping. The results of satellite image, Shuttle Radar Topography Mission (SRTM) digital elevation model (DEM), and aerial photograph analyses reveal several phases of paleochannels, relict fans, and large lobate landforms associated with the present-day rivers. In addition to this, a wealth of archaeological canals, of various types and shapes, and sites has been detected. Correlations of archaeological features with environmental attributes in a geographical information system (GIS) show that the spatial distribution of the settlements and canals was closely related to the dynamic nature of the rivers. With the available data, keys to interpret the changes of the rivers are presented and a relative chronology is suggested for the evolution of the landscape of the plain.

INTRODUCTION

The study area (Fig. 1) is located in the southern part of the Khuzestan province, southwest Iran, and is wedged between the head of the Persian Gulf to the south, the Zagros mountain front to the NE, and the Iraqi borderline to the west. It corresponds geographically to the southern extension of the Lower Mesopotamian plain but is separated from it by the marshlands east of the Tigris River. Numerous geomorphological and archaeological surveys and excavations have been undertaken in Mesopotamia (Turkey, Syria, Iraq) since the 1930s (Braidwood, 1937; Adams, 1962, 1965, 1981; Jacobsen, 1969; Algaze, 1989; Wilkinson, 1989, 1998; and many others), mainly via field campaigns. With the development of satellite images (*Corona*, Landsat, *SPOT*), digital mapping has been applied increasingly

in very recent years to Mesopotamia, and these surveys have successfully investigated the archaeological and geomorphological Mesopotamian landscape evolution (Pournelle, 2003; Hritz, 2004; Ur, 2005). Mesopotamia is a semiarid to arid environment that ranges from the northern areas of rain-fed agriculture to the southern part with irrigation agriculture. This irrigation is aided by a high water table and by melted snows from the mountains in southern Turkey (Pournelle, 2003). In the south, an area too arid to have sustained rain-fed agriculture, irrigation from the Tigris and Euphrates Rivers would have been possible where the rivers flow at plain level, and where river water is more manageable for irrigation purposes (Pournelle, 2003). The development of cities in the Lower Mesopotamian plain could only be sustained by the presence of water, supplied by a network of water channels providing irrigation for the cultivation of food crops and a means of transport of goods from city to city (Adams, 1981; Cole and Gasche, 1998; Morozova,

*laetitiadupin@yahoo.fr

Dupin, L., 2011, Mapping the landform assemblages and archaeological record of the Lower Khuzestan plain (SW Iran) using remote-sensing and GIS techniques, *in* Brown, A.G., Basell, L.S., and Butzer, K.W., eds., Geoarchaeology, Climate Change, and Sustainability: Geological Society of America Special Paper 476, p. 53–68, doi:10.1130/2011.2476(05). For permission to copy, contact editing@geosociety.org. © 2011 The Geological Society of America. All rights reserved.

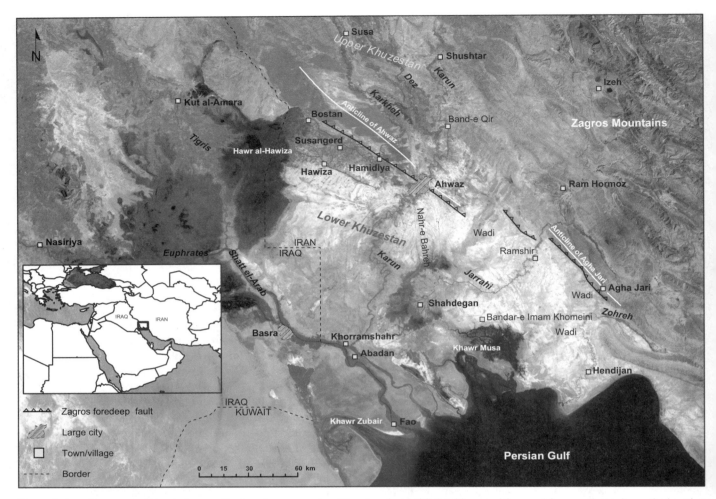

Figure 1. Location maps of the study area displayed on a mosaic of four Landsat MSS (Multispectral Scanner) images. Inset shows the location of the study area in the context of the Middle East.

2005). The rivers and canals are higher than the surrounding plain because of (1) built-up silt in the riverbeds, (2) overflooding bringing sediments onto the waterway banks, and (3) the style of maintenance of the canals, where excess of silt from the drainage bed was taken out and left on banks (Gasche and Cole, 2003). In that way, water for irrigation flowed into the fields by gravity using the levee slope. Although land nearer to the rivers was fertile and good for crops, portions of land further from the water were dry and largely uninhabitable. However, river shifting is an important phenomenon in Mesopotamia. The Tigris and Euphrates Rivers have avulsed several times across the Mesopotamian plain (Morozova, 2005). These river shifts involved an abandonment of the riverbed from one place, resulting in a loss of water supply for the population, and relocation of the river to another place. This fluvial process resulted in major population shifts (Gibson, 1973; Wilkinson, 2000; Morozova, 2005) following the trend of river migrations. Thus, water source and development of irrigation were very important for settlers of Mesopotamia.

The Lower Khuzestan plain shows similarities in the landscape with the southern part of the Mesopotamian plain in Iraq. However, in contrast to the profusion of regional and local archaeological and geomorphological studies in Iraq, Zagros Mountains and Upper Khuzestan, little attention has been paid to Lower Khuzestan. Currently, the cultural heritage of the Lower Khuzestan plain is increasingly threatened with destruction as many of the archaeological sites are either in very bad condition or are being bulldozed because of intensive agriculture, resource exploitation (oil and gas), and large urban development projects. It is not only archaeology in this region that suffers from a lack of data. Geomorphological studies cover only margins of the present study area (Kirkby, 1977; Baltzer and Purser, 1990), or have focused on specific natural or cultural features (Hansman, 1978; Potts, 2002), mainly due to the lack of visibility of most of the fluvial landforms on aerial photographs and unprocessed satellite images.

In this paper, an overview of recent investigations is provided, and is a step in understanding, for the first time, the general context of the Lower Khuzestan plain and associating geomorphological and archaeological data. It will aid in a second stage to focus on more specific areas, for excavations and geological studies. This study aims to present the results of detailed surface mapping of fluvial geomorphology and archaeology (Dupin, 2006; Baeteman et al., 2004/2005; Dupin, 2004) in order to determine the relationship between landscape history, primarily a product of changing fluvial processes and patterns, and the distribution and type of archaeological sites and ancient irrigation works. Field study, maps, and remote-sensing imagery provided the data; interpretation provided insight into spatial and process relationships; and available archaeological age data provide an approximate relative chronology.

METHODOLOGY

The study is based on the survey and mapping of geomorphological and archaeological features. Because field campaigns were too short in time to survey the whole study area (over 23,000 km²) and very few ancient maps with archaeological and geomorphological data were available, remote-sensing tools were very useful in order to reveal traces of past and recent human activities, as well as the trend of morphological changes and the dynamic behavior of the rivers. Satellite imagery has proven to be an invaluable resource in archaeology, and more specifically the *Corona* images, which aided in the recognition of archaeological sites and ancient landscape features in Mesopotamia (Challis et al., 2002; Challis and Howard, 2006; Pournelle, 2003; Fowler, 2004; Hritz, 2004; Ur, 2003, 2005).

However, the field study was also of great importance as geomorphological and archaeological information was collected, such as state of conservation of sites and canals, shape, soil surface texture, and composition, and all locations were recorded by global positioning system (GPS). The information was used as parameters for recognition of the specific spectral signatures of the different fluvial deposits and the spectral characteristics of mounds and canals on remotely sensed imagery. The ground truthing revealed that most of the geomorphological features were almost invisible from the ground because they are characterized by extensive surfaces with a smooth topography and a very gentle slope.

In this study, a large set of data was used that included: (1) Landsat imagery (1970s, 1990s, 2000s) with a resolution evolving from 120 m for the oldest images up to 15 m for the most recent, (2) panchromatic *SPOT* images (1970s) with a resolution of 10 m, (3) black-and-white aerial photographs (1968, maybe *Corona*, source unknown), with a resolution from 4 to 10 m, and (4) MODIS images (2004), with a resolution of 250 m. The use of more than one set of imagery was essential in the case of the Lower Khuzestan plain. The multitemporal coverage helped to overcome (1) the degree of vegetation cover, (2) the effect of the recent expansion of the agriculture, (3) the damages from the Iraq-Iran 1980s war, (4) the presence of clouds, and (5) the contrast between features and surroundings, which is enhanced during certain periods of the year. All these conditions can strongly affect the visibility of the features in the study area. The panel of image resolutions was necessary to survey a large category of various-scale objects since the smallest entity was a mound of 0.001 km² and the largest was a megafan of 970 km².

Selective image-processing techniques (namely image and edge enhancement, filtering, band combinations, ratioing, principal component analysis, data fusion) were performed to improve the quality of the image interpretability and the contrast between features, and enhance soil types. The applied techniques are described in more detail in Colwell (1983), Richards (1992), Lillesand and Kiefer (1994), Drury (2001), among others. The remote-sensing technique involves identifying a distinctive signature in the spectral response of a known element (field controlled) and using it as a sample. Such signatures serve as references for plotting other features of the same type throughout the images and the base for classification. The color composite ratio image (Landsat ETM) where band 4/band 5 is in red, band 4/band 7 is in green and band 5/band 7 is in blue, and the false band combination where band 2 is in red, band 5 is in green, and band 7 is in blue were two of the most relevant band combinations for both the geomorphological and the archaeological analyses.

The Shuttle Radar Topography Mission (SRTM) digital elevation model (DEM), with spatial resolution of 90 m, proved to be invaluable for mapping features even if the topographical variations are minor. The former were enhanced by shaded relief analysis and 25× vertical exaggeration.

Once georeferenced to the same coordinate system (WGS 84-UTM 39N), in a geographical information system (hereafter GIS), raster data (processed satellite images, aerial photographs, and maps) were used as a base for extracting vector data and linked databases. The major geomorphic categories obtained are past and recent earthquake epicenters (date, magnitude, depth, etc.), present-day perennial and temporary drainage systems, paleoriver courses, recent and ancient crevasse splay deposits, and channels, gullies, terraces, fans, etc.; archaeological categories are mounds (tells) and canals. Features in both categories were spatially correlated via the GIS.

REGIONAL SETTING AND FLUVIAL GEOMORPHOLOGY

The study area (Fig. 1) extends from latitude 31°44′42″N to 30°12′55″N and from longitude 47°54′27″E to 49°52′4″E. The wide and very flat region consists mainly of Holocene fluvial silt and clay sediments (Baeteman et al., 2004/2005). The Lower Khuzestan plain consists of 18% fertile land, corresponding to the floodplain area; 28% marshland, prone to dry-season desiccation and salinization; and the rest (54%) is barren land. Such a landscape in combination with a semiarid climate does not seem conducive for human settlement. The rain is concentrated between November and February and can cause disastrous floods. During the rest of the year, the weather is very dry with high potential evaporation. This does not allow much vegetation to grow, and most of the surface of the plain is covered by desiccation cracks and salt pans throughout the plain. Moreover, soil salinity makes agriculture difficult today.

The region relies on four rivers (Fig. 1): the Zohreh (not the focus of this paper), the Karkheh, the Jarrahi, and, most importantly, the Karun, with a catchment of 67,340 km^2 (Naff and Matson, 1984). Their present-day floodplains represent the most fertile and accessible land. The rivers reach peak discharge in April. The average discharge in the Lower Khuzestan plain is 1600 m^3/s for the Karun, 425 m^3/s for the Karkheh, and around 110 m^3/s for the Jarrahi River (State Hydrological Institute, 1999). Sediments are supplied to the plain predominantly by seasonal river floods, but also by the northwesterly Shamal wind (Foda et al., 1985), which brings in eolian dust and sand.

The coastal area to the south consists of a large tidal embayment with numerous tidal channels. The channels are bordered by mud flats, which in turn are fringed either by salt marshes or coastal sabkhas. The eastern part of the gulf coastline is very linear due to strong longshore drift.

The region is seismically active. Earthquakes can reach magnitude 6.5 (Berberian, 1995), but most earthquakes are relatively moderate (around 4–5). The tectonic activity is due to the convergence of the Arabian and Eurasian plates, which induces active faults parallel to the Zagros Mountains (Vernant et al., 2004). The plain is separated from the Zagros Mountain front by a thrust fault, the Zagros foredeep fault (Fig. 1), which is involved in the subsidence of the plain.

In the present study, four fluvial geomorphologic units were delineated after mapping the fluvial paleo- and active features on remotely sensed imagery.

Jarrahi System

In the SE part of the study area, the Jarrahi River enters the Khuzestan plain in a large left-hand bend from SE-NW in the Zagros to NE-SW in the plain, flowing 100 km, normally to debouch into marshes near Shahdegan (Fig. 1), but in severe floods reaching the Khawr Musa coastal embayment (MODIS images). Abandoned channel traces border the Jarrahi. Ephemeral channels (Fig. 1, wadi), up to 15 km wide, one NW and one SE of the Jarrahi, descend from the mountain front SW to the lowland or coastal wetlands. Wadi alignment is influenced by transverse slopes on the "megafans" of the major perennial rivers, Jarrahi and Karun. These fans have relief of ~6 m in ridges remaining unconsumed by fan dissection. The higher Jarrahi "megafan" (Fig. 2, fan I) covers ~120 km^2 and is bisected by the river, which is incised 8 m into it, with a terrace at 2 m below the fan surface. An older paleochannel (Fig. 2, J1) borders the fan southward; it is the product of a river diverted by the fan around its proximal margin, before it resumed a SW course (present-day Jarrahi River) to the Persian Gulf (Fig. 1).

Forty kilometers downstream along the Jarrahi, a second larger fan (Fig. 2, fan II) covers ~850 km^2, with an elevation at its center 10 m above its edges. Relict distributary channels radiate across the fan surface, originating at a sharp change in drainage direction from SW to NW.

A third "megafan" occurs 5 km further along the Jarrahi (Fig. 2, fan III). Covering 970 km^2, this fan is active today, with prominent radial distributaries. The river changes direction again, reverting to SW where it enters this fan. To the eastern edge of the present-day Jarrahi fan, there is a series of abandoned parallel and elongated lobes, whereas the western part is fully active. It shows a migration of the networks in use and a progradation SW toward Shatt el-Arab. This lowest fan is surrounded distally by marshes watered by the Jarrahi multibranching drainage system. A paleochannel (Fig. 2, J2) is visible on the opposite side of the marshes, crossed by the Karun.

The Jarrahi River is presently aggrading, depositing alluvial ridges on fans II and III, and changing pattern downstream abruptly from sinuous to straight. Adjacent to the modern river, crevasse splays are identified.

Karkheh System

The Karkheh River, in the NW of the study area, flows SE through the Zagros and crosses the Ahwaz anticline and the Zagros foredeep fault before debouching NW onto the plain and draining to the Hawr al-Hawiza marsh (Fig. 1). From where the river enters the plain, three generations of channels are recognized (Fig. 3, Kha, Khb, Kh1-Kh2). The Kh2 course shows variations in sinuosity, with a sinuous part in its Kh1-Kh2 segment, and then from the righthand bend to flow northwest, the section is linear. Ancient irrigation canals (Fig. 3, C) clearly led water from the axial stream (Kh2) diagonally across the floodplain toward the south and toward SE-NW–trending canals (Fig. 3, C1, C2).

An additional relict channel was observed to the south, toward the present-day Karun. Starting as the Kh1-Kh2, it bifurcates to the south to form the Kh1 (Fig. 2) and join a larger paleocourse (Fig. 2, K2). Crevasse splays are again a common feature of the Karkheh system.

Karun System

The Karun exits the Zagros southward, crosses the southerly extremity of the Ahwaz anticline, and then the line of the Zagros foredeep fault at Ahwaz, flowing SW then SSW to Shatt el-Arab at Khorramshahr (Fig. 1). Less than 10 km WSW of Ahwaz, there is a prominent paleochannel (Fig. 2, K2), which continues WSW to the Shatt el-Arab, ~70 km upstream of the present-day Karun and the Shatt el-Arab junction. This paleochannel is visible in adjacent alluvial ridges, lying above the floodplain, on the SRTM DEM, on satellite images, and aerial photos by moisture variations in scroll bars and meander belts. Other paleochannels radiate between the present-day Karun and K2 (Fig. 2, K1, K3). K1 shows a relatively straight path, maybe due to the coarse

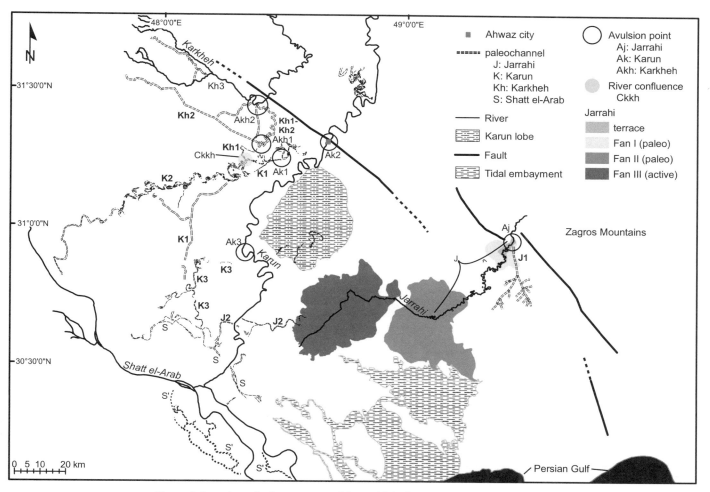

Figure 2. Location of paleocourses and fans with indication of the avulsion nodes.

resolution of the SRTM DEM. The major Karun lobe, to the south of Ahwaz, covers 950 km^2 and rises 9–14 m above its edges. Its surface is densely covered by a network of downslope-bifurcating irrigation channels, leading from the master channel (Fig. 1), Nahr-e Bahreh (Gasche, 2005).

Shatt el-Arab and Borders

Shatt el-Arab is formed first by the confluence of the Tigris and Euphrates, and it is joined 90 km lower down by the Karun at Khorramshahr, from where it follows a low-sinuosity course to the Persian Gulf. On the satellite images, paleocourses were detected on each side of the Shatt el-Arab, with the same trend some 15 km away to the SW (Fig. 2, S') and to the NE (Fig. 2, S). The northeasternmost relict river S shows a slightly different spectral response from K3 and J2 (Fig. 2), indicating a different sediment composition, as well as some relatively sharp junctions with the latter paleocourses coming from the north.

Interpretation of Paleochannel Changes

To the east of the study area, the dynamic character of the Tigris and Euphrates Rivers has long been known and has affected the settlement evolution in the Mesopotamian plain (Wilkinson, 2000). Avulsion is a phenomenon that particularly affected southern Mesopotamia, in Iraq (Hritz, 2004). The factors influencing shifting of rivers in this part of the world have been characterized by Morozova (2005), but avulsive rivers have been studied elsewhere (Mississippi, Ganges-Brahmaputra, Yellow, Rhine Rivers). The studies particularly point out the need of an original context (Mohrig et al., 2000; Slingerland and Smith, 2004), with high aggradation rates and alluvial ridges, confining the river above the adjacent floodplain, as being essential to the initiation of avulsion (Jones and Schumm, 1999; Törnqvist and Bridge, 2002; Slingerland and Smith, 1998, 2004), as well as a low-gradient alluvial plain (Makaske, 2001) and very sparse vegetation (Mohrig et al., 2000). In addition to this, a variety of factors such as

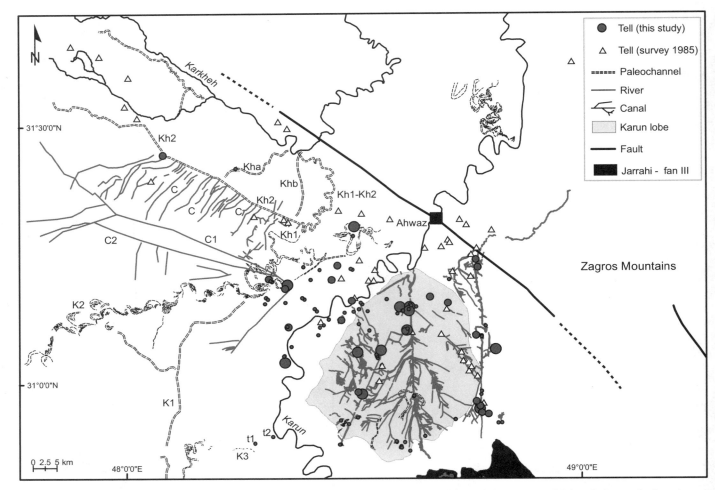

Figure 3. Spatial distribution of archaeological sites (from Alizadeh's survey [1985], and from the present study) in relation to the location of the canal network and fluvial features along the Karkheh and Karun Rivers. Variation in size of black circles represents three classes of tell size (in ha): 0.1–1.5, 1.5–5, and 5–15.

sea-level change, high floods and crevasse splays, channel blockage, in-channel aggradation, tectonic events, and human activities (Bridge and Leeder, 1979; Törnqvist, 1993; Stouthamer and Berendsen, 2000) can favor the occurrence of avulsion.

Here, I present an initial assessment of geological factors that would lead the Karun, Jarrahi, and Karkheh Rivers to avulse in the Lower Khuzestan plain.

Numerous alluvial ridges have been detected throughout the low-gradient plain (~0.2 m/km). They characterize present-day rivers as well as paleocourses and are the elements that allow the detection of rivers on the SRTM DEM. These aggradational features, developed year after year by overbank deposits during floods (Buringh, 1957; Gasche and Cole, 2003; Hritz, 2004), involve the gradual rise of the rivers flowing above the surrounding plain level. The course of the Karun River is observed in four different migratory stages: K1, K2, K3, and present-day Karun (Fig. 2). In the same way, the Karkheh has marked the landscape

with three different courses: Kh1, Kh2, and present-day Karkheh, and three stages are identified for the Jarrahi: J1, J2, and present-day river. The shift can relocate the rivers up to 100 km away from its previous setting. No other paleofeatures, such as meander scrolls, natural levees, and oxbow lakes, can be detected in between the different stages, indicating a rapid shift of the rivers rather than a gradual progressive lateral migration. Other causes of avulsion involve rainstorm events added to snowmelt coming from the Zagros Mountains and inducing high discharges, which can transport large volumes of sediment out of the Zagros Mountain range to the alluvial plain and to the coastal-fluvial interface zones (Baltzer and Purser, 1990). This process causes sediment overloading of the complete channel system, and the load is so great that the water cannot be evacuated via rivers only, and consequently ephemeral channels (Fig. 1, wadi) and crevasse splays develop. Catastrophic floods have occurred several times in the last 20 yr, according to the Dartmouth Flood Observatory, inducing breaks in the levees and creating splay deposits. Such an event was cited in the Dartmouth Flood Observatory database (Brakenridge et al., 2003): "Thunderstorms, heavy rainfalls and mudslides hit the southwestern province of Khuzestan, killing 13 people and causing damage to farmland and livestock. Thirty-four villages were inundated after the rivers Jarahi, Karkhe[h] and Karoun burst their banks" in March 1996. A similar event occurred in November 1994, when the Jarrahi and Zohreh Rivers overflowed their banks after torrential rains caused widespread flooding. The frequency of the flood occurrences in the plain follows an annual cycle linked to the rainy season, and the phenomenon is usually disastrous.

Numerous ancient and recent depositional crevasse splay features can be observed on aerial photographs and Landsat satellite images throughout the landscape: along the Karkheh and, more specifically, along the Jarrahi and the Karun Rivers. They are characterized either by their lobe-shaped form, often dissected by channels, and by the specific sandy material spectral signature found at the apex of the crevasse splay. Their size can vary from a few square kilometers up to ~475 km². The largest splays, more specifically located along the Karun, are at a slightly higher elevation than the surrounding floodplain and show well-marked crevasse channels. It is probably the accumulation of successive flood deposits that induces the elevation by aggradation, as well as the extension of the crevasse channels over distances up to 20 km.

The relocation of the rivers is mainly triggered by major flood events in arid and semiarid climates (Rust, 1981; Schumann, 1989), as depicted previously; however, other factors might have controlled the change of channel position in the plain, such as the response of the river to the Holocene sea-level rise (Baeteman et al., 2004/2005), with a landward extension of the Persian Gulf to at least 80 km north of the present-day shoreline at ca. 8000 cal. B.P. Tectonic movements occurring in the plain could also have triggered avulsion. It is clear that the avulsion nodes of the Karun in Ahwaz (Fig. 2, AK2) and Aj (Fig. 2) on the Jarrahi River at the foothills of the Zagros Mountain front are located where rivers cross the faults. Tectonic movements between the basin and the Zagros Mountain chain may have influenced the river behavior and can be a major parameter in the avulsion process. The only documented earthquake, which occurred in ancient time (ca. A.D. 840) in the study area, was of 6.5 in magnitude (Berberian, 1995). Its intensity was significant and estimated at Io ~VIII. The earthquake was destructive for infrastructure in Ahwaz and even involved a ground movement with fissures visible at the surface of the mountains overlooking Ahwaz. Moreover, in Ahwaz, the Karun River shows a sharp gradient break of ~1 m at the point where the fault and the river intersects, which suggests that tectonic vertical displacements occurred in the past.

A combination of floods, tectonic movements, and sea-level rise controls the mechanisms that cause avulsions in the Lower Khuzestan plain. However, given the available data, it is not possible to determine which of these geological processes has had the most significant impact on avulsion.

ARCHAEOLOGY

Detection and Classification

The Karkheh and the Karun Rivers originate in the central zone of the Zagros Mountains. The Karkheh was once known as the Choaspes or Eulaeus according to Greek and Latin sources (Potts, 2002). It passes west of Susa (Fig. 1), continues through Khuzestan (ancient Elam), and ends in the Hawr al-Hawiza marsh. Together with the Karun (ancient Pasitigris), the Karkheh sustains life on the plain (Kirkby, 1977; Hansman, 1978; Potts, 2002; Gasche and Cole, 2003).

The Karun and the Karkheh are the major rivers according to archaeological, philological, and historical studies. Nevertheless, human activity is also visible along the Jarrahi, known as the Hedyphon River (in the ancient Kingdom of Elymais).

Fragments of archaeological information can be found in the literature from the early travelers (Curzon, 1890; De Morgan, 1900; Kirkby, 1977), but it is not very significant for the area. One of the rare archaeological surveys in the Lower Khuzestan was undertaken by Gasche (2005, after a survey of Alizadeh, 1985). Nearly 50 mounds, mostly Parthian (125 B.C.–A.D. 226) and Sasanian (A.D. 226–637) in age—showing a similar population growth trend than in Mesopotamia (Adams, 1965; Wilkinson, 2005)—were mapped, but they were not accurately located. The present study identifies a greater human impact in the Lower Khuzestan than previously thought and locates some of the mounds surveyed by Alizadeh (1985).

Tells

A tell is a mound of collapsed mud-brick architecture and village waste that accumulates vertically and laterally as occupation is maintained in the same location over time. Its morphology provides information (1) on longevity, as high tells are usually long-lived settlements, and, on the contrary, small sites appear and disappear within a few generations (Pollock, 1999), and (2) on the population size, which is indicated by surface area. Since the structure is clay-made, it can be difficult to distinguish a tell from its surroundings on the satellite images, because they are often of a similar material. Therefore, the sites are not as apparent as in Upper Khuzestan, where they are better preserved, higher, and larger (Adams, 1962). Moreover, in spring, cultivated areas are identified by the strong spectral signature of growing vegetation. Because many mounds of the Upper Khuzestan plain are not cultivated but surrounded by fields, they are easily spotted, since their spectral response is sharply different (observed on satellite images). In Lower Khuzestan, this is not the case, since the tells are bulldozed to create more space for fields and removed to build irrigation canals. Large parts of the Lower Khuzestan plain are not cultivated, and the tell spectral response is similar to the surrounding barren soil. However, the color composite ratio image band 4/band 5 in red, band 4/band 7 in green, and band 5/band 7 in blue of the Landsat satellite allow the detection of these sites. The field observations reveal that the spectral response takes into consideration the roughness of the surface resulting from the disintegration of the mud bricks, which produces a less compact structure of the soil, or a different grain size from the surroundings. Moreover, the mound is topographically higher and retains less water, which induces a different spectral response than the moisture content patterns of the adjacent irrigated fields or swampy surroundings.

The large sites are easily detected with the SRTM DEM; at a resolution of 90 m, the tells need to have a size of at least 10–15 ha to be represented by sufficient pixels in order to be identified. Since the smallest mound delineated was as small as 0.1 ha, the investigation using the SRTM DEM data needed to be complemented by Landsat images and aerial photographs for this survey. The Landsat false color compositions and ratios (resolution of 15–30 m) were used for the identification of medium-size mounds, and the aerial photographs were used for the small-size tells. On the latter, shape, brightness (the moisture content is characterized by darker shades), and the presence of canals were explored to detect the tells. This work was based on the known archaeological sites visited during the fieldwork. Their position was recorded by GPS and integrated in the GIS. So far, 150 sites (tells) have been found, and most of them are located on the Karun lobe and along the Jarrahi River, particularly concentrated at the foothill of the mountains.

The tells have been entered into a database assigning information for the following criteria: (1) ground truth data; (2) description (shape, name, date, artifact types, if available); (3) measurement (area, height, and visibility from satellite imagery); (4) human disturbances affecting representativeness (agriculture activities, road works, villages, brick factories); (5) nearby natural and cultural drainage features (river, ephemeral river, or canal); (6) coordinates; and (7) source of the detection (Landsat images, aerial photographs, SRTM DEM). These criteria were used to test the reliability of the data and the spatial analyses, and to assign an age to the canals or channels. Cross-checks using different imagery led to confirmation; consistency across three or four data sets was defined as positive, whereas inconsistency led to rejection.

Canal Network

In Khuzestan, written documentation of canals is very sparse (Alizadeh et al., 2004); however, information on canals is revealed by the satellite images and photographs, even if older canal structures are not always obvious or are masked by the modern infrastructures. Out of all the image-processing techniques, the application of Sobel or Laplacian filters (especially on aerial photographs) was found to optimize acquisition of data on canals.

In the Lower Khuzestan plain, the irrigation canals are mainly located on the Karun lobe and in the westernmost Jarrahi region. Canals were constructed to optimize delivery of water to the greatest area of agricultural land by combining the flow velocity and the natural slope. Depending on location and condition, seven patterns of canal were defined (Fig. 4). Over barren land far from the river, the main canal is normally constructed in a straight line downslope (Fig. 4A), and secondary canals branch off it with an angle between 30° and 70°, and within a few kilometers, change direction to follow the slope. A second type of canal network (Fig. 4B) occurs where secondary canals branch from the main canal. They are straight all the way to the chosen place, in the case when the main canal is not directly in the downsloping direction.

In both cases, the canal network is constructed according to the slope (gravity-flow irrigation system) to be sufficient to lead the water to the required place, probably (1) so it has an adequate flow velocity to avoid too much silting up of the canal, and (2) at the same time so it is not too great to cause erosion and wastage. The former factors were the main problems in canal maintenance in ancient times (Pournelle, 2003).

In the case where the canal network is established in the vicinity of a river, the setting is slightly different. The river is the major source point from which most of the secondary canals start. Generally, the canals are more or less perpendicular to the river (Fig. 4C). Therefore, the lateral canals use the levee backslope of the river to bring the water to the fields. The third-order canals start from the lateral canals with a slight angle and are straight. In the case of the Karkheh and Jarrahi Rivers, which end by a bird's foot distributary system into freshwater marshes, the canals are generally parallel to the main river branch (Fig. 4D). The lack of space in between the channel branches does not allow perpendicular canals. Moreover, the slope is probably not steep enough to provide an appropriate flow velocity. These canals are characterized by a long and sinuous pattern more or less similar to the main river branch.

Because the canal works required considerable labor in order to construct, it was a gain of time and human resources to use existing natural waterways. Some examples of these can be observed where some of the ancient canal patterns, coming from the river, have a natural meandering characteristic (Fig. 4E). From these meandering canals, numerous small-scale linear canals originate, showing traces of well-delineated square field boundaries in between. This meandering pattern is typical of the depositional zone along a river, which is characterized by crevasse splays and dissected by channels. In this way, the natural waterways are reused and form the basis for human-made canals.

At the foothill part of the Jarrahi, the spatial architecture of the canals is not as well organized because the river is deeply incised into the fan surface and does not allow gravity-flow irrigation. Here, the canals form a stellar pattern (Fig. 4F). The canal was probably built for providing water only to the settlements and their close surroundings. The primary canals originate in the mountains and follow the slope. They connect the tells, and several other shorter canals radiate from the tells (star shape pattern), and some of them show field pattern boundaries alongside.

The present-day canal network is engineered in a very different way and forms a generally very regular and perpendicular

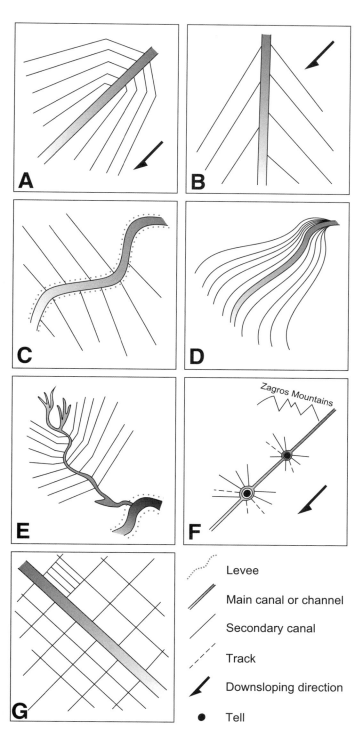

Figure 4. Representation of the different types of irrigation canals. (A) Main canal in the downsloping direction and secondary canals showing a change of direction. (B) Main canal with straight secondary branching canals. (C) River course as a main canal and perpendicular secondary canals. (D) River course as a main canal and similar-trending secondary canals. (E) Crevasse splay channels as main canal. (F) Star pattern canal. (G) Modern canal organization.

pattern (Fig. 4G) with rectangular field boundaries. The natural slope is not always taken into account, as irrigation system is now machine-assisted. Most of the ancient waterways have been leveled and are replaced by the modern network.

The common aspect of the different canal networks is the presence of a large waterway as a start. The largest canals are located on the Karun lobe. The main canal, the Nahr-e Bahreh, is 100 m wide, and the parallel canal, some 15 km further east, is 100–150 m wide. The branching canals get progressively smaller and smaller as they get further away from the main canal.

Analysis of the Spatial Location of Archaeological Features

The mounds are spatially distributed, with 32% along the Jarrahi, 30% on the Karun lobe, 16% along the Karun, 13% between the present-day Karun and the paleoriver course, 7% along the eastern part of the Nahr-e Bahreh canal, and 2% along the Karkheh.

In the Karun area, the largest sites are concentrated in the north of the Karun lobe (Fig. 3), while the smallest are located at the southern edge. The decrease in the tell size (from 5 to 15 ha to less than 1 ha) reflects (1) the diminution of the water amount from the source to the southern part of the lobe and (2) the strategic and empowered position of the upstream tells over their downstream neighbors (Morozova, 2005).

On the Karun lobe, the largest tells are located predominantly at the intersection of two major canals. The large sites (between 5 and 15 ha) around the Ahwaz area are located along canals, whereas the Karun River is surrounded by small mounds (Fig. 3).

Most of the ancient canals on the Karun lobe are abandoned and have suffered from a progressive siltation, reducing the efficiency of water transmission. The reason they were neglected may be due to the decline of an empire, involving less human resources, as it is believed that it was principally slaves that were used for canal maintenance (Nelson, 1962). Since the canals were easily choked with silt, constant dredging was essential, as long as the manpower was available. Another reason why the area could have been abandoned is the accumulation of salt on fields, which sterilizes the soil and brings agriculture to an end.

The Jarrahi area revealed the largest detected tells (20–25 ha) mainly concentrated upstream of the present-day Jarrahi (Fig. 5). In this area, the distribution of the tells and the organization of the canals are completely different depending on their location in the fluvial system and the type of fluvial sedimentation. Three different zones along the Jarrahi were defined: the sediment erosion zone (Fig. 5), mainly on the relict fan I where large gullies prevail and the river is entrenched; further downstream of the Jarrahi river and away from the relict fan I, the sediment transport zone (Fig. 5) is a stable fluvial zone with rare gullies; and toward fan II and fan III, the sediment depositional zone (Fig. 5) is characterized by abundant crevasse splays because the river is not confined anymore. The majority of the sites are located in the sediment erosion zone where the canals come directly from the mountains

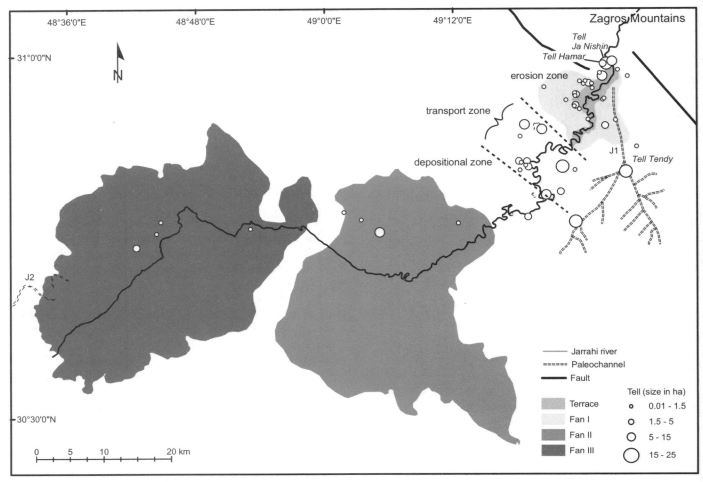

Figure 5. Spatial distribution of archaeological sites according to their size and relation to the different types of sedimentation zones along the Jarrahi River: (I) erosion zone, (II) transport zone, and (III) deposition zone.

and show stellar patterns. In this zone, the tells are all located at the edge of the fluvial terrace (Fig. 5) on fan I, probably because it is a much safer place, away from river erosion and floods. In the sediment transport zone, the number of tells slightly decreases, but their size on average increases slightly. This was a propitious place to settle because the river was stable, and thus safe from catastrophic floods. Here, the canals originate directly from the river, which is no longer entrenched. In the sediment depositional area, much larger in surface, the number of sites decreases. This distribution does not necessarily mean that tells were not built, it might rather indicate that mounds have been buried under sediments (see following), including crevasse splay deposits. On the margin of this site distribution, some tells, including Tell Tendy, the largest and the highest (8 m high on SRTM DEM), were identified. This tell location is revealed to be at a significant junction of the distributary system of the Jarrahi abandoned branch (Fig. 5), detected recently on satellite images.

The canals throughout the plain can be classified into two distinctive groups: anthropogenic or natural. The linear, orga-

nized fluvial features are typical of human-made structures. In fact, linear features can occur tectonically, or artificially, induced by humans (Bridge, 2003). No tectonic structures have been observed in the plain; the only faults are along the mountain front.

In view of the spatial configuration, it is more likely that certain geomorphological and environmental characteristics contributed to the decision-making process regarding the site locations. However, the representativeness and visibility of the sites and canals across the landscape of the plain may be dependent on taphonomic processes affecting their detection on the satellite images. The apparent lack of archaeological records may occur as a result of geological processes (Brown, 1997; Bettis and Mandel, 2002). Thus, various degrees of sedimentation have resulted in the burial of the archaeological record in the Lower Khuzestan plain, acting as a "geologic filter" (Bettis and Mandel, 2002). This phenomenon is also recognized in the Upper Khuzestan plain (Brookes, 1989; Alizadeh et al., 2004); in the Lower Mesopotamian plain, in Iraq (Hritz, 2004; Wilkinson, 2000), where deep alluviation, marsh, and wadi development covered earlier period settlement; and in the Lower Khuzestan plain, where the present-day fan sediments of the Jarrahi River (Fig. 5, fan III) cover paleochannel J2 (observed on the satellite images). Erosion caused by flooding and eolian processes can also affect the preservation of archaeological features in the plain. However, geological processes are not the only phenomena that can affect the site visibility. Human-induced disturbances to archaeological sites are among the most severe impacts on the archaeological records in the plain over the centuries, with construction of roads, canals, reuse of ancient infrastructure material, and wars. These natural and cultural issues would explain the under-representation of archaeological features, (1) along the Jarrahi River, as described previously in the three sedimentation type zones; (2) in between the Karun lobe and Jarrahi fans and to the SE of the Jarrahi River, with the effect of the wadi development (Fig. 1); and (3) the important gap in the record in the SW part of the plain, which underwent three phases of the Karun relocation and thus aggradation of the river ridges, as well as the Iraq-Iran 1980s war. It could also explain the under-representation of settlements prior to Sasanian and Parthian time, maybe buried under sediments, and the fact that no settlement has been detected along the three paleocourses of the Karun, usually the locus of settlement, when in use.

DISCUSSION

Relative Fluvial Evolution in Space and Time

Given the evidence for former channel locations, strong presumption for avulsion occurrence, the use of the archaeological information, the degree of visibility of the fluvial channels on the satellite images, and crosscutting relationships between channels, sequences of channel locational change may be suggested as an initial assessment.

The paleochannel K1 (Fig. 2) trends south from the paleocourse K2 for ~40 km and disappears. This may be the very oldest of the detected Karun paleocourses, since it was identified by the SRTM DEM only. K1 was most probably masked by more recent sediments, since it is invisible on the satellite images and aerial photographs. However, it is still expressed on the SRTM DEM because of the elevation of its alluvial ridges. An avulsion (Fig. 2, Ak1) triggered the change in the course direction, causing the relocation of the course to the K2 position. At one point, the K2 course cuts across the paleocourse K1, thus demonstrating that K1 is older than K2. K2 built up pronounced and easily identifiable alluvial ridges. This is the reason why K2 is reported in most of the geomorphological and archaeological surveys of the area. This major paleoriverbed goes from Ahwaz toward Shatt el-Arab. Another paleochannel, Kh1, originating from the Karkheh, joins it near Ahwaz. Identification of the confluence (Fig. 2, Ckkh) of the two paleorivers might solve the ambiguity around the interpretation of the major fossil alluvial ridges. Several authors (Curzon, 1890; Kirkby, 1977; Gasche and Cole, 2003) have interpreted the abandoned course K2 either as being

the paleocourse of the Karun between Ahwaz and Shatt el-Arab or being a former course of the Karkheh. However, the identification of a confluence, in this study, suggests that both rivers joined into a single channel.

Another avulsion (Fig. 2, Ak2) relocated the Karun course again (Fig. 2, K3) to a SSW-NNE direction. Its first part corresponds more or less to the present-day Karun, between Ak2 and Ak3, but downstream it diverged to the southwest, leading to paleocourse K3 (Fig. 2). This feature has a strong signature on satellite images and is clearly visible on panchromatic *SPOT* images taken in the 1970s, when no extensive canals, agriculture, and war structures disturbed the surface. Furthermore, the feature K1 seems to disappear where K3 crosses its path. These factors suggest that the K3 is younger than K1 and K2, as the riverbed is more clearly visible.

The K3 channel did not keep this position long enough to build up large alluvial ridges, unlike in the previous channel situation. The latest avulsion (Fig. 2, Ak3) brought the Karun to its present-day position. Its avulsion point (Fig. 2, Ak3) might be positioned on the present-day Karun as the paleocourse K3 tends to go in this direction. Moreover, the presence of two small tells (Fig. 3, t1, t2) may indicate that K3 channel lay nearby. However, a large zone of more recent crevasse splay deposits and extensive agriculture activities mask the northern segment of this paleocourse. The present-day Karun, in the same way as its previous courses, joins Shatt el-Arab, even though the latter was most probably further north (Fig. 2, S) than its current position. This sequencing cannot be supported by any archaeological age data because no remains have been detected in the SW part of the plain.

The relocation of the Karun course from K2 to K3 triggered a change in the orientation of the Karkheh. The Karkheh avulsed (Fig. 2, Akh1) and changed from a SSW to a NW direction (Fig. 2, Kh2). The paleofeature Kh2 has a much clearer spectral response than its previous course, suggesting a more recent setting.

The path of the Karkheh, Kh2, shows a rather straight trend, which contrasts with all the other meandering courses. Moreover, numerous abandoned canals surround Kh2, and some show a similar trend and length (Fig. 3, C1, C2). These very linear and organized features are completely artificial, human-made structures. The state of paleocourse Kh2 and the ancient land-use traces suggest that a large part of Kh2 is artificial. As the avulsion occurred, the river, in the process of developing a new course, most probably used an existing canal path as an easy way to flow, as has been observed in the Mesopotamian plain, Iraq (Morozova, 2005).

The last avulsion (Fig. 2, Akh2) causing the change to the Kh3 position (Fig. 2) is located 5 km to the south of Hamidiya (Fig. 1) and was induced after the collapse of a dam located some 24 km north of the city (Layard, 1846). It occurred in 1837, and the river shifted further north from its previous position.

The changes in the river position and the relative chronology based on the visibility of the patterns on the images are reinforced by age data from archaeological sites (Gasche, 2005).

Archaeological sites along the earliest paleocourses of the Kark-heh (Kh1) and the Karun (K1) are abundant and have a Seleucid (331–125 B.C.), Parthian/Elymean (125 B.C.–A.D. 226), or Sasanian (A.D. 226–637) origin, whereas further along the second paleocourse of the Karkheh, the sites date from the Islamic period (A.D. 637–1500), and their number decreases. Very few sites are present along the present-day Karkheh; they are mostly Islamic mounds located on the SW branch of the present-day Karkheh. The spatial distribution of the sites and their sequence emphasize the cultural adaptation toward the river evolution and changes. Indeed, the relative locations of the channels and their association with dated sites potentially provide evidence for the sequence in which they were in use.

The Karun lobe (Fig. 3), south of Ahwaz, can be attested to have been in use at least from the Seleucid-Parthian time mainly, and until Islamic time, according to the age of tells located along the canals (Kirkby, 1977; Gasche, 2005).

The evolution of the Jarrahi River is visible but delicate to date because very few archaeological sites have datation inputs. Only three have been dated (Gasche, 2005); nevertheless, they are of great interest. Tell Tendy (Fig. 5), located at the confluence of two paleoriver branches, is of Achaemenid origin (539–331 B.C.) and was occupied throughout Parthian times, and apparently no longer after this time. On the bank of the present-day Jarrahi at the head of fan I, Tell Ja Nishin may have a Hellenistic foundation and was almost certainly inhabited through the Parthian, Sasanian, and Islamic times. Another much smaller site, Tell Hamar, located nearby, indicates Sasanian times or maybe slightly older. This information constrains the timing of the avulsion and the abandonment of the Jarrahi paleochannel (Figs. 2 and 5, J1). Tell Tendy probably was abandoned during Parthian times, as no material from the Sasanian or Islamic was discovered. Its abandonment was probably due to the change of river course, causing an acute water shortage, leading to depopulation of the site. The Jarrahi River acquired its present-day location at fan I, and mounds developed along its new position, as the sites are slightly younger and inhabited until the Islamic times. This shift in population associated with the river relocation has also been observed in Mesopotamia with the Euphrates and Tigris Rivers (Wilkinson, 2000; Morozova, 2005).

From fan I, the Jarrahi River prograded southwestward, probably because of the availability of more accommodation space due to the seaward progradation of the coast (Baeteman et al., 2004/2005), which started between A.D. 600 and 700. This was provoked by the shifting of the locus of main deposition, which generated several paleofans (Fig. 2, fans I and II).

From the present-day Jarrahi fan, a paleochannel once meandered from the fan to the west (Figs. 2 and 5, J2). This is crossed by the present-day Karun River and joins the paleo–Shatt el-Arab (Fig. 2, S), suggesting that the Jarrahi prograded to the west. The last avulsion of the Karun (Fig. 2, Ak3) with relocation of its course (present-day Karun), most probably crossed and blocked the Jarrahi River (J2). As a consequence, the Jarrahi started to develop a fan (Fig. 2, fan III) to the east side of the present-day

Karun. The presence of the tomb of Imamzadeh Robein-ibn-Yakub, along the present-day Karun, dated between the twelfth and fourteenth centuries (Gasche, 2005), would attest to the presence of the Karun at this time and would indicate that the avulsion occurred previous to this time period. Thus, the development of the Jarrahi fan may be constrained from at least the twelfth to fourteenth centuries, throughout the seventeenth century, with the foundation of Darak, a city located at the beginning of fan III (Gasche, 2005) to the eighteenth-century city foundation of Fallahiya (Fig. 1, Shahdegan), until now.

Human Interaction

Humans had, and still have, an important impact on the configuration of the channels on the plain and natural processes. Because a large part of the plain was unfertile for agriculture and thus for subsistence, the ancient population developed irrigation networks to allow cultivation. Thus, comparison of ancient and modern irrigation patterns in the study area reveals that the ancient population exploited up to twice the land surface for agriculture purposes as is used today.

Some canal works were carried out reusing natural waterways. The crevasse channels were exploited by the population as canals and formed the base of secondary canals (Hritz, 2004; Morozova, 2005). Along the present-day Karkheh, most of the ancient crevasse channels are integrated in the agricultural landscape as irrigation systems. This contrasts with the linear abandoned paleocourse of the Karkheh, where the canals are also linear and have an anthropogenic origin.

The Karun lobe shows a wealth of canal networks, which suggests a human-made intervention. Most of the features are arranged throughout the lobe, with linear branches originating from the major canal Nahr-e Bahreh. Moreover, it is an important locus of settlement. Even if the Karun lobe appears to be artificial, its origin might be natural. Indeed, the very beginning of Nahr-e Bahreh shows (1) a sinuous character with no linear previous trace, and (2) the presence of a 2 km² deposit, characterized by a strong sandy spectral signature on satellite images. This kind of deposit can be observed at the beginning of crevasse splays, more particularly along the Karun. Moreover, two other sinuous canals (only visible on the aerial photographs from 1968) seem to converge toward the place where the Nahr-e Bahreh branches. The evidence suggests that a large crevasse splay with channels (Figs. 4 and 6A) is at the origin of the Karun lobe. The ancient population took advantage of this natural feature and built some canals from the natural waterways (Fig. 6B), extending the network. During the rainy season, the system suffered from floods and the successive overbank deposits. During this period, the excess of water and sediment reaching the end of the canals was loose, and formed small lobes and channels (Fig. 6C). In order to expand area of agricultural land, the canal network was probably extended over the years by reusing the natural channels (Figs. 6D and 6E) that appeared during the flood period. This process can be observed throughout the plain but on a much smaller scale.

In the Karun lobe, the flow was probably significant enough to allow the progradation of such a feature.

A similar scenario might have happened within the different Jarrahi megafans (Fig. 7). A succession of floods provided excess water and sediments, which initiated crevasse splays and channels (Figs. 7A and 7B), which were then reused as canals and prolongated (Figs. 7C, 7D, and 7F) until another flood period brought enough water and sediments to the end of the canals and formed other splays (Fig. 7E). The episodes of splay formation and canal extension were interrupted by periods of shifting of the main locus of sedimentation (Fig. 7E), and the whole process led to the formation of a series of three separate megafans (Fig. 7G). The successive occurrences of crevasse splay deposition at a similar location caused aggradation of the ground level and caused a local floodplain relief, which allowed the detection of the Karun lobe and Jarrahi megafans on the SRTM DEM. What is considered as a natural bird's foot distributary system (fan III) might in fact be human induced, supported by a representation of an early traveler (Layard, 1846), where most of the different branches of present-day Jarrahi distributary system are named canals. Moreover, recent crevasse splays observed on the satellite images in the interdistributary areas of fan III favor the formation of new distributary channels on the fan surface, which are recycled for agriculture purposes and illustrate ancient practice.

The humans interacted at other levels along the natural river course. Indeed, in this hostile land, enduring floods, the local population attempted to prevent catastrophes from happening. With this perspective, the straightening of channel prevented crevasse splays from forming, which took place more likely on the concave side of the river where the streamflow is high (Slingerland and Smith, 2004), and even more when the water and sediment supply increased. The excess water and sediment was dissipated via the numerous canals emanating from the channel, and the straightening of the river segment helped to control the flow. This method prevented floods only along the straightened section (Nelson, 2004), if well maintained. However, it is hard to distinguish in some parts of the rivers whether the course was straightened by humans or if the straight channel is due to the natural river evolution.

CONCLUSION AND PERSPECTIVE

In this chapter, digital mapping is a first step in setting up the general context of the Lower Khuzestan plain and its evolution by integrating fluvial landform mapping into a regional archaeological survey. In that way, important insights are obtained for the interpretation of past human behavior in the face of natural processes. The combination of both archaeological and geomorphological surveys in GIS allow us to spatially understand the mechanisms that contributed to shape the last evolutionary steps of the Lower Khuzestan plain and the distribution of the archaeological sites and canals. The relationship between the sedimentation history of the plain and the human settlement is clarified as (1) the ancient population was looking for perennial water, a crucial element for their subsistence in this semiarid area, (2) preference was given for stable places, less subject to

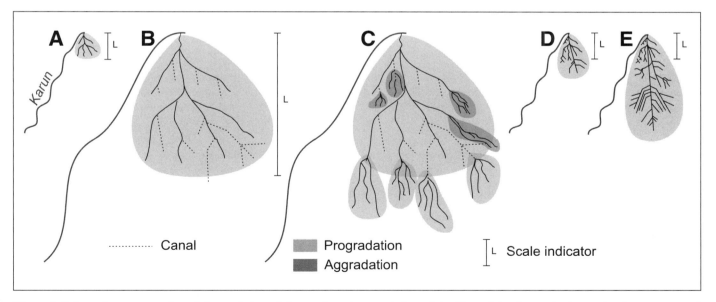

Figure 6. Schematic representation of the evolution of the southward progradation of the Karun lobe due to the interaction between natural processes and human activities. (A) First phase of the Karun lobe development: crevasse splay and channels develop from a break in the Karun levee. (B) Close-up on the crevasse splay: second phase, human intervention by the construction of canals using the crevasse channels. (C) Third phase: the floods involve an excess of water going through the existing crevasse channel/canal systems, which is dissipated at the end of the waterways in the form of small depositional lobes and channels. (D–E) Broad view of the progradation of the Karun lobe: splay and channel formation followed by canal construction.

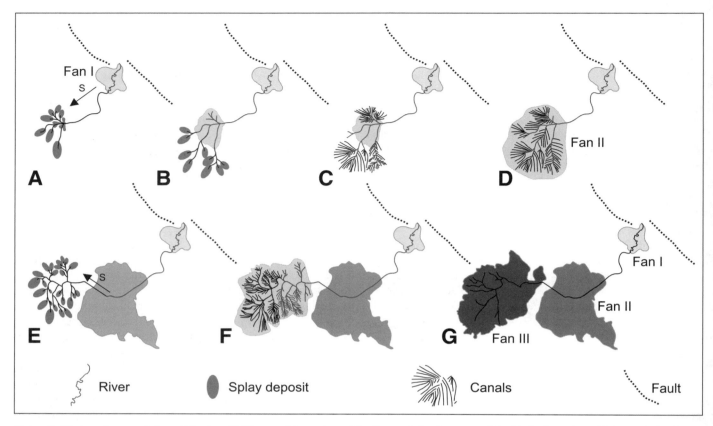

Figure 7. Westward progradation of the Jarrahi River and formation of the fans and development of the bird's foot–shaped lobes: (A–B) Phases of splay deposits; (C–D) phases of canal constructions; (E) shifting of the main locus of deposition (S) and phases of splay deposits; (F) phases of canal constructions; and (G) present-day spatial distribution of the different Jarrahi fans.

river migration, erosion, or floods, (3) the human activity tended to follow the natural or environmentally driven evolution of the fluvial landscape, (4) human irrigation practices tended to use the topography initiated by river changes and aggradation, and (5) some channel-management practices altered natural fluvial processes. Life in the Lower Khuzestan plain was not easy, as the population had to adapt to the river relocations when avulsions occurred.

The historical record contains many other examples where societies and settlements had to adapt in the face of abrupt environmental change. In order to further interpret the record of settlement and evolution more comprehensively for future research in the Khuzestan plain, it is necessary to look at a wider range of influences, including social factors, the political economy, and environmental fluctuations. Indeed, parallel studies conducted in arid and semiarid areas in the Southwest United States (Bayman, 2001; Waters and Ravesloot, 2001; Ravesloot and Waters, 2004), Peru (Dillehay et al., 2004), India (Berger, 2006), Pakistan (Belcher and Belcher, 2000), North Africa (Gilbertson et al., 2000), Near East (Butzer, 1997), and Sudan (Woodward et al., 2001), and Mesopotamia (Wilkinson, 2000, 2005; Wilkinson

et al., 2004), where the ancient population relied heavily on fluvial water for agriculture purpose and thus for living, have shown that agents of change and collapse of a society can be led by (1) climatic fluctuations, flood (river migration, destruction of infrastructures, and livestock), and drought (agriculture cannot sustain population), (2) soil degradation (natural or human-induced such as agricultural field salinization), (3) canal sedimentation, (4) invasion and war, and (5) diseases. However, economic and cultural practices such as long-distance trading (which could supply food from elsewhere) and pastoral practice (mixed economy with irrigation agriculture) must have been capable of over-riding climatic short event limitations.

These factors should be further investigated, in the Lower Khuzestan plain by more local geological and archaeological surveys to (1) improve knowledge on the population, and their evolution (growth and decline), which would explain over-representation of Parthian and Sasanian settlements compared to previous and subsequent settlement periods, Achaemenid and Islamic, keeping in mind questions of site visibility altered by taphonomic processes; (2) better constrain the timing of avulsion; and (3) provide further evidence on avulsion triggers.

ACKNOWLEDGMENTS

The Archaeological Institute in Ahwaz is thanked for their logistic support. I am grateful to Eric Goemaere (Geological Survey of Belgium) and Bart Ooghe (Archaeology, University of Ghent) for providing complementary information, as well as Ian A. Brookes (retired professor, York University, Toronto), Yves Vanbrabant (Geological Survey of Belgium), Cecile Baeteman (Geological Survey of Belgium), Andrew Farrant (British Geological Survey), and Christian Burlet (Geological Survey of Belgium) for their reviews and comments, which improved the manuscript. Financial support for this research was provided by the Interuniversity Attraction Poles Programme–Belgian State–Belgian Science Policy.

REFERENCES CITED

Adams, R.M., 1962, Agriculture and urban life in early southwestern Iran: Science, v. 136, p. 109–122, doi:10.1126/science.136.3511.109.

Adams, R.M., 1965, Land behind Baghdad: A History of Settlement on the Diyala Plains: Chicago, University of Chicago Press, 187 p.

Adams, R.M., 1981, Heartland of Cities; Surveys of Ancient Settlement and Land Use on the Central Floodplain of the Euphrates: Chicago, University of Chicago Press, 362 p.

Algaze, G., 1989, A new frontier: First results of the Tigris-Euphrates archaeological reconnaissance project, 1988: Journal of Near Eastern Studies, v. 48, p. 241–281, doi:10.1086/373408.

Alizadeh, A., 1985, Elymaean occupation of Lower Khuzestan during the Seleucid and Parthian Periods: A proposal: Iranica Antiqua, v. 20, p. 175–195, doi:10.2143/IA.20.0.2014081.

Alizadeh, A., Kouchoukos, N., Wilkinson, T.J., Bauer, A.M., and Mashkour, M., 2004, Human-environment interactions on the upper Khuzestan plains, southwest Iran: Recent investigations: Paléorient, v. 30, p. 69–88.

Baeteman, C., Dupin, L., and Heyvaert, V., 2004/2005, Geo-environmental investigation, *in* Gasche, H., ed., The Persian Gulf Shorelines and the Karkheh, Karun, and Jarrahi Rivers: A Geo-Archaeological Approach: Akkadica, v. 125, p. 155–215, v. 126, p. 1–12.

Baltzer, F., and Purser, B.H., 1990, Modern alluvial fan and deltaic sedimentation in a foreland tectonic setting: The Lower Mesopotamian plain and the Arabian Gulf: Sedimentary Geology, v. 67, p. 175–197, doi:10.1016/0037-0738(90)90034-Q.

Bayman, J.M., 2001, The Hohokam of Southwest North America: Journal of World Prehistory, v. 15, no. 3, p. 257–311.

Belcher, W.R., and Belcher, W.R., 2000, Geologic constraints on the Harappa archaeological site, Punjab Province, Pakistan: Geoarchaeology International Journal (Toronto, Ontario), v. 15, no. 7, p. 679–713.

Berberian, M., 1995, Master "blind" thrust faults hidden under the Zagros folds: Active basement tectonics and surface morphotectonics: Tectonophysics, v. 241, p. 193–224, doi:10.1016/0040-1951(94)00185-C.

Berger, A.R., 2006, Abrupt geological changes: Causes, effects and public issues: Quaternary International, v. 151, p. 3–9, doi:10.1016/j.quaint.2006.01.011.

Bettis, E.A., III, and Mandel, R.D., 2002, The effects of temporal and spatial patterns of Holocene erosion and alluviation on the archaeological record of the central and eastern Great Plains: Geoarchaeology, v. 17, p. 141–154, doi:10.1002/gea.10006.

Braidwood, R.J., 1937, Mounds in the Plain of Antioch: An Archaeological Survey: Chicago, Oriental Institute Publication 48, 67 p.

Brakenridge, G.R., Anderson, E., and Caquard, S., 2003, Flood Inundation Map DFO 2003-282: Hanover, USA, Dartmouth Flood Observatory, digital media, http://www.dartmouth.edu/~floods/2003282.html (accessed August 2008).

Bridge, J.S., 2003, Rivers and Floodplains: Forms, Processes and Sedimentary Record: Oxford, Blackwell Publishing, 504 p.

Bridge, J.S., and Leeder, M.R., 1979, A simulation model of alluvial stratigraphy: Sedimentology, v. 26, p. 617–644, doi:10.1111/j.1365-3091.1979.tb00935.x.

Brookes, I.A., 1989, The physical geography, geomorphology and late Quaternary history of the Mahidasht Project area, Qara Su Basin central west Iran: Toronto, Royal Ontario Museum, Mahidasht Project, 48 p., pls. I–V.

Brown, A.G., 1997, Alluvial Geoarchaeology, Floodplain Archaeology and Environmental Change: Cambridge, UK, Cambridge University Press, 377 p.

Buringh, P., 1957, Living conditions in the Lower Mesopotamian plain in ancient times: Sumer, v. 13, p. 30–46.

Butzer, K., 1997, Sociopolitical discontinuity in the Near East c. 2200 B.C.E.: Scenarios from Palestine and Egypt, *in* Dalfes, H.N., Kukla, G., and Weiss, H., eds., Third Millennium BC Climate Change and Old World Collapse: Berlin, Springer, North Atlantic Treaty Organization Advanced Study Institute Series I: Monographs in Global Environmental Change, v. 49, p. 245–296.

Challis, K., and Howard, A.J., 2006, A review of trends within archaeological remote sensing in alluvial environments: Archaeological Prospection, v. 13, no. 4, p. 231–240, doi:10.1002/arp.296.

Challis, K., Priestnall, G., Gardner, A., Henderson, J., and O'Hara, S., 2002, *Corona* remotely-sensed imagery in dryland archaeology: The Islamic City of al-Raqqa, Syria: Journal of Field Archaeology, v. 29, p. 139–153, doi:10.2307/3181489.

Cole, S.W., and Gasche, H., 1998, Second and First Millennium B.C. rivers in northern Babylonia, *in* Gasche, H., and Tanret, M., eds., Changing Watercourses in Babylonia: Towards a Reconstruction of the Ancient Environment in Lower Mesopotamia: Ghent, University of Ghent, and Chicago, Illinois, Oriental Institute, p. 1–64.

Colwell, R.N., 1983, Manual of Remote Sensing (2nd ed.): Falls Church, Virginia, Sheridan, Volumes 1 and 2, 2440 p.

Curzon, G., 1890, The Karun River and the commercial geography of southwest Persia: Proceedings of the Royal Geographical Society, v. 12, p. 509–532.

De Morgan, J., 1900, Etude géographique sur la Susiane: Mémoires de la Délégation en Perse, v. 1, p. 1–32.

Dillehay, T., Kolata, A.L., and Pino, M.Q., 2004, Pre-industrial human and environment interactions in northern Peru during the late Holocene: The Holocene, v. 14, no. 2, p. 272–281, doi:10.1191/0959683604hl704rp.

Drury, S.A., 2001, Image Interpretation in Geology (3rd ed.): London, Chapman and Hall, 290 p.

Dupin, L., 2004, Satellite imagery technique for an interpretation of the fluvial-marine geomorphology in SW Iran: International Geoscience Programme Project 495 "Quaternary Land-Ocean Interactions: Driving Mechanisms and Coastal Responses," Program and Abstracts, Bar Harbor, Maine, USA, 14–17 October 2004: Bar Harbor, University of Maine, p. 11; available at http://web.gg.qub.ac.uk/people/postgrad/harman/IGCP495Program.pdf (accessed 22 November 2007).

Dupin, L., 2006, Natural and human-induced processes: Impact on the landscape of the Lower Khuzestan plain (SW Iran) revealed by remote sensing, *in* Broadening Horizons, Multidisciplinary Approaches to the Study of Past Landscapes, Programme and Abstracts, Ghent, Belgium, 27–28 February 2006; available at http://www.broadeninghorizons.ugent.be/indexUK.htm (accessed on 29 April 2008).

Foda, M.A., Khalaf, F.I., and Al-Kadi, A.S., 1985, Estimation of dust fallout rates in the northern Arabian Gulf: Sedimentology, v. 32, p. 595–603, doi:10.1111/j.1365-3091.1985.tb00473.x.

Fowler, M.J.F., 2004, Archaeology through the keyhole: The serendipity effect of aerial reconnaissance revisited: Interdisciplinary Science Reviews, v. 29, p. 118–134, doi:10.1179/030801804225012635.

Gasche, H., 2005, Repères archéologiques dans le bas Khuzestan, *in* Gasche, H., ed., The Persian Gulf Shorelines and the Karkheh, Karun, and Jarrahi Rivers: A Geo-Archaeological Approach: Akkadica, v. 126, p. 13–42.

Gasche, H., and Cole, S.W., 2003, Fleuves, irrigation et inondations en Basse Mésopotamie et en Susiane, *in* Scienze moderne & Antiche Sapienze: Le radici del sapere scientifico nel Vicino Oriente Antico, Atti del Convegno Internazionale, Milano, 25 January 2003: Milano, p. 67–89.

Gibson, M., 1973, Population shift and the rise of Mesopotamian civilization, *in* Renfrew, C., ed., The Explanation of Culture Change: Models in Prehistory: London, Duckworth, p. 447–463.

Gilbertson, D., Hunt, C., and Gillmore, G., 2000, Success, longevity and failure of arid-land agriculture: Romano-Libyan floodwater farming in the Tripolitanian pre-desert, *in* Barker, G., and Gilbertson, D., eds., The Archaeology of Drylands: Living at the Margins, One World Archaeology: London, Routledge, p. 137–159.

Hansman, J.F., 1978, The Mesopotamian delta in the first millennium, BC: Geographical Journal, v. 144, no. 1, p. 49–61.

Hritz, C., 2004, The hidden landscape of southern Mesopotamia: Akkadica, v. 125, p. 93–106.

Jacobsen, T., 1969, A survey of the Girsu (Telloh) region: Sumer, v. 25, p. 103–109.

Jones, L.S., and Schumm, S.A., 1999, Causes of avulsion: An overview, *in* Smith, N.D., and Rogers, J., eds., Fluvial Sedimentology VI: International Association of Sedimentologists Special Publication 28, p. 171–178.

Kirkby, M.J., 1977, Land and water resources of the Deh Luran and Khuzistan plains, *in* Hole, F., ed., Studies in the Archeological History of the Deh Luran Plain: The Excavation of Chagha Sefid: Memoirs of the Museum of Anthropology, v. 9, p. 251–288.

Layard, A.H., 1846, A description of the province of Khuzestan: Journal of the Royal Geographical Society of London, v. 16, p. 1–105, doi:10.2307/1798222.

Lillesand, T.M., and Kiefer, R.W., 1994, Remote Sensing and Image Interpretation (3rd ed.): New York, Wiley & Sons, 750 p.

Makaske, B., 2001, Anastomosing rivers: A review of their classification, origin and sedimentary products: Earth-Science Reviews, v. 53, p. 149–196, doi:10.1016/S0012-8252(00)00038-6.

Mohrig, D., Heller, P.L., Paola, C., and Lyons, W.J., 2000, Interpreting avulsion process from ancient alluvial sequences: Guadalope-Matarranya system (northern Spain) and Wasatch Formation (western Colorado): Geological Society of America Bulletin, v. 112, no. 12, p. 1787–1803, doi:10.1130/0016-7606(2000)112<1787:IAPFAA>2.0.CO;2.

Morozova, G.S., 2005, A review of Holocene avulsions of the Tigris and Euphrates Rivers and possible effects on the evolution of civilizations in Lower Mesopotamia: Geoarchaeology, v. 20, p. 401–423, doi:10.1002/gea.20057.

Naff, T., and Matson, R., 1984, Water in the Middle East: Conflict or Coordination?: Boulder, Colorado, Westview Press, 236 p.

Nelson, H.S., 1962, An abandoned irrigation system in southern Iraq: Sumer, v. 18, p. 67–72.

Nelson, S., 2004, Flooding Hazards, Prediction & Human Intervention: New Orleans, Tulane University, Lecture Note, p. 1–8; available at http://www.tulane.edu/~sanelson/geol204/floodhaz.htm.

Pollock, S., 1999, Ancient Mesopotamia: The Eden That Never Was: Cambridge, UK, Cambridge University Press, 259 p.

Potts, D.T., 2002, Elamite Ula, Akkadian Ulaya, and Greek Choaspes: A solution to the Eulaios problem: Bulletin of the Asia Institute, v. 13, p. 27–44.

Pournelle, J., 2003, Marshland of Cities: Deltaic Landscapes and the Evolution of Early Mesopotamian Civilization [Ph.D. thesis]: San Diego, Department of Anthropology, University of California, 314 p.

Ravesloot, J.C., and Waters, M.R., 2004, A geoarchaeological approach to interpreting archaeological site patterning along the middle Gila River Valley, Arizona: Journal of Field Archaeology, v. 29, p. 203–214, doi:10.2307/3181493.

Richards, J.A., 1992, Remote Sensing Digital Image Analyses: An Introduction (2nd ed.): Berlin, Springer, 340 p.

Rust, B.R., 1981, Sedimentation in an arid-zone anastomosing fluvial system: Cooper Creek, Central Australia: Journal of Sedimentary Petrology, v. 51, p. 745–755.

Schumann, R.R., 1989, Morphology of Red Creek, Wyoming, an arid-region anastomosing channel system: Earth Surface Processes and Landforms, v. 14, p. 277–288, doi:10.1002/esp.3290140404.

Slingerland, R., and Smith, N.D., 1998, Necessary conditions for a meandering-river avulsion: Geology, v. 26, p. 435–438, doi:10.1130/0091-7613(1998)026<0435:NCFAMR>2.3.CO;2.

Slingerland, R., and Smith, N.D., 2004, River avulsions and their deposits: Annual Review of Earth and Planetary Sciences, v. 32, p. 257–285, doi:10.1146/annurev.earth.32.101802.120201.

State Hydrological Institute, 1999, World Water Resources and Their Use: http://espejo.unesco.org.uy/ (accessed 17 February 2007).

Stouthamer, E., and Berendsen, H.J.A., 2000, Factors controlling the Holocene avulsion history of the Rhine Meuse delta (The Netherlands): Journal of Sedimentary Research, v. 70, no. 5, p. 1051–1064, doi:10.1306/033000701051.

Törnqvist, T.E., 1993, Holocene alternation of meandering and anastomosing fluvial systems in the Rhine-Meuse Delta (central Netherlands) controlled by sea-level rise and subsoil erodibility: Journal of Sedimentary Petrology, v. 63, p. 683–693.

Törnqvist, T.E., and Bridge, J.S., 2002, Spatial variation of overbank aggradation rate and its influence on avulsion frequency: Sedimentology, v. 49, p. 891–905, doi:10.1046/j.1365-3091.2002.00478.x.

Ur, J.A., 2003, *Corona* satellite photography and ancient road networks: A northern Mesopotamian case study: Antiquity, v. 77, p. 102–115.

Ur, J.A., 2005, Sennacherib's northern Assyrian canals: New insights from satellite imagery and aerial photography: Iraq, v. 67, p. 317–345.

Vernant, P., Nilforoushan, F., Hatzfeld, D., Abbassi, M.R., Vigny, C., Masson, F., Nankali, H., Martinod, J., Ashtiani, A., Bayer, R., Tavakoli, F., and Chéry, J., 2004, Present-day crustal deformation and plate kinematics in the Middle East constrained by GPS measurements in Iran and northern Oman: Geophysical Journal International, v. 157, no. 1, p. 381–398, doi:10.1111/j.1365-246X.2004.02222.x.

Waters, M.R., and Ravesloot, J.C., 2001, Landscape change and the cultural evolution of the Hohokam along the middle Gila River and other river valleys in south-central Arizona: American Antiquity, v. 66, p. 285–299, doi:10.2307/2694609.

Wilkinson, T.J., 1989, Extensive sherdscatters and land use intensity: Some recent results: Journal of Field Archaeology, v. 16, p. 31–46, doi:10.2307/529879.

Wilkinson, T.J., 1998, Water and human settlement in the Balikh Valley, Syria: Investigations from 1992–1995: Journal of Field Archaeology, v. 25, p. 63–87, doi:10.2307/530458.

Wilkinson, T.J., 2000, Regional approaches to Mesopotamian archaeology: The contribution of archaeological surveys: Journal of Archaeological Research, v. 8, no. 3, p. 219–267, doi:10.1023/A:1009487620969.

Wilkinson, T.J., 2005, Soil erosion and valley fills in the Yemen Highlands and southern Turkey: Integrating settlement, geoarchaeology, and climate change: Geoarchaeology, v. 20, no. 2, p. 169–192, doi:10.1002/gea.20042.

Wilkinson, T.J., Miller, N., Reichel, C., and Whitcomb, D., 2004, On the margin of the Euphrates, settlement and land use at Tell Es-Sweyhat and in the Upper Lake Assad area, Syria: Chicago, Illinois, Oriental Institute Publications, v. 124, 276 p.; available at oi.uchicago.edu/pdf/OIP124.pdf.

Woodward, J.C., Macklin, M.G., and Welsby, D.A., 2001, The Holocene fluvial sedimentary record and alluvial geoarchaeology in the Nile Valley of Northern Sudan, *in* Maddy, D.R., Macklin, M.G., and Woodward, J.C., eds., River Basin Sediment Systems: Archives of Environmental Change: Rotterdam, the Netherlands, Balkema, p. 327–356.

MANUSCRIPT SUBMITTED 23 NOVEMBER 2007
MANUSCRIPT ACCEPTED BY THE SOCIETY 3 AUGUST 2010

The Geological Society of America
Special Paper 476
2011

Geomorphological study and paleogeographic evolution of NW Kefalonia Island, Greece, concerning the hypothesis of a possible location of the Homeric Ithaca

Kalliopi Gaki-Papanastassiou
Hampik Maroukian
Department of Geography and Climatology, Faculty of Geology and Geoenvironment, University of Athens,
GR-15784, Athens, Greece

Efthimios Karymbalis
Department of Geography, Harokopio University, 70 E. Venizelou Str., GR-17671, Athens, Greece

Dimitris Papanastassiou
Institute of Geodynamics, National Observatory of Athens, GR-11810, Athens, Greece

ABSTRACT

In the past two centuries, several researchers, based on different interpretations of the Homeric poems, have proposed that the ancient homeland of Odysseus may not have been the present Ithaca Island in the Ionian Sea but somewhere else. Among them, there is the opinion that the Homeric Ithaca was the western part of Kefalonia Island, the Paliki peninsula, separated at that time from the main island by a channel.

The aim of this study is to verify, based on geological and geomorphological field observations, the existence of the proposed "channel" during the Homeric era, and its filling by a series of landslides originating from the eastern mountains, and to determine the paleogeographic evolution of the study area in the late Holocene. Detailed geological and geomorphological mapping was performed focusing on different landforms of fluvial origin, slope changes, planation and depositional surfaces, karst features, mass wasting features, and faults. Topographic diagrams and maps, aerial photographs, and satellite images were used, accompanied by extensive field-work. For the geological mapping, field observations were combined with previous works. A spatial database derived from the aforementioned material and work was constructed using geographic information system (GIS) techniques. A digital terrain model (DTM) of the study region was also created.

All the geological and geomorphological evidence refutes the hypothesis for the existence of a channel in NW Kefalonia. Moreover, there is a serious discordance in the time period needed for the formation and evolution of the landscape, considering the rock type and the Mediterranean climate of the area.

Gaki-Papanastassiou, K., Maroukian, H., Karymbalis, E., and Papanastassiou, D., 2011, Geomorphological study and paleogeographic evolution of NW Kefalonia Island, Greece, concerning the hypothesis of a possible location of the Homeric Ithaca, *in* Brown, A.G., Basell, L.S., and Butzer, K.W., eds., Geoarchaeology, Climate Change, and Sustainability: Geological Society of America Special Paper 476, p. 69–79, doi:10.1130/2011.2476(06). For permission to copy, contact editing@geosociety.org. © 2011 The Geological Society of America. All rights reserved.

INTRODUCTION

Narrative epic poems have been very popular in the Aegean region, starting when the first Greek races settled down in the area ca. 2000 B.C. and flourishing during the eleventh to eighth centuries B.C. The epic poems of Homer, *Iliad* and *Odyssey*, were composed in the eighth century B.C. and describe the Trojan War and the return of the warriors to their homes after the termination of the war, events that had taken place in the broader Aegean area much earlier, during the twelfth century B.C. For thousands of years, people believed that these poems were mythological tales, until the end of the nineteenth century when Heinrich Schliemann, a wealthy German, discovered Troy and Mycenae. Soon after, other places mentioned in the poems were identified, verifying in this way Homer's poems.

The *Odyssey* narrates the story of Odysseus (Ulysses), the king of Ithaca Island in the Ionian Sea, who, sailing back home after the Trojan War, lost his way and spent 10 yr navigating around the Mediterranean. According to today's geography, seven islands exist in the Ionian Sea. The largest among them,

from north to south, are Corfu, Lefkada, Kefalonia, Ithaca, and Zakynthos. Kefalonia and Ithaca lie side by side separated by a channel; Kefalonia is situated to the west (Fig. 1).

Homer, in the *Odyssey* (rhapsody 'ι' lines 19–26), describes the geographical location of the isle of Ithaca thoroughly through a narration by Odysseus in the court of the king of Corfu Island. The following is a translation, given by the Perseus digital library (www.perseus.tufts.edu/):

19 εἴμ' Ὀδυσεύς Λαερτιάδης, ὅς πᾶσι δόλοισιν
20 ἀνθρώποισι μέλω, καί μευ κλέος οὐρανόν ἴκει.
21 ναιετάω δ᾽ Ἰθάκην εὐδείελον· ἐν δ᾽ ὄρος αὐτή,
22 Νήριτον εἰνωσίφυλλον ἀριπρεπές· ἀμφί δε νῆσοι
23 πολλαί ναιετάουσι μάλα σχεδόν ἀλλήλησι,
24 Δουλίχιόν τε Σάμη τε καί ὑλήεσσα Ζάκυνθος.
25 αὐτή δε χθαμαλή πανυπερτάτη εἰν ἁλί κεῖται
26 πρός ζόφον, αἱ δε τ᾽ ἄνευθε πρός ἠῶ τ᾽ ἠέλιόν τε,

I am Odysseus *son of* Laertes, *renowned among humankind for all manner of subtlety, so that my kleos ascends to heaven.*

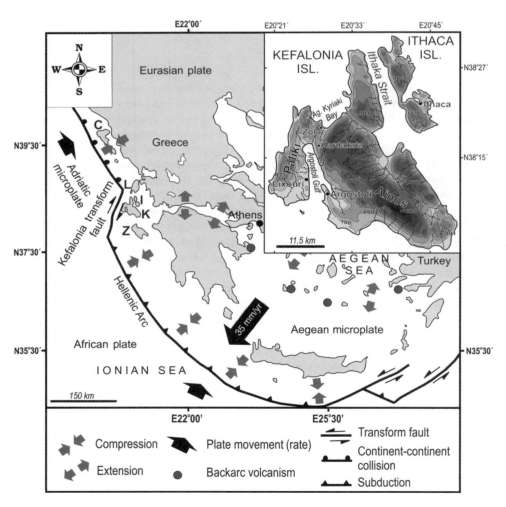

Figure 1. Location map of the Ionian Islands and the geodynamic setting of the broader area of the Aegean. Letters C, L, K, I, and Z stand for the larger islands of the Ionian Sea: Corfu, Lefkada, Kefalonia, Ithaca, and Zakynthos, respectively. Inset gives a larger-scale map of Kefalonia and Ithaca area.

I live in Ithaca, *where there is a high mountain*
called Neritum, *covered with forests; and not far from it*
there is a group of islands very near to one another
Dulichium, *Same, and the wooded island of* Zakynthos.
It lies squat on the horizon, all highest up in the sea
towards the sunset, while the others lie away from it
towards dawn,

Another interpretation for lines 21–26 is given by Luce
(1998):

21 My home is in clear-seen Ithaca. In it rises a mountain,
22 Neriton, conspicuous, with quivering foliage. Around lie
23 Numerous inhabited islands, very close to one another,
24 (including) Doulichion and Same and wooded Zakynthos.
25 Ithaca itself is low and is set farthest out in the sea
26 towards the dark quarter. The other islands lie away
towards the dawn and the sun.

These lines are considered to be the most important that
Homer gives us concerning the location of ancient Ithaca in relation to the nearby islands, but they are also the most disputed.
Almost every item in this selection has been the subject of pro-
longed discussion and controversy from antiquity onward. One
should think that Homeric scripts are not written text but narrative poems, so a literal interpretation of the Homeric poems
may lead to different meanings. It is no wonder that it took
Schliemann's discovery of Troy and Mycenae and then the identification of other places mentioned in the poems to verify, in this
way, Homer's experience with the places in the poems.

During the past two centuries, in addition to the view that
the ancient homeland of Odysseus was modern Ithaca (Gell,
1807; Leake, 1830, 1835; Rennell, 1927), several other opin-
ions were put forward that placed Homeric Ithaca on different
Ionian islands or places of the Homeric world or even faraway.
Wilhelm Dörpfeld, a famous German archaeologist, identified
Lefkada Island as Homer's Ithaca (1927). A. Goekoop (1908)
and C. Goekoop (1990) believed that it was Kefalonia Island.
Severin (1987), by sailing within the Aegean and Ionian area, in
a re-created Homeric (late Bronze) galley, attempted to locate the
entire geography of Odysseus' voyage. He gave evidence supporting the location of many Homeric places, but he did not manage to solve the problem of identifying Ithaca. Recently, Luce
(1998), in his book *Celebrating Homer's Landscapes: Troy and*
Ithaca Revisited, gives all the archaeological proofs that Homeric
Ithaca is the modern one. He also demonstrates that the topography of Ithaca is sketched with such accuracy that Homer must
have had firsthand knowledge of the terrain.

This chapter deals with one of the claims concerning the
location of ancient Ithaca. Homer (§671, o29, 33) and also the
Greek historian Strabo, who lived in the first century B.C. (Geog-
raphies, book I, 452), reported that the two islands, Same (Kefalonia) and Ithaca were separated by a channel. Some researchers
have expressed the opinion that the ancient Ithaca was the western

part of Kefalonia Island, the Paliki peninsula, separated from the
main island by a channel. In other words, they maintain that during the Homeric era, around 3200 yr ago, the island of Kefalonia
was separated into two parts by a narrow "channel" of NE-SW
direction located in the isthmus between Agia Kyriaki Bay and
Argostoli Gulf (Agia Sotira), in NW Kefalonia (Figs. 2 and 3).

These researchers were G. Volteras (1903), who first proposed that Paliki peninsula was the Homeric Ithaca, and Gilles le
Noan (2001, 2003, 2004), who initially suggested the same but
afterward, based on the geological conditions of the island, completely revised his opinion. Recently, R. Bittlestone et al. (2005)
also proposed that Paliki peninsula is the Homeric Ithaca. The last
research team suggests a series of successive channels (Fig. 3).
Eventually, they end up proposing that the most probable location is the eastern one, along the base of the western slopes of
Imerovigli mountain. They also claim that following the Homeric
years, successive landslides originating from the eastern mountains (Imerovigli mountain) filled the "channel." These landslides
created a huge lake at the SW part of the filled channel. Later, the
lake breached one or both of its northern and southern earth barriers, emptying and deepening the two existing channels running
toward the north and the south, creating the present landscape.
However, their field observations seem to be superfluous, and
they come to a questionable conclusion.

The aim of this study is not to solve the literary or the archaeological problem of the location of ancient Ithaca derived from
different interpretations of the Homeric poems, but to verify,
based on geological and geomorphological field observations,
the existence of the proposed "channel" by Bittlestone et al.
(2005) during the Homeric era and the filling of this "channel"
by a series of landslides, and to determine the paleogeographic
evolution of this area in the late Holocene.

In order to investigate the possibility of the existence of the
channel 3200 yr ago and draw conclusions about the paleogeographic evolution of the area, detailed geological (Fig. 4) and
geomorphological (Fig. 5) mapping was performed, focusing on
landforms of fluvial origin (gorges, valley morphology, alluvial
cones), slope changes, planation and depositional surfaces, karst
features (dolines), mass wasting features (landslides, mudflows,
and debris flows), and faults.

In the present study, topographic diagrams at 1:5000 scale
and maps at 1:50,000 scale (Hellenic Military Geographical
Service, HMGS), aerial photographs at a scale of 1:33,000, and
satellite images were used, accompanied by extensive fieldwork.
For the geological mapping, field observations were combined
with previous works, including the 1:100,000 and 1:50,000 geological maps of the Institute of Geology and Mining Exploration
(IGME) (1971) and (1985), respectively, as well as the geological map of the study area constructed by Underhill (1989). A
spatial database, derived from the aforementioned topographical
and geological maps, geometrically corrected aerial photographs,
satellite images, and fieldwork data confirmed with global positioning system (GPS) data, was constructed using geographical
information systems (GIS) techniques. A digital terrain model

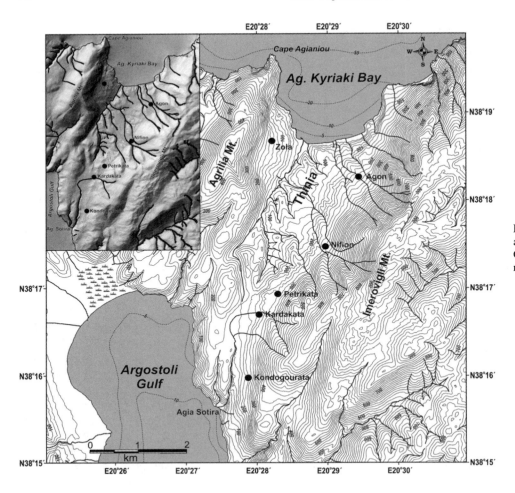

Figure 2. Topographic map of the study area of the isthmus between Argostoli Gulf and Agia Kyriaki Bay. Digital terrain model is shown in the inset.

(DTM) of the study region was also created using appropriate data (topography, drainage networks) and specialized GIS functions (Fig. 2).

TECTONICS, GEOLOGY, AND SEISMOLOGY OF KEFALONIA ISLAND

Kefalonia is the biggest and most mountainous island in the Ionian Sea. It has an area of 688 km², and a large part of the island is occupied by Ainos mountain, with the highest peak at 1628 m. The island of Kefalonia holds an important pivotal position along the Hellenic arc system. Geodynamic processes occurring in the region are related to the active subduction of the African lithosphere beneath the Eurasian plate, which progressively becomes continental convergence in northwestern Greece. The transition occurs along the Kefalonia fault zone (Fig. 1), a prominent dextral strike-slip fault, located offshore west of Kefalonia and Lefkas Islands (Scordilis et al., 1985; Louvari et al., 1999). The basement of the island consists of east-dipping, NW- to NNW-striking, thrust sheet fragments of a carbonate platform, belonging mainly to the Paxos geotectonic zone (Under-

hill, 1985, 1989). The Ionian zone is also present, occupying a relatively small part of the eastern island.

The study area is composed of a tectonic trough bordered by NE-SW–trending normal faults. The older formations outcropping in the study area are Upper Cretaceous thin-bedded pelagic limestones, overlain by Eocene–Oligocene (?) massive, thick-bedded limestones. On top of them, Upper Oligocene to Upper Miocene formations consist of a rhythmic series of conglomerates, limestones, and brecciated limestones with marl alternations in the upper parts. A small outcrop of Pliocene sediments south of Zola village reaches an elevation of 100 m. The Holocene deposits consist of alluvial cones and talus as well as fluviotorrential sediments along the stream channels and karst solutional depression fillings (Fig. 4).

A drilling operation in the central part of the isthmus (Thinia) at an elevation of 191.62 m and down to a depth of 260 m through Eocene limestones enclosed by Miocene marls encountered brine ground water at a depth of 258 m (absolute depth is −66 m). The study showed that these brines were hypersaline fossil water enriched primarily with Cl and Na and secondarily with Ca and Mg. These waters were formed at an early stage of seawater

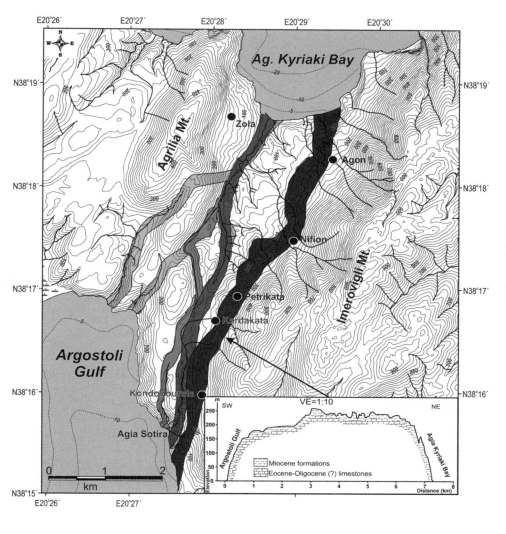

Figure 3. Topographic map showing the different courses of channels proposed by Bittlestone et al. (2005). The cross-sectional profile of the final proposed channel is depicted in the lower right-hand corner.

evaporation, probably during Miocene times, in the Messinian salinity crisis (Hsu, 1983). Since then, these waters had remained there for millions of years, without any hydraulic connection with the surface or adjacent ground waters (Koumantakis and Mimides, 1989).

The area is characterized by intense seismicity, with strong frequent earthquakes. The island of Kefalonia has been influenced by long-term positive land movements during the Quaternary. Pleistocene marine deposits forming terraces are found at different sites along the south coast at altitudes between 6.5 and 21.6 m and are considered to be Tyrrhenian (Last Interglacial, 125,000 yr old) in age (Braune, 1973; IGME, 1985). Other marine sediments of Pliocene age, reaching 200 m in altitude, have been observed in the same area (Sorel, 1976). During the past millennia, two vertical displacements associated with coseismic uplift, which affected most of the island, have been verified. The first occurred between A.D. 350 and 710 and the second during the 1953 earthquake, which uplifted mainly the southeastern part of the island by 50 and 70 cm (Pirazzoli et al., 1994; Stiros et al., 1994).

Recent precise GPS studies (Cocard et al., 1999; Hollenstein et al., 2006; Lagios et al., 2007) have confirmed the southwestward movement of the Ionian islands with a velocity of 7 mm/yr, increasing toward the south. A coseismic horizontal displacement of the area of several centimeters and interseismic subsidence of up to 4 mm/yr have also been found. The latter is in contradiction to the long-term geological evidence of uplift, indicating that uplift of the island is exclusively a coseismic result.

GEOMORPHOLOGICAL OBSERVATIONS IN THE AGIA KYRIAKI BAY AND ARGOSTOLI GULF ISTHMUS

The study area constitutes a tectonic depression bounded by NE-SW–trending tectonic lines. On the eastern side of the depression, there is Imerovigli mountain (994 m), and on the western side, there is Agrilia mountain (517 m). The area of the proposed channel is drained by two drainage systems today, the main channel flow directions of which have opposite courses to the north

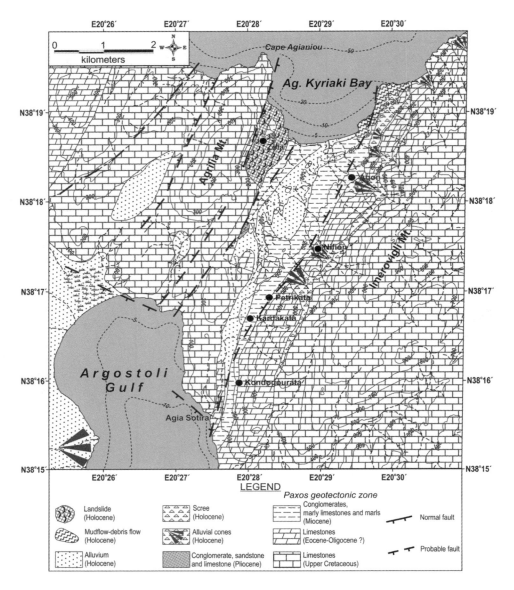

Figure 4. Modified geological map of the study area based on the maps by IGME (1971 and 1985) and detailed fieldwork.

(Agia Kyriaki Bay) and to the south (Argostoli Gulf) (Figs. 2 and 5). The watershed that separates the two drainage networks has an elevation of 180 m and is composed of fluviotorrential and some scree material from the torrents of Imerovigli mountain in the east.

The drainage system of the northern part exhibits a striking asymmetry. The main channel coincides with the original proposed channel of the early hypothesis by Bittlestone et al. (2005) (Fig. 3), and was probably affected by the presence of a normal fault having a NE-SW orientation. It has a length of 3.98 km and a southwest-northeast flow direction, emptying into Agia Kyriaki Bay. The tributaries extend only to the east of the main channels and drain the western slopes of Imerovigli mountain. They have formed V-shaped valleys on the Eocene–Cretaceous limestones in their upper reaches and Miocene for-

mations (mainly marls) in their lower portions. Alluvial deposits are present along the main channel of this drainage system (Fig. 5). Along the southern part of the proposed channel by Bittlestone et al. (2005) (Fig. 3), the main course of the very small drainage system has a total length of 2.22 km and has an almost north to south flow direction, emptying into Argostoli Gulf in the Agia Sotira region. The deep dissection of the main channel has formed an almost 60-m-deep gorge.

At the eastern limestone slopes of the "channel" (Imerovigli mountain), where the scar of the proposed landslide should be located, there are well-developed small drainage networks with V-shaped valleys, while at the geological boundary between the Cretaceous limestones and the Oligocene-Miocene formations, conspicuous alluvial cones have developed. The most important of these networks are those of Agon and Nifion (Fig. 6). There

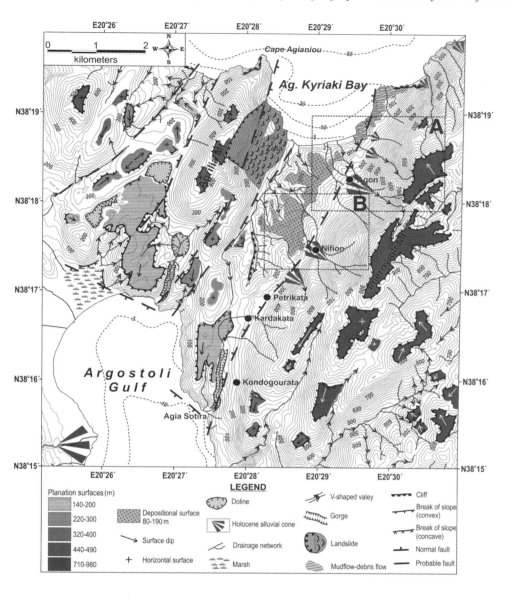

Figure 5. Geomorphological map of the study area. Boxes A and B correspond to Figure 6.

is no indication of any lacustrine deposits indicating the presence of a sizable lake, which, upon breaching its southern and northern banks, formed the two deep channels of Agia Kyriaki and Agia Sotira.

In the study area, there are some planation surfaces, which include scattered dolines and karst depressions located at different elevations ranging from 140 m in the west to more than 900 m in the east (Imerovigli mountain). These surfaces were grouped according to their elevation. It is possible that they represent remnants of an older single erosional surface that was tectonically broken into smaller pieces located at different elevations today (Fig. 5).

In the course of the fieldwork, various landforms (landslides, mudflows, and debris flows) were recognized and mapped having to do with mass wasting, as well as limestone boulders that slid down the steep slopes of Mount Agrilia in the west, probably triggered by the activation of a normal NE-SW–trending fault located west of Zola village or by a strong earthquake. The sliding process could also have been generated by the nearly identical slope of the mountain sides of Mount Agrilia and the dip of the rock strata. The fact that there are no indications of a developing drainage network on the slide material or on the scar left by the landslide is an important proof that this natural phenomenon occurred some hundreds of years or a few thousand years ago.

Along the slopes of the eastern coast of Agia Kyriaki Bay, mudflows and debris slides are observed. The activation of these slides was greatly assisted by the lithology of the Miocene formations, which are composed of alternating strata of conglomerates, marly limestones, and marls, which are especially susceptible to slide phenomena.

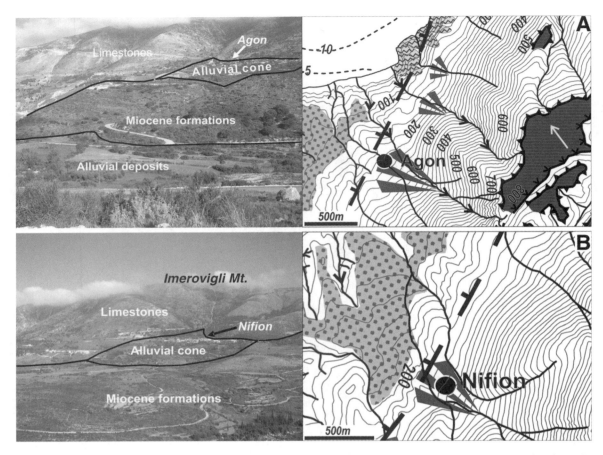

Figure 6. Large-scale topographic sections of Imerovigli mountain with corresponding photographs looking from the west. (A) Agon village area and (B) Nifion village area showing V-shaped drainage systems developed on the limestone of Imerovigli mountain, alluvial cones, Miocene formations, and Holocene alluvial deposits. For interpretation of the symbols, see the legend of Figure 5.

PALEOGEOGRAPHICAL EVOLUTION OF THE STUDY AREA

Using detailed fieldwork and geomorphological mapping, it was possible to reconstruct the recent paleogeographical evolution of the study area, starting with the end of the last glacial period 18,000 yr ago, when sea level was ~120 m below today's mean sea level (Shackleton and Opdyke, 1977; Chappell and Shackleton, 1986). At that time, the stream of Agia Kyriaki was downcutting intensively, trying to reach the lower sea level. There followed a rapid sea-level rise of ~110 m until 6000 yr ago. This transgression drowned the valleys on both sides of the isthmus, giving rise to the flat valley floor of Agia Kyriaki stream. Since that time, the sea has been eroding intensively the Miocene marly coasts of Agia Kyriaki Bay in the north, and wherever there is high water content in the Miocene marls landslides, debris slides and mudflows occur. On the contrary, in the Agia Sotira area, the presence of resistant limestone formations resulted in the creation of the very narrow gorge of Agia Sotira stream and the

very slow retreat of the coastline. The asymmetric evolution of the main drainage network of Agia Kyriaki is due to the presence of the higher mountain mass of Imerovigli mountain in the east, on which the main tributaries of the network are located. Along the base of the mountain, where the villages are located, there is the exit of at least three streams, where alluvial cones have formed near the contact of the Cretaceous limestones of Imerovigli mountain and the Eocene limestones or the Miocene marls of the area (Fig. 6). Scree or talus material is located only along the western front of Imerovigli mountain and the village of Zola in the west, where a significant landslide has occurred during the Holocene.

DISCUSSION

Our detailed geomorphological study and mapping of the isthmus region lead to several observations. The area of the proposed channel is drained by two drainage networks, main channels of which flow in opposite directions. The northern drainage network, emptying into Agia Kyriaki Bay, exhibits intense asymmetry with V-shaped tributaries located only on the slopes of Imerovigli mountain in the east, while the principal characteristic of the southern channel, which empties into Argostoli Gulf, is an intense main channel downcutting of ~60 m.

Small-scale landslides and mudflows were recognized and mapped in the study area. One significant landslide was identified near Zola village, west of the proposed channel, the material from which has slid along the slopes of Agrilia mountain. The absence of any drainage patterns on the slide material as well as on the scar left on the mountain sides denotes that this natural phenomenon occurred in very recent times, perhaps some hundreds of years ago. Mudflows and debris flows resulting from the presence of lithologic formations like marls that are prone to mass wasting were identified in the region along the steep slopes of the eastern Agia Kyriaki Bay.

The hypothesis offered by Bittlestone et al. (2005) asserts that Paliki peninsula was the Homeric Ithaca, which was separated from Kefalonia by a channel that was eventually filled by a series of landslides. It also created a lake that eventually breached its northern and/or southern ends and deepened the preexisting drainage system. In order to support their theory, the authors make some assumptions and presumptions that go a long way to even approaching the solution to their problem.

However, the geomorphological study of this area provides evidence that refutes their hypothesis. The hypothesis of occurrence of huge landslides presupposes the existence of a deep valley that was filled with landslide material. Traces of landslide material along the main channels of the two drainage networks of Agia Kyriaki and Agia Sotira should have been found, but none has been detected. On the contrary, in situ strata have been found instead of slipped material, as, for example, the Miocene marly formations in the Agia Kyriaki area (Fig. 7). The only slide material observed in the study area is the presence of some limited mudflows and debris flows on the eastern side of the proposed channel and in the northern area along the coastline of Agia Kyriaki Bay, along with the landslide at Zola village, which, however, is of local scale and originated from Agrilia mountain in the west. The material that moved down along the eastern slopes of Agrilia mountain lies on marly layers, creating an amphitheatric scar that is clearly visible in the DTM of the area (Fig. 2). Thus, it is highly unlikely that this material came from the east (Imerovigli mountain). Landslide material is found along the eastern slopes of the "channel" (west slopes of Imerovigli mountain), and small debris flows are found at the northern part of the area, along the coastline of Agia Kyriaki Bay, triggered by the presence of the Miocene marls, which are especially prone to sliding when there is an increase of water content. The only material originating from Imerovigli mountain is scree material at the base of the western slopes of the mountain.

At the eastern limestone slopes of the "channel" (Imerovigli mountain), where the scar of the proposed landslide is supposed to be located, there are well-developed small drainage networks with V-shaped valleys, while at the geological boundary between

Figure 7. In situ Miocene marly formations located in the Agia Kyriaki area.

the Cretaceous limestones and the Oligocene-Miocene formations, conspicuous alluvial cones have evolved. The most important of these networks are those of Nifion and Agon.

Even in the case of the "channel" being a wide valley, as proposed by Underhill in Bittlestone et al., 2005 (figure 27.6, p. 367), having the shape of a inverted triangular prism with dimensions of 250 m and 200 m for the base length and the height of the triangle and 6000 m for the height (length) of the prism, the shape would require an enormous volume of material (3×10^8 m^3) to have slipped from Imerovigli mountain. Given that the western slopes of Imerovigli mountain also have a length of 6000 m, a scar of similar dimensions to the filled area, 250 m wide and 200 m deep, should exist, something that in no way appears in the DTM (Fig. 2). In conclusion, there are no indications for the occurrence of sizeable landslides from Imerovigli mountain nor any sign of a significant scar on the mountain.

So a simple question arises, where did the fill material come from? Bittlestone and his colleagues have no convincing explanation for this. Given that Strabo (first century B.C.) reported the existence of a channel between Ithaca and Same (Kefalonia), which according to Bittlestone et al. (2005) is between Paliki and Kefalonia, in this very short time period of 2000 yr since Strabo's time, it is most improbable that such large-scale events could have occurred in order to fill such a deep and wide channel. This presupposes a period of intense seismicity followed by downcutting, and then a period of tectonic quiescence in order to have today's deep valleys. In this time period, one should consider the present semiarid Mediterranean climatic conditions as well as our knowledge of the last centuries of the seismic behavior of the area and the response of the landscape to them.

The latest hypothesis by Bittlestone et al. (2005) proposes the existence of a channel running immediately east of Imerovigli mountain and the villages along the road, filled with the landslide material. According to the various geological maps, the supposed "channel" is partly located in Eocene limestones or Miocene marls, which refutes the above hypothesis. One of the authors, J. Underhill, in his doctoral dissertation (1985) and in subsequent publications (Underhill, 1988, 1989) does not map any kind of extensive landslide material (Fig. 8).

It is also noteworthy that the region of western Kefalonia Island is an area with the highest seismic activity in Greece, where strong earthquakes are very frequent. In the past 110 yr with instrumental observations on seismicity, more than 50 strong events with magnitudes greater than 5.0 on the Richter scale (five of them greater than 6.0) have taken place in the area of Kefalonia (data from the archives of the Geodynamic Institute of Athens, http://www.gein.noa.gr/services/cat.html), without any massive landslides. An example is the recent strong event on 17 January 1983, of magnitude 6.2, that triggered only some rockfalls from steep slopes. Moreover, none of these events of the past 110 yr was accompanied by coseismic uplift in the Paliki area.

Beyond the geomorphological comments already made, another problem is also worth discussing, that of the time required to accomplish the sequence of events needed to complete the evolution of the landscape. Bittlestone et al. (2005) used the writings of Herodotus (book 2 of the Persians wars) and Thucydides (book 10 of the Peloponnesian war) in order to maintain that in the fifth century B.C., the island of Kefalonia was joined with Paliki peninsula, meaning that the proposed "channel" was filled up to sea level between 3200 and 2500 yr ago. This means that the filling of the narrow and shallow channel took place in 700 yr. Furthermore, they continue their contradictory and arbitrary "geomorphological" story and refer to Strabo's sources (first century B.C.) stating that "the channel was hardly navigable" at that time, which means that in 400 yr (fifth to first centuries B.C.), the channel topography remained almost unchanged. This leaves a much shorter time till today (nearly 2000 yr) for the area to have been filled up to 180 above sea level with landslide material, the formation of a lake, its breaching, the ensuing intense downcutting, and finally the formation of the present drainage systems.

CONCLUSION

Bittlestone et al. (2005) proposed that during the Homeric era, Ithaca was Paliki peninsula, the westernmost part of Kefalonia Island. At some time after, Kefalonia Island and Paliki peninsula were separated by a channel, which was filled by a series of landslides originating from Imerovigli mountain located at the east. In this study, based on detailed geological and geomorphological fieldwork and mapping, but also on previous studies, it is demonstrated that the hypothesis proposed by Bittlestone et al. (2005) is not valid. All the geological and geomorphological evidence refutes this hypothesis.

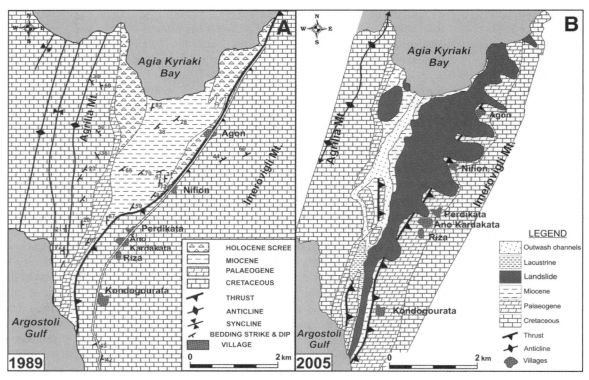

Figure 8. Geological maps of the study area as presented by Underhill (A) in 1989 and (B) in 2005 (Bittlestone et al., 2005). Figure 8B copyright © 2005 Robert Bittlestone. Reprinted with the permission of Cambridge University Press.

Once again it should be mentioned that in order to have this geomorphic evolution in the study area after the Homeric period, time is of vital importance, because if we consider the type of rocks and the temperate Mediterranean climate of the region, these changes are usually very slow and last for thousands of years. In the study area, the time period of 3200 yr is too short to have such major changes occurring in the natural environment. Moreover, this paper demonstrates that a proper straightforward, uncomplicated, and detailed geomorphological study can give answers to problems of the evolution of the landscape.

REFERENCES CITED

Bittlestone, R., Diggle, J., and Underhill, J., 2005, Odysseus Unbound: The Search for Homer's Ithaca: Cambridge, UK, Cambridge University Press, 598 p.

Braune, K., 1973, Die rezenten und pleistozaenen Sedimente des Sublitorals von Kephallinia (Ionische Inseln): Senckenbergiana Maritima, v. 5, p. 99–133.

Chappell, J., and Shackleton, N.J., 1986, Oxygen isotopes and sea level: Nature, v. 324, p. 137–140, doi:10.1038/324137a0.

Cocard, M., Kahle, H.-G., Geiger, A., Veis, G., Felekis, S., Biliris, H., and Paradissis, D., 1999, New constraints on the rapid crustal motion of the Aegean region: Recent results inferred from GPS measurements (1993–1998) across the West Hellenic Arc, Greece: Earth and Planetary Science Letters, v. 172, p. 39–47, doi:10.1016/S0012-821X(99)00185-5.

Dörpfeld, W., 1927, Alt-Ithaka. Ein Beitrang zur Homer-Frage, 2 volumes: Munich, Uhde, 442 p. with 33 figures and 89 engravings.

Gell, W., 1807, The Geography and Antiquities of Ithaca: London, Longman, Hurst, Rees and Orme, 119 p.

Goekoop, A.E.H., 1908, Ithaque la grande: Athens, Beck & Barth, 38 p.

Goekoop, C.H., 1990, Op zoek naar Ithaka: Weesp, Heureka, 114 p.

Hollenstein, Ch., Geiger, A., Kahle, H.-G., and Veis, G., 2006, CGPS time-series and trajectories of crustal motion along the West Hellenic Arc: Geophysical Journal International, v. 164, p. 182–191, doi:10.1111/j.1365-246X.2005.02804.x.

Hsu, K., 1983, The Mediterranean Was a Desert: Princeton, New Jersey, Princeton University Press, 197 p.

Institute of Geology and Mineral Exploration (IGME), 1971, The British Petroleum Co, Ltd.: The Geological Results of Petroleum Exploration in Western Greece, Report no. 10: Athens, Institute for Geological and Subsurface Research, 73 p. with 6 plates.

Institute of Geology and Mineral Exploration (IGME), 1985, Geological Map of Kefalonia Island: Athens, scale 1:50,000.

Koumantakis, I., and Mimides, Th., 1989, Brines in an enclosed limestone body of Kefalonia: Bulletin of the Geological Society of Greece, v. XXIII, no. 3, p. 61–76.

Lagios, E., Sakkas, V., Papadimitriou, P., Parcharidis, I., Damiata, B.N., Chousianitis, K., and Vassilopoulou, S., 2007, Crustal deformation in the central Ionian Islands (Greece): Results from DGPS and DInSAR analyses (1995–2006): Tectonophysics, v. 444, p. 119–145, doi:10.1016/j.tecto.2007.08.018.

Leake, W., 1830, Travels in the Morea with a Map and Plans: London, John Murray, 568 p.

Leake, W., 1835, Travels in Northern Greece: London, J. Rodwell, 530 p.

le Noan, G., 2001, A la recherche d'Ithaque: Essai sur la localization de la partie d'Ulysee: Quincey-sous-Senart, Editions Tremen, 118 p.

le Noan, G., 2003, La Ferme d'Eumee: Nouvelle recherche sur l'Ithaque Homerique: Quincey-sous-Senart, Editions Tremen, 114 p.

le Noan, G., 2004, Le Palais d'Ulysse: Quincey-sous-Senart, Editions Tremen, 91 p.

Louvari, E., Kiratzi, A.A., and Papazachos, B.C., 1999, The Cephalonia transform fault and its extension to western Lefkada island (Greece): Tectonophysics, v. 308, p. 223–236, doi:10.1016/S0040-1951(99)00078-5.

Luce, J.V., 1998, Celebrating Homer's Landscapes, Troy and Ithaca Revisited: New Haven, Connecticut, Yale University Press, 260 p.

Pirazzoli, P.A., Stiros, S.C., Laborel, J., Laborel-Deguen, F., Arnold, M., Papageorgiou, S., and Morhange, C., 1994, Late Holocene shoreline changes related to palaeoseismic events in the Ionian Islands, Greece: The Holocene, v. 4, no. 4, p. 397–405, doi:10.1177/095968369400400407.

Rennell of Rodd, Lord, 1927, Homer's Ithaca: A Vindication of Tradition: London, Arnold, 160 p.

Scordilis, E., Karakaisis, G., Karakostas, B., Panagiotopoulos, D., Comninakis, P., and Papazachos, B., 1985, Evidence for transform faulting in the Ionian Sea: The Cephalonia Island earthquake sequence of 1983: Pure and Applied Geophysics, v. 123, p. 388–397, doi:10.1007/BF00880738.

Severin, T., 1987, The Ulysses Voyage: Sea Search for the Odyssey: London, Hutchinson, 251 p.

Shackleton, N.J., and Opdyke, N.D., 1977, Oxygen isotope and paleomagnetic evidence for early Northern Hemisphere glaciation: Nature, v. 270, no. 5634, p. 216–219, doi:10.1038/270216a0.

Sorel, D., 1976, Etude Néotectonique des îles Ioniennes de Céphalonie et de Zante et de l'Elide Occidentale (Grèce) [Thèse 3e cycle]: Orsay, University Paris Sud, 200 p.

Stiros, S.C., Pirazzoli, P.A., Laborel, J., and Laborel-Deguen, F., 1994, The 1953 earthquake in Cephalonia (Western Hellenic Arc): Coastal uplift and halotectonic faulting: Geophysical Journal International, v. 117, p. 834–849, doi:10.1111/j.1365-246X.1994.tb02474.x.

Underhill, J., 1985, Neogene and Quaternary Tectonics and Sedimentation in Western Greece [Ph.D. thesis]: Cardiff, University of Wales, 500 p.

Underhill, J., 1988, Triassic evaporates and Plio-Quaternary diapirism, western Greece: Journal of the Geological Society of London, v. 145, p. 269–282, doi:10.1144/gsjgs.145.2.0269.

Underhill, J., 1989, Late Cenozoic deformation of the Hellenide foreland, western Greece: Geological Society of America Bulletin, v. 101, p. 613–634, doi:10.1130/0016-7606(1989)101<0613:LCDOTH>2.3.CO;2.

Volteras, G., 1903, A Critical Study on the Homeric Ithaca: Athens, Rapsani, Papageorgiou, 109 p. (in Greek).

MANUSCRIPT ACCEPTED BY THE SOCIETY 3 AUGUST 2010

The Geological Society of America
Special Paper 476
2011

Sand dune morphodynamics and prehistoric human occupation in NW Ireland

Jasper Knight*

*School of Geography, Environment, and Earth Sciences, Victoria University of Wellington,
P.O. Box 600, Wellington, New Zealand*

Helene Burningham*

Department of Geography, University College London, Pearson Building, Gower Street, London, WC1E 6BT, UK

ABSTRACT

   Interrelationships between coastal sand dune dynamics and prehistoric human activity are explored from three sites along the sandy, high-energy Atlantic coast of County Donegal, NW Ireland. Dunes at these sites yield artifacts and shell middens of Bronze Age to Medieval date. The detailed sedimentary context of shell middens and associated dark-stained occupation horizons and hearths was investigated from exposures within dune faces. Occupation horizons show mixed shells dispersed throughout, and wind-eroded and lagged upper surfaces. Shells located within these horizons are distinguished from those located within unstained sand, which are interpreted as middens formed marginal to semipermanent occupation sites. Sediments immediately overlying midden and hearth sites contain components (including shell fragments and charcoal) derived directly from these anthropogenic layers. The influence of this sediment source, tracked by the presence and abundance of shell and charcoal fragments, decreases rapidly upward. This field evidence suggests that changes in the nature of the land surface (by devegetation, sediment compaction, development of occupation horizons, hearths) may cause temporary changes in subsequent dune sedimentation processes and sediment characteristics. This also suggests that, as well as being difficult to evaluate using conventional geoarchaeological techniques, the sedimentological impact of past human activity in the coastal zone has probably been underestimated.

INTRODUCTION

   The interplay between coastal landscape development and human activity, in response to late Holocene climate and environmental changes, is well established from different coastal settings on a conceptual basis (Wickham-Jones and Woodman, 1998).

Schematically, this interplay can often be considered as consisting of periods of rapid change punctuated by periods of relative stability (e.g., McFadgen, 1994; Tolan-Smith, 1998; Gilbertson et al., 1999), although this viewpoint may be oversimplified in complex, shifting coastal landscapes (Bailey and Parkington, 1988; Anderson et al., 2006). Support for this landscape-human relationship, however, comes from point-specific dating,

*E-mails: drumlin@hotmail.com; h.burningham@ucl.ac.uk.

Knight, J., and Burningham, H., 2011, Sand dune morphodynamics and prehistoric human occupation in NW Ireland, *in* Brown, A.G., Basell, L.S., and Butzer, K.W., eds., Geoarchaeology, Climate Change, and Sustainability: Geological Society of America Special Paper 476, p. 81–92, doi:10.1130/2011.2476(07). For permission to copy, contact editing@geosociety.org. © 2011 The Geological Society of America. All rights reserved.

stratigraphic, and contextual archaeological evidence, which provides a limited understanding of landscape-human changes at a single location over (usually) a short time period (e.g., Caseldine et al., 2005; McFadgen and Goff, 2005; Boomer et al., 2007). For these point data to be linked together to understand wider spatial and temporal patterns of landscape-human development, we require closely spaced, high-resolution records that can be interpreted with a high degree of confidence (Woodman, 1992). From this, the timing and controls on changing landscape-human relations can be evaluated (e.g., Dark, 2006).

The conceptual, geoarchaeological approach outlined here can be used as a tool to track those changes in landscape morphology, environments, and processes that are both a driver for, and a response to, human activity and landscape impact (e.g., Bailey and Parkington, 1988; McFadgen, 1994; Gilbertson et al., 1999; Knight and Burningham, 2007; Mikkelsen et al., 2007; Sommerville et al., 2007). As such, this geoarchaeological approach is predictive, quantitative, and can be used to help monitor human impact over time through variables such as sediment fluxes, response times and time lags, and landscape recovery. An alternative conceptual tool in understanding landscape-society relations is one that considers landscapes as ritual and task spaces replete with cultural meanings that are contextualized by relations between society and space and their changes over time (e.g., McNiven, 2004; Conneller and Warren, 2006). This dynamic approach moderates landscape-human relations beyond the functional and views the formation of "lived" landscapes as a construct of social processes, and thus (preserved) archaeological landscapes as the product of these processes (Cooney and Grogan, 1999; Bell and Renouf, 2004; Westerdahl, 2005). This alternative approach is also useful because it helps fill in gaps in the archaeological record (Woodman, 1992), and it focuses on landscape changes such as changes in paleogeography and resource availability that impact directly on social patterns (Bailey and Parkington, 1988; Bell and Renouf, 2004).

Understanding of the timing, origin, and controls on landscape-human development is informed by both these approaches, particularly in landscape settings such as sand-dominated coasts that are morphologically dynamic over short (seasonal to decadal) time scales (Carter et al., 1987; Bailey and Parkington, 1988; Carter, 1990; McFadgen and Goff, 2005). In these coastal settings, changes in paleogeography (by coastal erosion and accretion) explicitly control the geomorphology, sedimentary processes, and landscapes of adjacent land areas, which may include estuaries, sand dunes, and salt marshes. In turn, these may control patterns of resource availability (including freshwater, the locations of freshwater and marine fish, shellfish, and seaweed) and strongly influence the location of shelterbelts, defensive sites, routeways, and settlements (Bailey and Parkington, 1988; Bell and Renouf, 2004; Boomer et al., 2007; Mikkelsen et al., 2007). In summary, therefore, past landscape-human relationships (broadly defined) along sandy coasts are the most dynamic, yet perhaps least visible, part of the archaeological record because they reflect the interplay among physical processes, changes in paleogeography,

and human activity and social processes over short time scales (Carter, 1990; Gilbertson et al., 1999; Anderson et al., 2006; Mikkelsen et al., 2007).

Dynamics of Sandy Coasts

The sand-dominated coasts of the glaciated midlatitudes (including the British Isles, western Europe, western United States, New Zealand) exhibit particularly dynamic morphological behavior over short (submillennial to event) time scales (e.g., Wickham-Jones and Woodman, 1998; Gilbertson et al., 1999; Cannon, 2000; May and Hansom, 2003; Erlandson et al., 2005; Sommerville et al., 2007; Burningham, 2008). This dynamism is due largely to their late Quaternary glacial inheritance, whereby glacigenic sediments were transported away from ice margins located on coastal lowlands and continental shelves (Carter, 1990; Shaw and Carter, 1994). Postglacial sea-level changes resulting from glacioisostatic unloading were important in reworking this sediment onshore, forming landforms such as barrier island chains, sandy beaches, coastal sand dunes, and estuary infills (Shaw and Carter, 1994; FitzGerald and van Heteren, 1999; Gutierrez et al., 2003; May and Hansom, 2003).

Many studies from the sandy coasts of the British Isles have shown the dynamic morphological behavior of coastal landforms, and their responsiveness to external forcing by sea-level change, wind and wave climate, and storms on short time scales (e.g., Hansom, 2001; Knight and Burningham, 2001; Wilson et al., 2001; Knight et al., 2002; May and Hansom, 2003; Burningham, 2005). Other studies have looked at relationships between human presence/activity and landscape dynamics (e.g., Gilbertson et al., 1999; Wilson et al., 2004; Boomer et al., 2007), focusing mainly, but not exclusively, on the timing of phases of land surface instability/stability in coastal sand dunes and thus, by extension, periods of dune development. Fewer studies, however, have considered in detail the role of human activity on the sedimentary and morphological processes that lead to land surface instability/stability and dune development (Gilbertson et al., 1999; Sommerville et al., 2007). These processes, however, are important because they relate closely to issues such as landscape carrying capacity and threshold disturbance, as well as wider issues such as climatic regime, sediment supply, and paleogeography. This paper focuses on interpreting these processes and wider issues from the geoarchaeological record of coastal sand dunes in County Donegal, NW Ireland.

AIMS AND METHODS

This paper has three main aims. These are to (1) describe field evidence for prehistoric human occupation from the inner margins of three Atlantic-facing estuaries in County Donegal, NW Ireland; (2) discuss the morphological and sedimentary processes that are associated with human disturbance in these sensitive coastal landscapes; and (3) set this human activity within a wider geographical and temporal context. The sand dune sediments and structures described in this paper were observed and logged in cliff section and georeferenced to Irish Grid using a differential global positioning system (GPS). Sediment grain-size distribution was established by dry sieving bulk samples at 0.25ϕ intervals between 63 and 2000 μm (4ϕ to -1ϕ). Calcium carbonate content was determined by dissolution with HCl; loss on ignition (combustible organic content) was determined by heating at 430 °C for 8 h.

PHYSICAL SETTING OF THE NW IRELAND COAST

Coastal sand dunes and other sand accumulations (in beaches and estuary fills) are common across northern and western Ireland, an area that was strongly affected by glacial erosion and deposition during the late Pleistocene (Knight et al., 2004). A dominant NE-SW structural alignment has restricted these sand accumulations to pocket beaches and estuary-mouth fills located within bedrock-defined embayments (King, 1965; Burningham, 2008). Furthermore, postglacial sea-level transgression (Shaw and Carter, 1994) has helped move sediment onshore into these embayments and estuaries, forming, in places, extensive supratidal strandflats, dune fields, and spits (Delaney and Devoy, 1995; Duffy and Devoy, 1999). Radiocarbon and luminescence dating shows that coastal sand dunes in northern and western Ireland started to accumulate from ca. 5 ka onward, as the rate of postglacial sea-level rise slowed (Carter and Wilson, 1993; Wilson et al., 2004). In addition, associated pollen, organics, metalwork, and other artifactual evidence shows that human activity has been present in these landscapes episodically and over long time periods (Mallory and McNeill, 1991; Wilson and Braley, 1997; Plunkett, 2004; Wilson et al., 2004). Several recent studies have highlighted the sensitivity of NW Ireland coastal sand accumulations to external forcing by decadal and shorter-scale changes in wind and wave climate, storminess and sediment supply (e.g., Burningham and Cooper, 2004; Burningham, 2005; Cooper et al., 2007). These studies show that, broadly, the most dynamic coastal change (including changes in coastal morphology, sediment dynamics, and sediment processes) coincides with periods of climate transition, in particular, the intensification of onshore winds and waves under cooler climates in association with positive phases of the winter North Atlantic Oscillation index (Burningham, 2005; Sommerville et al., 2007). While these processes (in isolation) are likely drive coastal morphological change, they also make coastal landscapes more sensitive to the effects of human disturbance, including coastal settlement, changes in land use (by deforestation, scrub clearance, agriculture) and land-management practices (grazing, rabbit breeding) (Tipping et al., 2008). This is thought to be the case during the unstable, cooler climate of the Little Ice Age (ca. A.D. 1550–1850), during which population pressure on coastal resources became exacerbated (Grove, 1988; Wilson et al., 2004). By contrast, "stable" and warmer climates are more conducive to land-surface stability and soil development and decreased sediment movement (Gilbertson et al., 1999; Sommerville et al., 2007; Tipping et al., 2008).

Coastal sand dunes are present in the innermost parts of Gweebarra Bay and two estuaries within the adjacent Loughros Bay, County Donegal, NW Ireland (Fig. 1). Sand dunes are found at Dooey, on the north side of the mouth of the Gweebarra River, where it exits into Gweebarra Bay. These dunes (1.3 km^2 in area and up to 50 m in height) back a wide, west-facing beach and comprise shore-parallel foredunes, dissected by both vegetated and active blowouts that degrade landward into low dune hummocks. Two west-facing, funnel-shaped estuaries (Loughros More, Loughros Beg) are present within Loughros Bay. Sand dunes (1.5 km^2 area) at Magheramore, on the north side of Loughros More, comprise a range of dune forms associated with the west-facing beach and estuary-margin setting. A steep, active scarp face (<25 m high) attests to present estuary-margin dune retreat, which has persisted since about A.D. 1900 (Burningham, 2002, 2008). The sand dunes at Maghera (0.75 km^2 in area), on the south side of Loughros Beg, back a wide, supratidal sand flat and comprise embryo and foredune ridges, which grade inland to relict and overgrown blowouts and residual dune hummocks.

The timing of dune development in these three substantial systems is poorly constrained, not least because buried (dateable) soils are not observed from the Dooey and Magheramore dunes. At Loughros Point, on the north side of the Loughros Beg estuary, blanket peat overlying perched dune sand has been dated to 4205 ± 80 ^{14}C yr B.P. (4690 [4765–4620] cal. yr B.P.) (Pearson, 1979). This is broadly consistent with dated evidence for land-surface stability from other locations in the north of Ireland (e.g., Delaney and Devoy, 1995; Wilson et al., 2004). In other places, dune sand has migrated across intertidal and back-barrier peats. One such sub–sand peat, on the south side of Gweebarra Bay, has been dated to 2095 ± 100 ^{14}C yr B.P. (1675 [1795–1555] cal. yr B.P.) (Shaw, 1985). These radiocarbon ages provide only inferential evidence for the timing of dune activity; to date, no luminescence ages have been retrieved from west County Donegal dunes. Archaeological evidence can also be used in a relative-dating context, but, although materials spanning the Bronze Age to Medieval periods have been recovered from all three dune systems (e.g., Brunicardi, 1914); to date no consistent patterns in age structure or location have been identified.

FIELD EVIDENCE

Dooey, Gweebarra Bay

Although there is a rich archaeological record in the Dooey dunes, including metalwork, pottery, flint tools, settlement structures, and human bones that span the Iron Age to Medieval periods (MacGill, 1947; Ó Ríordáin and Rynne, 1961; Ó Floinn, 1995), most finds have been recovered from back-dune (sand transgression) locations, not within the main dunes themselves. As such, middens and occupation sites from within the dunes have not been recorded in detail, but they can be observed at the northernmost end of the Dooey dunes, where the foredune ridges are lowest (6–10 m high) and onlap onto bedrock to the

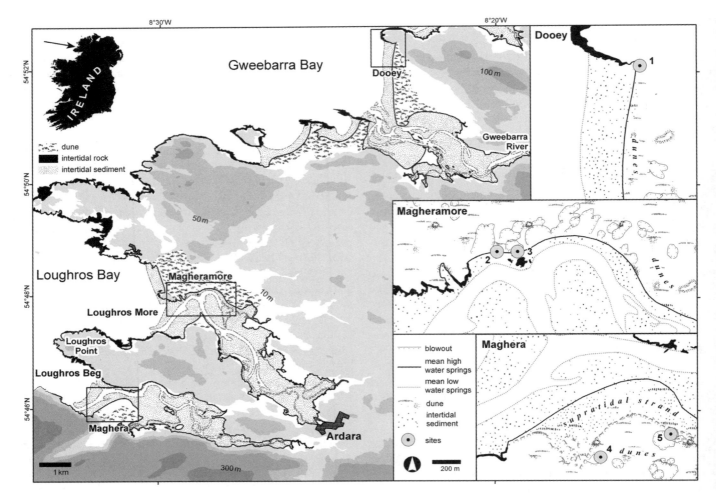

Figure 1. General location map of NW Ireland showing the sand dune systems discussed and (inset) the coastal geomorphology and location of sites 1–5 in the three estuaries.

north (site 1 on Fig. 1, at Irish Grid reference 175428, 403095 [54°52.498′N, 08°23.011′W]). Here, an erosional foredune scarp is fronted by developing embryo dunes. Sediments exposed in the scarp face comprise flat-lying, laterally continuous beds of well-sorted medium to fine sand, which is generally massive and occasionally planar stratified (Fig. 2A). A flat-lying and laterally continuous dark-stained bed, containing archaeological materials and shells and other fragments, is exposed ~6 m below the dune top at 5.8–6.0 m above mean sea level (Fig. 3). This bed, 0.25 m thick, has sharp and planar upper and lower boundaries and is characterized by higher organic and lower CaCO$_3$ content compared to the sand above and below, and it is also coarser in comparison to these beds (Fig. 2A). The highest CaCO$_3$ values (broken millimeter-scale marine shell fragments) are found in the sand bed immediately overlying the dark-stained bed. The dark-stained bed itself contains dispersed whole and fragmented shells (located particularly toward the bottom of the bed) that vary in concentration and composition laterally. The shells are not arranged in layers and do not show any internal organization.

The shell fauna is dominated (84%) by mussels (*Mytilus edulis*) (Fig. 2B). Charcoal fragments are likewise dispersed throughout. Small fragments of bone, sheep teeth, and metal slag (1–2 cm in length) are also present within this bed. Cockles (*Cerastoderma edule*) and charcoal fragments are found dispersed within the sand immediately below the dark-stained bed.

More widely, the dark-stained bed and mixed shell faunas observed here are consistent with previous observations elsewhere in the Dooey dunes (MacGill, 1947). The dark-stained bed is interpreted as an occupation horizon, not as a buried soil, as evidenced by its sharp lower boundary and absence of plant macrodebris within the layer. The associated, disseminated shells are interpreted as debris accumulated around a settlement place and not related specifically to a kitchen site. The other materials found within this bed (bone, teeth, metal slag) suggest a Medieval age (Lacey, 1983; Ó Floinn, 1995). The flat-lying morphology and lateral continuity of the dark-stained bed suggest that it represents a stable sand plain or broad, shallow depression located landward of foredunes that has since been eroded by wind, possibly down

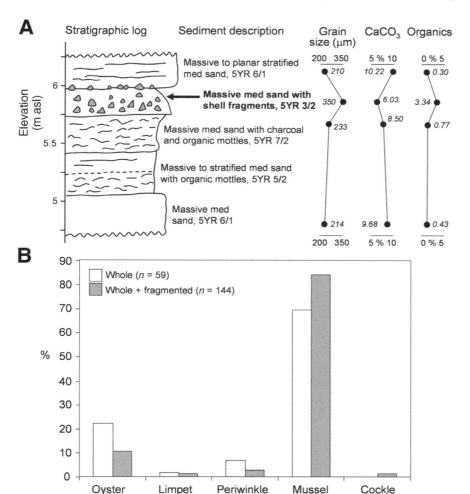

Figure 2. Site 1 at Dooey, Gweebarra Bay (location in Fig. 1), showing (A) generalized stratigraphic log, and (B) graph of recovered shell fauna from within the occupation horizon (arrowed).

to the level of the water table. Active wind erosion can account for the presence of a surface shell lag over the bed (Ceci, 1984). The identical texture of sand within the beds immediately above and below the occupation horizon suggests that this horizon was associated with temporary environmental disturbance of the dune depositional system (e.g., Sommerville et al., 2007; Tipping et al., 2008), and this was followed by a return to previous conditions when the site was abandoned. The CaCO₃-rich sand layer immediately overlying the occupation horizon may also suggest a process of sediment reworking, discussed in detail later.

Magheramore, Loughros More

Continued foredune erosion, caused by ebb channel migration (Fig. 4), has revealed shell middens and other archaeological features within the sand dunes at Magheramore (location in Fig. 1). Artifacts recovered from throughout these dunes include an anvil stone, a stone cist, part of a bronze cauldron, early Bronze Age pins, daggers, and Medieval items (Brunicardi, 1914; Lacey,

Figure 3. Photo of the occupation horizon at site 1.

Figure 4. Photo of the dune face at Magheramore dunes, Loughros More (location of sites 2 and 3). The dune face is 20 m high.

1983; Ó Floinn, 1995). Shell middens with both single species and mixed faunas have also been observed (Brunicardi, 1914). Archaeological horizons are observed in section on the actively eroding dune face. Two locations are described (sites 2 and 3 on Fig. 1, at Irish Grid reference 169020, 394958 [54°48.092′N, 08°28.948′W]).

Site 2, located at 4 m above mean sea level and toward the bottom of the dune scarp face (20 m high), shows layers of medium to coarse sand, 10–30 cm thick, in a coarsening-up overall sequence interbedded with thin and discontinuous shell layers (Fig. 5A). Combustible organic carbon is low throughout (0.22%–0.46%). The sand beds are massive to planar laminated, with the laminations developed in the coarser sediments. Two flat-lying shell layers are observed here. The uppermost layer (10 cm thick) consists mainly of marine shells (77% of total) that are dominated (73% of all marine shells) by cockles, with lesser amounts of limpets (*Patella vulgata*) and mussels (Fig. 5B). The bivalves are disarticulated, and the shells do not touch one another, nor do they show evidence of having been burnt. The terrestrial shells (23% of total) include the common European snail species *Cepaea hortensis* and *Cepaea nemoralis*, both of which are characteristic of dune environments. These snail shells are mixed in with the marine shells. The lowermost shell layer has a similar composition and structure to the uppermost layer. Above, below, and separating these two shell layers, there are vertically repeated, fining-upward sequences of coarse to medium-fine sand. Immediately overlying the shell layers, coarse sand interbeds are composed (mainly) of broken shell fragments (Fig. 6A). Calcium carbonate values are over twice as high here than in subjacent beds. These interbeds pinch out ~10 cm above the shell layers.

At site 3, located 7 m above mean sea level and 150 m to the east of site 2, medium sand with planar and discontinuous thin streaks of organic-stained materials and charcoal fragments overlies a shell-rich and red/brown-stained horizon (Fig. 5C). The red/brown-stained horizon is 2–4 cm thick with sharp upper and lower boundaries, is planar and continuous, and contains organic fragments including plant stems (1.8%–2.6% organics) and bone fragments. This sediment grades downward to a pink color in pure sand and contains large charcoal fragments (<8 mm) and local schist clasts (2–12 cm diameter) that are fire-blackened. This layer also contains an assemblage of fire-blackened shells dominated by periwinkles (*Littorina littorea*) (Fig. 5D). Above this horizon, planar, massive, medium sand beds (15 cm thick) are separated by planar and discontinuous seams of charcoal fragments (<5 mm diameter), which are vertically repeated in the profile (Fig. 6B).

The vertically repeated stratigraphy (shell layer, fining-up sand) at site 2 attests to repeated episodes of midden/shell-layer formation followed by landscape response (enhanced sand accumulation). This is also evidenced by the vertical repetition of charcoal layers at this site. Both of these examples show the relationship between sediment source (shell layer and hearth, respectively) and reworking of that sediment into coarser overlying layers. The mixed shell layers at both sites suggest utilization of different intertidal environments and resources, with sandy and rocky substrates being favorable habitats for cockles and periwinkles, respectively. The shells at site 2 show that both sandy-coast and dune environments were used as (summer) food sources (e.g., Bailey and Craighead, 2003; Jones et al., 2008). Furthermore, the position of the discarded shells in clean sand argues for deposition in an unvegetated dune-front setting away from an occupation surface. The shell-rich coarse sand immediately overlying the shell layer, however, suggests reworking locally from a restricted shell sediment source. Together, these inferences suggest deposition along the margins of a beach-facing blowout or where a dune ridge has been dissected by wind erosion. The red/brown-stained horizon at site 3 is interpreted as a hearth, supported by the presence of charcoal, fire-blackened materials, and pink (fire-heated) subjacent sand (Sergant et al., 2006). The association of rock-living limpets, periwinkles, and mussels with this hearth suggests a temporary (seasonal or shorter) meal or camp site that was later abandoned. A backshore or beach-fronting interdune hollow location is likely. At present, rocky coastal outcrops are exposed within a few tens of meters of this site (Fig. 1).

Maghera, Loughros Beg

The sand dunes at Maghera, within the Loughros Beg estuary, are separated from the active tidal channel by a wide (several hundred meters) supratidal strand (Fig. 1). As a result, the dunes have experienced limited recent marine erosion and may yield, potentially, a longer preserved record of human activity. The dunes themselves are mature back dunes (<25 m high) that have stable, vegetated blowouts. These dunes have a sharp, erosional scarp face around the northern and eastern edge of the dune field. Prograding foredune and embryo dune ridges are present on the west-facing side of the dune field. Throughout the dune

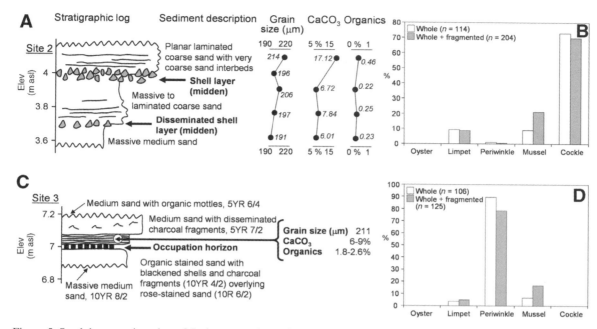

Figure 5. Sand dune stratigraphy at Magheramore dunes, Loughros More, showing (A) the stratigraphic log at site 2 and (B) graph of shell fauna within the uppermost shell layer; and (C) stratigraphic log at site 3 and (D) graph of shell fauna within the occupation horizon.

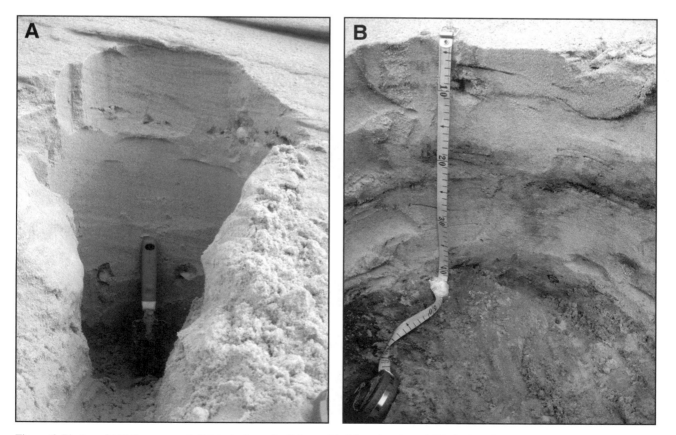

Figure 6. Photos of (A) the coarse shell interbeds at site 2 (trowel is 15 cm long), and (B) the hearth at site 3 at Magheramore dunes, Loughros More. Excavated face is 40 cm deep (scale on tape measure).

field, a wide range of archaeological material has been recovered, including bronze implements, flints, pottery, and bones (Brunicardi, 1914; D'Evelyn, 1933; MacGill, 1947; Ó Floinn, 1995). Mixed- and single-species shell middens have also been reported (Brunicardi, 1914).

Within the mature dunes, a laterally extensive buried soil is present. At site 4, within an abandoned blowout (at 12.75 m above mean sea level, at Irish Grid reference 166420, 390879 [54°45.528′N, 08°31.182′W]), the soil is 1.5 m thick and is overlain by 8 m of massive to stratified and cross-bedded medium sand (Fig. 7). The upper and lower boundaries of the soil are deformed by worm casts; organic and $CaCO_3$ content is generally low throughout. Dispersed charcoal fragments (<8 mm diameter) and fire-blackened local quartzite clasts are very common throughout. The soil has been dated to 3415 ± 135 ^{14}C yr B.P. (3695 [3555–3835] cal. yr B.P.) from charcoal fragments at its base (Carter and Wilson, 1991). Fire-blackened pottery fragments of early Bronze Age style have been recovered from the soil (Knight and Burningham, 2007), which is consistent with this age (Mallory and McNeill, 1991).

At site 5 (between 3.3 m and 6.8 m above mean sea level, at Irish Grid reference 166928, 391054 [54°45.979′N, 08°30.873′W]), a midden and associated buried soil are exposed on the flanks of a blowout at the edge of the dune system (Fig. 8). Sediments here consist of planar stratified medium to fine sand with disseminated charcoal fragments, exposed at the bottom of the blowout, developing upward into trough cross-bedded sand. Organic and shell material and organic-stained sand are exposed at several levels within the blowout. These materials constitute discontinuous accumulations of (sometimes decalcified) cockles that are associated laterally with accumulations of charcoal and woody fragments, small bones, and metal slag. Together, this material forms a flat-lying layer that is very variable in thickness (0.1–1.2 m thick) and composition but that has

a sharp upper surface. In detail, the cockle shells are often nested inside one another, are not burnt but are sometimes broken, and may be either scattered in a flat layer or else clustered together in U-shaped depressions (Fig. 8). No other shell species are present.

The presence of cockles is consistent with the sandy foreshore environment of this site and tidal flushing through the adjacent ebb channel. The shell clusters observed here reflect burial of shells within the sand itself, whereas the scatter of shells (interior side down) likely represents a lagged deflation surface. The lateral variability in layer thickness is also best explained as later wind erosion that has beveled off a stable land surface. Overall, this evidence strongly suggests that this is part of an occupation horizon in a sand-plain environment located landward of any foredunes, and recording a period or multiple periods of occupation, followed by abandonment, wind erosion, and later dune sand inundation.

DISCUSSION

Faunal, artifactual, and sedimentary evidence from these three sand dune sites reveals the interplay between prehistoric human activity and dune processes and environments, which is a topic that has been explored in detail in a few previous studies (e.g., Gilbertson et al., 1999; Sommerville et al., 2007; Jones et al., 2008). Evidence from the Donegal sites shows that there are specific physical mechanisms (erosion, transport, and deposition processes) and products (sedimentary beds) that may link human activity with coastal landscape change (or vice versa), and that these mechanisms and products can be identified in the dune geological record. This link is evidenced by (1) the formation and characteristics of occupation horizons; and (2) the composition of sediments that overlie these horizons.

Occupation horizons are observed at sites 1, 3, and 5. These can be identified on the basis of concentrations of shell debris,

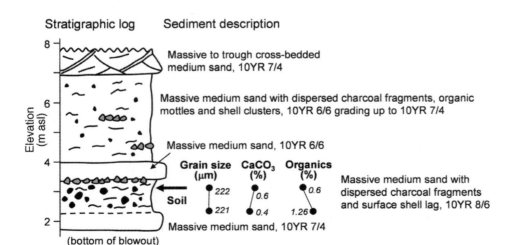

Figure 7. Stratigraphic log of exposed dune sediments at Loughros Beg (site 4), showing the location of the buried soil and associated shell accumulations.

Figure 8. Photo of cockle layers and clusters at Loughros Beg (site 5).

charcoal, and other fragments (including bone) that form a flat-lying and distinct layer with sharp upper and lower boundaries. As such, occupation horizons can be distinguished from in situ soils, which are deeper, may have a gradational lower boundary, and may contain micromorphological evidence for biological activity such as worm casts. The occupation horizons are all flat-lying, laterally continuous, and have wind-eroded and lagged upper surfaces. This evidence indicates surface devegetation and compaction during use, followed by wind erosion and surface deflation after site abandonment (Gilbertson et al., 1999; Sommerville et al., 2007). A kitchen (hearth) is observed at site 2 at Magheramore and is identified on the basis of rose-mottled (fire-heated) and discolored sand that immediately underlies the organic-stained horizon containing fire-blackened shells and clasts. Occupation horizons and hearths can be considered as lateral equivalents, set within contemporary landscapes that show human use of locally sourced materials.

The sediments that immediately overlie the shell layers at sites 1, 2, and 3 show two key characteristics—they are stratigraphically repeated over a scale of a few tens of centimeters, and they contain material that is derived from the underlying shell-rich layer. At sites 1 and 2, coarse shell fragments enrich sand layers immediately overlying the occupation horizon, and decrease upward in fining-upward sequences (Fig. 6A). At site 3, charcoal from the underlying hearth is reworked (and concentrated) into distinct and stratigraphically repeated layers in the overlying sand (Fig. 6B). A likely process responsible for this is wind circulation within an interdune hollow or blowout behind the main foredunes.

This evidence argues that formation of these archaeological layers first interrupted, and then enhanced, overlying sediment reworking and accumulation by surface deflation. This two-stage process represents a temporary response of the sediment system

to disequilibrium, probably on a short (seasonal to decadal) time scale associated with land-surface disturbance. It also highlights the role of site geomorphology in determining sediment supply, exposure, and the continuum of degree of disturbance in coastal settings, from changes in land use and development of routes through the dunes, to occupation horizons, to development of hearths and living spaces such as encampments. These different activities likely took place (as at present) in different parts of the dune environment and over different time scales.

These human-induced changes in dune sediment dynamics have been considered, thus far, independently of climate forcing. Distinguishing between human and climate forcing, however, is important because they often have similar geological signatures (e.g., Gilbertson et al., 1999; Wilson et al., 2004; Sommerville et al., 2007). Although late Holocene dunes in NW Ireland show distinct phases of instability/stability that very broadly correspond to cooler/windier climates (Wilson and Braley, 1997; Plunkett, 2004; Wilson et al., 2004), this regional picture emerges on a longer time scale than that discussed here. It is likely, therefore, that cycles of human-induced sediment dynamics were nested within longer-scale patterns of climate forcing, which may have influenced the sensitivity of the coastal environment to geomorphic change (e.g., Gilbertson et al., 1999; May and Hansom, 2003; Tipping et al., 2008). This may explain, for example, why coastal sand dune change in the British Isles appears most marked during the Medieval period (Little Ice Age) (e.g., Wilson et al., 2001, 2004; Knight et al., 2002) and Bronze Age (Bailey and Craighead, 2003).

The shell layers located within the dune sands described here could have accumulated under normal dune conditions and environments unaffected by human activity. The location of low-water tidal channels in the inlets of all three estuaries is subject to major decadal-scale variability, which is also associated with significant shifts in sedimentation patterns around estuary mouths and on adjacent beaches (Burningham, 2008). For example, dune erosion within Gweebarra Bay releases sediment to the beach and estuary, as well as to back-dune environments (Burningham, 2000). Marine shells found at high levels within the dunes and not in association with erosional unconformities are unlikely to have been lifted there by storm waves. The presence of human activity within the sand dunes is also necessary in order to yield the charcoal, metal slag and other fragments observed here. Stratigraphically, the presence of these non-natural materials can be used to indicate the extent of human disturbance of background rates of natural dune processes.

Significance of Middens

A key characteristic of these coastal sites is the presence of shell layers and middens. These are significant, not only because they help inform interpretations of contemporaneous human activity, seasonality, sedimentary environment, nutrition, etc. (e.g., Ceci, 1984; Mallory and Woodman, 1984; Bailey and

Craighead, 2003; Jones et al., 2008), but also because they are by far the most common (and still in situ) archaeological remains in these dunes (Lacey, 1983). The small size of the shell middens, in comparison to those reported from other coastal Ireland locations (e.g., Milner and Woodman, 2006), suggests that they reflect temporary and opportunistic activities within the coastal landscape, that midden sites were not reoccupied over time, and that the middens are of different ages (cf. Tonner, 2005; Jones et al., 2008). Another important characteristic here is that the larger and more laterally continuous middens are of mixed faunas, similar to those reported elsewhere in Ireland (Milner and Woodman, 2006), whereas the smaller and more dispersed middens are mainly of single-species composition (e.g., site 5). The smaller shell accumulations may reflect short (seasonal or shorter) occupation periods associated with the exploitation of very specific intertidal resources (Tonner, 2005; Jones et al., 2008).

The Wider Context

The localized evidence for landscape-human interrelationships described here mirrors that of other sensitive, sandy coasts in the British Isles (Gilbertson et al., 1999; Plunkett, 2004; Boomer et al., 2007; Sommerville et al., 2007), North America (Cannon, 2000; Bell and Renouf, 2004), New Zealand (McFadgen, 1994; Brook, 1999), and South Africa (Compton and Franceschini, 2005; Tonner, 2005). It shows in detail the feedback processes of landscape development occurring through human-induced changes in land-surface stability and sediment supply (Gilbertson et al., 1999; Anderson et al., 2006; Sommerville et al., 2007). Although it is likely that the occupation horizons and middens described here are broadly contemporaneous with others elsewhere, certainly in western Europe, their wider climatic significance is unclear (cf. Bailey and Craighead, 2003). In the absence of much tighter dating control, a focus on the local-scale interpretation of sedimentary processes and environments, as developed here, is probably a more useful research strategy, and one that can help inform debate on the sensitivity of regional-scale coastal systems to human activity over long time scales.

CONCLUSIONS

Sand dunes at the mouths of three NW Ireland estuaries show evidence for the interplay between prehistoric human activity and sedimentary processes. They suggest that even low-intensity human activity can influence sediment dynamics, processes, and sediment supply. They also suggest that, as well as being difficult to evaluate using conventional geoarchaeological techniques, the sedimentological impact of human activity in the coastal zone has probably been underestimated in the past.

Coastal sand dune environments, developed at the land-sea interface, are probably most sensitive to small-scale changes in boundary conditions that help drive these dynamic processes. Even relatively subtle changes in human activity, location, or density have potential to change coastal morphodynamics dramati-

cally, particularly on sand-dominated coasts. As such, the likely *impacts* of human activity on these coasts are probably much greater than the *evidence* actually suggests. Since this archaeological evidence is exposed in eroded cliff sections or blowouts, it is both selective and unevenly distributed, and thus may lead to an unbalanced view of the type or age of evidence available and interpretations of human activity based thereon (Bailey and Parkington, 1988; Woodman, 1992; Anderson et al., 2006). Noninvasive ground-penetrating radar studies (e.g., Neal and Roberts, 2000) and luminescence dating (e.g., Sommerville et al., 2007) are techniques that can yield further insight into archaeological patterns in these sand dunes.

REFERENCES CITED

Anderson, A., Roberts, R., Dickinson, W., Clark, G., Burley, D., de Biran, A., Hope, G., and Nunn, P., 2006, Times of sand: Sedimentary history and archaeology at the Sigatoka Dunes, Fiji: Geoarchaeology, v. 21, p. 131–154, doi:10.1002/gea.20094.

Bailey, G., and Craighead, A.S., 2003, Late Pleistocene and Holocene coastal palaeoeconomies: A reconsideration of the molluscan evidence from northern Spain: Geoarchaeology, v. 18, p. 175–204, doi:10.1002/gea.10057.

Bailey, G., and Parkington, J., 1988, The Archaeology of Prehistoric Coastlines: Cambridge, UK, Cambridge University Press, 154 p.

Bell, T., and Renouf, M.A.P., 2004, Prehistoric cultures, reconstructed coasts: Maritime Archaic Indian site distribution in Newfoundland: World Archaeology, v. 35, p. 350–370, doi:10.1080/0043824042000185766.

Boomer, I., Waddington, C., Stevenson, T., and Hamilton, D., 2007, Holocene coastal change and geoarchaeology at Howick, Northumberland, UK: The Holocene, v. 17, p. 89–104, doi:10.1177/0959683607073281.

Brook, F.J., 1999, Stratigraphy, landsnail faunas, and paleoenvironmental history of coastal dunefields at Te Werahi, northernmost New Zealand: Journal of the Royal Society of New Zealand, v. 29, p. 361–393, doi:10.1080/03014223.1999.9517603.

Brunicardi, M., 1914, The shore-dwellers of ancient Ireland: Journal of the Royal Society of Antiquaries of Ireland, v. 44, part III, p. 185–213.

Burningham, H., 2000, Short-term changes at an inlet margin dune barrier: Dooey spit, Gweebarra estuary, north-west Ireland: Periodicum Biologorum, v. 102, supp. 1, p. 505–511.

Burningham, H., 2002, Meso-scale morphological changes in the Loughros More estuary: Proceedings of Littoral 2002: The Changing Coast, v. 3, p. 265–270.

Burningham, H., 2005, Morphodynamic behaviour of a high-energy coastal inlet: Loughros Beg, Donegal, Ireland, *in* FitzGerald, D.M., and Knight, J., eds., High Resolution Morphodynamics and Sedimentary Evolution of Estuaries: New York, Springer, p. 215–242.

Burningham, H., 2008, Bedrock control on ebb channel behaviour in a mesotidal estuary: Geomorphology, v. 97, p. 300–320, doi:10.1016/j.geomorph.2007.08.009.

Cannon, A., 2000, Settlement and sea-levels on the central coast of British Columbia: Evidence from shell midden cores: American Antiquity, v. 65, p. 67–77, doi:10.2307/2694808.

Carter, R.W.G., 1990, Coastal processes in relation to geographic setting, with special reference to Europe: Senckenbergiana Maritima, v. 21, p. 1–23.

Carter, R.W.G., and Wilson, P., 1991, Chronology and geomorphology of the Irish dunes, *in* Quigley, M.B., ed., A Guide to the Sand Dunes of Ireland: Dublin, European Union for Dune Conservation and Coastal Management, p. 18–41.

Carter, R.W.G., and Wilson, P., 1993, Aeolian processes and deposits in northwest Ireland, *in* Pye, K., ed., The Dynamics and Environmental Context of Aeolian Sedimentary Systems: Geological Society of London Special Publication 72, p. 173–190.

Carter, R.W.G., Johnston, T.W., McKenna, J., and Orford, J.D., 1987, Sea-level, sediment supply and coastal changes: Examples from the coast of Ireland: Progress in Oceanography, v. 18, p. 79–101, doi:10.1016/0079-6611(87)90027-9.

Caseldine, C., Thompson, G., Langdon, P., and Hendon, D., 2005, Evidence for an extreme climatic event on Achill Island, Co. Mayo, Ireland around 5200–5100 cal. yr BP: Journal of Quaternary Science, v. 20, p. 169–178, doi:10.1002/jqs.901.

Ceci, L., 1984, Shell midden deposits as coastal resources: World Archaeology, v. 16, p. 62–74, doi:10.1080/00438243.1984.9979916.

Compton, J.S., and Franceschini, G., 2005, Holocene geoarchaeology of the sixteen mile beach barrier dunes in the western cape, South Africa: Quaternary Research, v. 63, p. 99–107, doi:10.1016/j.yqres.2004.09.006.

Conneller, C., and Warren, G., 2006, Mesolithic Britain and Ireland—New Approaches: Stroud, UK, Tempus, 224 p.

Cooney, G., and Grogan, E., 1999, Irish Prehistory—A Social Perspective: Bray, Ireland, Wordwell, p. 276.

Cooper, J.A.G., McKenna, J., Jackson, D.W.T., and O'Connor, M., 2007, Mesoscale coastal behaviour related to morphological self-adjustment: Geology, v. 35, p. 187–190, doi:10.1130/G23016A.1.

Dark, P., 2006, Climate deterioration and land-use change in the first millennium BC: Perspectives from the British palynological record: Journal of Archaeological Science, v. 33, p. 1381–1395, doi:10.1016/j.jas.2006.01.009.

Delaney, C., and Devoy, R., 1995, Evidence from sites in western Ireland of late Holocene changes in coastal environments: Marine Geology, v. 124, p. 273–287, doi:10.1016/0025-3227(95)00045-Z.

D'Evelyn, A.M., 1933, A sandhill settlement, Maghera, Co. Donegal: Journal of the Royal Society of Antiquaries of Ireland, v. 63, p. 88–100.

Duffy, M.J., and Devoy, R.J.N., 1999, Contemporary process controls on the evolution of sedimentary coasts under low to high energy regimes: Western Ireland: Geologie en Mijnbouw, v. 77, p. 333–349, doi:10.1023/A:1003619813284.

Erlandson, J.M., Rick, T.C., and Peterson, C., 2005, A geoarchaeological chronology of Holocene dune building on San Miguel Island, California: The Holocene, v. 15, p. 1227–1235, doi:10.1191/0959683605hl893rp.

FitzGerald, D.M., and van Heteren, S., 1999, Classification of paraglacial barrier systems: Coastal New England, USA: Sedimentology, v. 46, p. 1083–1108, doi:10.1046/j.1365-3091.1999.00266.x.

Gilbertson, D.D., Schwenninger, J.-L., Kemp, R.A., and Rhodes, E.J., 1999, Sanddrift and soil formation along an exposed North Atlantic coastline: 14,000 years of diverse geomorphological, climatic and human impacts: Journal of Archaeological Science, v. 26, p. 439–469, doi:10.1006/jasc.1998.0360.

Grove, J.M., 1988, The Little Ice Age: London, Methuen, 498 p.

Gutierrez, B.T., Uchipi, E., Driscoll, N.W., and Aubrey, D.G., 2003, Relative sea-level rise and the development of valley-fill and shallow-water sequences in Nantucket Sound, Massachusetts: Marine Geology, v. 193, p. 295–314, doi:10.1016/S0025-3227(02)00665-5.

Hansom, J.D., 2001, Coastal sensitivity to environmental change: A view from the beach: Catena, v. 42, p. 291–305, doi:10.1016/S0341-8162(00)00142-9.

Jones, T.L., Kennett, D.J., Kennett, J.P., and Codding, B.F., 2008, Seasonal stability in late Holocene shellfish harvesting on the central California coast: Journal of Archaeological Science, v. 35, p. 2286–2294, doi:10.1016/j.jas.2008.03.002.

King, C.A.M., 1965, Some observations on the beaches of the west coast of County Donegal: Irish Geography, v. 5, p. 40–50, doi:10.1080/00750776509555596.

Knight, J., and Burningham, H., 2001, Development of bedrock-cut coastal ventifacts and their relationship to late Holocene environmental change, County Donegal, northwestern Ireland: The Journal of Geology, v. 109, p. 647–660, doi:10.1086/321959.

Knight, J., and Burningham, H., 2007, Coastal morphodynamics and prehistoric human occupation, County Donegal, NW Ireland: Journal of Coastal Research, v. 50, Special Issue, p. 104–108.

Knight, J., Orford, J.D., Wilson, P., and Braley, S.M., 2002, Assessment of temporal changes in coastal sand dune environments using the log-hyperbolic grain size method: Sedimentology, v. 49, p. 1229–1252, doi:10.1046/j.1365-3091.2002.00493.x.

Knight, J., Coxon, P., McCabe, A.M., and McCarron, S.G., 2004, Pleistocene glaciations in Ireland, in Ehlers, J., and Gibbard, P.L., eds., Quaternary Glaciations—Extent and Chronology: Part 1: Europe: Amsterdam, Elsevier, p. 183–191.

Lacey, B., 1983, Archaeological Survey of County Donegal: Lifford, Donegal County Council, 401 p.

MacGill, P.J., 1947, Notes on shore dwellers and sandhill settlements (Dooey, Lettermacaward, Co. Donegal): Journal of the County Donegal Historical Society, p. 27–35.

Mallory, J.P., and McNeill, T.E., 1991, The Archaeology of Ulster from Colonization to Plantation: Belfast, Institute of Irish Studies, Queen's University of Belfast, 367 p.

Mallory, J.P., and Woodman, P.C., 1984, Oughtymore: An early Christian shell midden: Ulster Journal of Archaeology, v. 47, p. 51–62.

May, V.J., and Hansom, J.D., 2003, Coastal Geomorphology of Great Britain: Geological Conservation Review Series 28: Peterborough, Joint Nature Conservation Committee, 754 p.

McFadgen, B.G., 1994, Archaeology and Holocene sand dune stratigraphy on Chatham Island: Journal of the Royal Society of New Zealand, v. 24, p. 17–44, doi:10.1080/03014223.1994.9517454.

McFadgen, B.G., and Goff, J.R., 2005, An earth systems approach to understanding the tectonic and cultural landscapes of linked marine embayments: Avon-Heathcote Estuary (Ihutai) and Lake Ellesmere (Waihora), New Zealand: Journal of Quaternary Science, v. 20, p. 227–237, doi:10.1002/jqs.907.

McNiven, I.J., 2004, Saltwater people: Spiritscapes, maritime rituals and the archaeology of Australian indigenous seascapes: World Archaeology, v. 35, p. 329–349, doi:10.1080/0043824042000185757.

Mikkelsen, J.H., Langohr, R., and Macphail, R.I., 2007, Soilscape and land-use evolution related to drift sand movements since the Bronze Age in eastern Jutland, Denmark: Geoarchaeology, v. 22, p. 155–179, doi:10.1002/gea.20162.

Milner, N., and Woodman, P., 2006, Deconstructing the myths of Irish shell middens, in Milner, N., Craig, O.E., and Bailey, G.N., eds., Shell Middens in Atlantic Europe: Oxford, Oxbow, p. 55–64.

Neal, A., and Roberts, C.L., 2000, Applications of ground-penetrating radar (GPR) to sedimentological, geomorphological and geoarchaeological studies in coastal environments, in Pye, K., and Allen, J.R.L., eds., Coastal and Estuarine Environments: Sedimentology, Geomorphology and Geoarchaeology: Geological Society of London Special Publication 175, p. 139–171.

Ó Floinn, R., 1995, Sandhills, silver and shrines—Fine metalwork of the Medieval period from Donegal, in Nolan, W., Ronayne, L., and Dunlevy, M., eds., Donegal, History and Society: Dublin, Geography Publications, p. 85–148.

Ó Ríordáin, A.B., and Rynne, E., 1961, A settlement in the sandhills at Dooey, Co. Donegal: Journal of the Royal Society of Antiquaries of Ireland, v. 91, p. 58–64.

Pearson, G.W., 1979, Belfast radiocarbon dates IX: Radiocarbon, v. 21, p. 274–290.

Plunkett, G., 2004, Archaeology and palaeoenvironment at Grangemore dunes: Co Derry: Ulster Journal of Archaeology, v. 63, p. 1–13.

Sergant, J., Crombé, P., and Perdaen, Y., 2006, The 'invisible' hearths: A contribution to the discernment of Mesolithic non-structured surface hearths: Journal of Archaeological Science, v. 33, p. 999–1007, doi:10.1016/j.jas.2005.11.011.

Shaw, J., 1985, Holocene Coastal Evolution, Co. Donegal, Ireland [Ph.D. thesis]: Coleraine, University of Ulster, 278 p.

Shaw, J., and Carter, R.W.G., 1994, Coastal peats from northwest Ireland: Implications for late-Holocene relative sea-level change and shoreline evolution: Boreas, v. 23, p. 74–91, doi:10.1111/j.1502-3885.1994.tb00588.x.

Sommerville, A.A., Hansom, J.D., Housley, R.A., and Sanderson, D.C.W., 2007, Optically stimulated luminescence (OSL) dating of coastal aeolian sand accumulation in Sanday, Orkney Islands, Scotland: The Holocene, v. 17, p. 627–637, doi:10.1177/0959683607078987.

Tipping, R., Davies, A., McCulloch, R., and Tisdall, E., 2008, Response to late Bronze Age climate change of farming communities in north east Scotland: Journal of Archaeological Science, v. 35, p. 2379–2386, doi:10.1016/j.jas.2008.03.008.

Tolan-Smith, C., 1998, Radiocarbon chronology and the late glacial and early postglacial resettlement of the British Isles: Quaternary International, v. 49–50, p. 21–27, doi:10.1016/S1040-6182(97)00051-7.

Tonner, T.W.W., 2005, Later Stone Age shellfishing behaviour at Dunefield Midden (Western Cape, South Africa): Journal of Archaeological Science, v. 32, p. 1390–1407, doi:10.1016/j.jas.2005.03.017.

Westerdahl, C., 2005, Seal on land, elk at sea: Notes on and applications of the ritual landscape at the seaboard: International Journal of Nautical Archaeology, v. 34, p. 2–23, doi:10.1111/j.1095-9270.2005.00039.x.

Wickham-Jones, C.R., and Woodman, P.C., 1998, Studies on the early settlement of Scotland and Ireland: Quaternary International, v. 49–50, p. 13–20, doi:10.1016/S1040-6182(97)00050-5.

Wilson, P., and Braley, S.M., 1997, Development and age structure of Holocene coastal sand dunes at Horn Head, near Dunfanaghy, Co Donegal, Ireland: The Holocene, v. 7, p. 187–197, doi:10.1177/095968369700700206.

Wilson, P., McGourty, J., and Bateman, M.D., 2004, Mid- to late-Holocene coastal dune event stratigraphy for the north coast of Northern Ireland: The Holocene, v. 14, p. 406–416, doi:10.1191/0959683604hl716rp.

Wilson, P., Orford, J.D., Knight, J., Braley, S., and Wintle, A.G., 2001, Late-Holocene (post-4000 years BP) coastal dune development in Northumberland, northeast England: The Holocene, v. 11, p. 215–229, doi:10.1191/095968301667179797.

Woodman, P.C., 1992, Filling in the spaces in Irish prehistory: Antiquity, v. 66, p. 295–314.

Manuscript Accepted by the Society 3 August 2010

The Geological Society of America
Special Paper 476
2011

Holocene sedimentation in a pericoastal river system (South Wales, UK): Relationship to sea level, human activity, and coastal sediment flux

Simon K. Haslett*

School of STEM, University of Wales, Front Suite 1st Floor, Park House, Greyfriars Road, Cardiff, CF10 3AF, UK

ABSTRACT

The role of fluvial systems in coastal sediment dynamics, particularly regarding sediment storage in floodplains, the flux of sediment to the coast, and its influence on coastal evolution, is currently being widely considered. This study contributes to this debate through a geoarchaeological approach to reconstructing floodplain sedimentation rates in the Olway-Usk Valley system in South Wales, which is a tributary to the Severn Estuary, a coastal feature of global importance because it has the world's second highest tidal range. Archaeological and radiocarbon-dated horizons within alluvium indicate that floodplain deposition was initiated as Holocene sea levels rose toward present levels around 6500 yr B.P. River drainage appears to have been impeded at this time, leading to ground surface-water logging, sporadic peat formation in valley bottoms, and subsequent overbank deposition of alluvium. The mean Holocene sedimentation rate is 0.44 ± 0.02 mm yr^{-1}, but this includes a rise to around 1 mm yr^{-1} after the medieval period, rising again to around 10 mm yr^{-1} since the early nineteenth century. This increase reflects human activity, especially agricultural land use within the catchment such as widespread ploughing, which was not introduced until the nineteenth century. The volume of accumulated fluvial fine sediment stored within the Olway-Usk valley system is estimated to be 5.25×10^7 m^3 (7.09×10^7 t). These data are used here as a proxy for total fluvial sediment input into the Severn Estuary since marine inundation first occurred around 8500 yr B.P. The combined sediment contribution from rivers and intra-estuarine bedrock erosion is estimated to be 1.13×10^{10} t. This corresponds precisely to a previously estimated amount of Holocene sediment lying beneath the coastal wetlands of the Severn Estuary. These independent estimates give confidence to our understanding of the sediment dynamics in the Severn Estuary through the Holocene, and the investigation provides a new case study to contribute to the wider debate of alluvial sediment storage and fluvial fine sediment flux to the coast.

---

*s.haslett@wales.ac.uk

Haslett, S.K., 2011, Holocene sedimentation in a pericoastal river system (South Wales, UK): Relationship to sea level, human activity, and coastal sediment flux, *in* Brown, A.G., Basell, L.S., and Butzer, K.W., eds., Geoarchaeology, Climate Change, and Sustainability: Geological Society of America Special Paper 476, p. 93–103, doi:10.1130/2011.2476(08). For permission to copy, contact editing@geosociety.org. © 2011 The Geological Society of America. All rights reserved.

INTRODUCTION

The influence of sea-level changes on fluvial sediment distribution and deposition has received increased attention over the past 15 yr or so, both in theoretical terms (e.g., Schumm, 1993; Thorne, 1994; Zaitlin et al., 1994; van Heijst and Postma, 2001) and in empirical Holocene studies of sites in, for example, eastern North America (Ashley and Sheridan, 1994; Belknap et al., 1994), Gulf of Mexico (Blum and Aslan, 2006; Knox, 2006; Autin and Aslan, 2001), central America (Esker et al., 1998), Papua New Guinea (Harris, 1994), Australia (Rustomji et al., 2006), Europe (Long et al., 2000; Wilkinson et al., 2000; Stouthamer and Berendsen, 2001; Rommens et al., 2006), and China (Hori et al., 2002). Rivers are considered to be the primary source of sediment delivered to the oceans; however, there is still consider-

able uncertainty about the role and behavior of alluvial stores in determining the flux of sediment delivered to the sea, particularly during the Holocene, when climate and sea level have been variable (Phillips, 2003; Phillips and Slattery, 2006). Soft-sediment coastlines are often dependent upon riverborne sediments, and temporal variation in input may, at least locally, strongly influence coastal systems and their evolution (Haslett, 2008).

This paper examines an alluvial sequence in the Olway-Usk river valley system in South Wales (UK) that drains into the Severn Estuary, a coastal inlet that has the second highest tidal range in the world (~14.5 m; Fig. 1). The aim of this paper is to provide estimates of alluvial sedimentation rates through the Holocene to increase our understanding of sediment delivery to the coast. The study adopts, out of necessity, a geoarchaeological approach to construct alluvial sedimentation rates based on

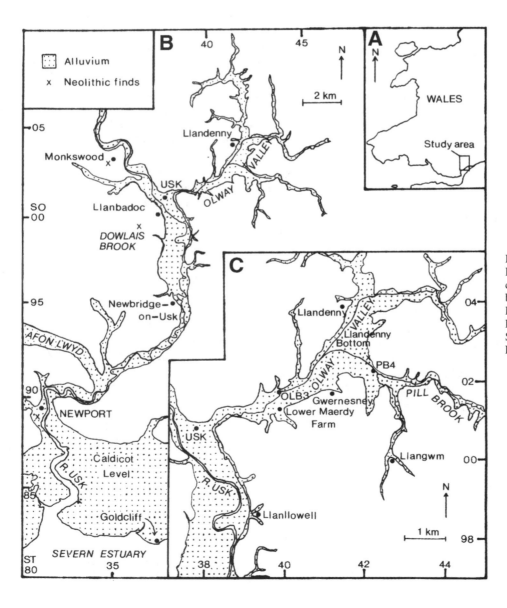

Figure 1. Distribution of alluvium in the lower Olway-Usk Valley system. (A) Location of study area in Wales; (B) distribution of alluvium; and (C) detail of the location of sites investigated (from Haslett, 2003). Coordinates use the Ordnance Survey of Great Britain National Grid Reference.

dated archaeological horizons within minerogenic deposits spanning the past 2000 yr, and radiocarbon dating of organic deposits of various ages where they occur. A close temporal relationship is apparent between sea level and the onset of alluviation in the mid-Holocene, coincident with a significant change in the coastal depositional environment of the Severn Estuary margins. Subsequent rate changes in alluviation are attributed to human activity within the catchment. Estimations of fluvial sedimentation rates, volumes, and inputs into the Severn Estuary are made by exploring the use of the Olway-Usk tributary as a proxy for basinwide changes in the Severn Estuary catchment. Through this, this study contributes to the emerging debate regarding fluvial sediment storage and supply to the coast.

GEOLOGICAL SETTING

The Olway Valley is situated in southeast Wales (Fig. 1), extending east of the town of Usk (Haslett, 2003). The principal watercourse in the valley is the Olway Brook, which drains into the River Usk. It was selected as a study site because the stratigraphy was well documented through geotechnical investigations prior to the construction of a major trunk road within the valley in 1974 (Soil Mechanics Ltd., 1966; Haslett, 2003; Fig. 2). The headwaters of the Olway Brook rise at an altitude of ~230 m OD (Ordnance Datum, Newlyn). Initially, it flows within a narrow valley, but it emerges from the upland to flow within a broad valley (up to ~1 km wide). This broad lower valley possesses

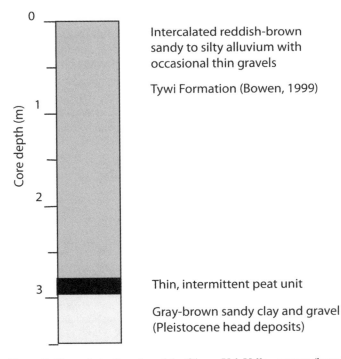

Figure 2. General stratigraphy of the Olway-Usk Valley system (based on Haslett, 2003).

an extensive floodplain, falling over a distance of ~5.5 km from ~30 m to ~17 m OD. At the town of Usk, the Olway Brook flows southward into the Usk Valley for a further ~3 km to its confluence with the River Usk, near Llanllowell, which then outflows into the Severn Estuary near Newport, with the tidal limit presently extending upriver as far as Newbridge-on-Usk (Fig. 1). The Olway Brook has a number of important tributaries, including the Pill Brook, which was also investigated; its headwaters are at an altitude of ~200 m OD, and it flows through a relatively narrow valley to its emergence and confluence with the Olway Brook.

The solid geology of the Olway catchment is almost entirely of Silurian-Devonian Old Red Sandstone (Welch and Trotter, 1961; Haslett, 1998), with the exception of a small intrusion of igneous rock near Llanllowell (Haslett, 1990, 1992). The general dip of the Old Red Sandstone in the catchment is to the south and east, being the east limb of the north-south–trending Usk anticline (George, 1956), which has influenced the development of a number of escarpments that structurally determine the course of the Olway and Usk valleys. The floodplain of the Olway Valley has been mapped as river alluvium by the British Geological Survey (Welch and Trotter, 1961), and termed the Tywi Formation by Bowen (1999), but it is subdivided by the Soil Survey of England and Wales (1983) into several different soil associations.

The River Severn drains a considerable catchment in the West Midlands and eastern Wales, and important tributaries, such as the River Usk, enter the estuary and contribute 1.9×10^6 t yr^{-1} of sediment into the estuary (Collins, 1987). Within the estuary, up to 1.3×10^7 t of fine sediment are held in suspension, which is roughly ten times the annual fluvial input (Collins, 1987; Severn Tidal Power Group, 1989; Allen, 1990a). However, in addition, 5.5×10^5 t yr^{-1} are contributed through the erosion of bedrock within and on the sides of the estuary (Allen, 1990a). The typical suspended sediment concentration in the Severn Estuary is 5000 mg L^{-1}; however, at slack water, this begins to settle out, forming a basal ~1-m-thick layer of "fluid mud" with a sediment concentration of 200,000 mg L^{-1}. Although this layer is resuspended as tidal velocities increase following slack water, deposition can occur, particularly in the high intertidal zone, creating mudflats and salt marshes (e.g., Haslett, 2006). Parker and Kirby (1982) estimated that some 2.7×10^8 t of fine sediment deposits exist in the present active estuary. The Holocene floodplain sequences of the River Severn, including sedimentation rates, have been investigated by Brown (1987, 1991).

Holocene paleo-intertidal deposits underlie the coastal lowlands (Severn Estuary Levels) and consist of intercalated estuarine silts and freshwater/terrestrial peats (Allen, 2001a; Haslett et al., 2001a) that are related to fluctuations in sea-level rise (Haslett et al., 2001b). The sequence, known as the Wentlooge Formation in South Wales and the Somerset Levels Formation in England (Bowen, 1999), possesses an essentially tripartite lithostratigraphy consisting of lower and upper silt units separated by a substantial layer of peat (Kidson and Heyworth, 1976; Haslett and Davies, 2002; Haslett et al., 2006). Thinner peats are sometimes encountered within the silt units. Recently, close to the mouth of the River Usk, Allen and Haslett (2002, 2007) analyzed the full Holocene sequence through granulometric, micropaleontological, and radiocarbon techniques, and at one site described an ~5-m-thick lower silt unit (with three minor peat layers) and an ~1-m-thick peat layer overlain by ~4 m of an upper silt unit (with one minor peat layer). Laminations occur within the silt units, which Allen and Haslett (2006) interpreted as annual banding reflecting seasonal changes in estuarine water characteristics. The Holocene sequence is in places dissected by infilled paleochannels (Allen et al., 2006) that represent either former river courses or tidal creeks. Successive human settlers have progressively embanked the surface of the coastal lowlands over the past 2000 yr, especially during the Roman and medieval periods (Rippon, 1996, 1997). Significant for this study, Allen and Haslett (2007) also suggested that it is reasonable to assume that the rivers draining into the Severn Estuary have been the source of the silts that have accumulated at the coast throughout the Holocene.

General Holocene sea-level change within the Severn Estuary is reasonably well understood, and several authors have published sea-level curves (Hawkins, 1971a, 1971b; Kidson and Heyworth, 1973; Heyworth and Kidson, 1982; Haslett et al., 1998a, 1998b). The late Pleistocene lowstand stimulated erosion and the formation of river channels incised into bedrock now buried under later sediments (Williams, 1968; Kidson and Heyworth, 1976; Allen, 2001b). Upon deglaciation, a relatively rapid rate of sea-level rise of ~10 mm yr^{-1} occurred in the early Holocene, slowing considerably or even falling in the mid-Holocene before rising again through the late Holocene, but at a lower rate of ~1–2 mm yr^{-1} (Allen and Haslett, 2007). Accommodation space was continually being made available through rapid sea-level rise in the early Holocene, and, as a result, the intertidal surface was positioned relatively low in the tidal frame (Allen, 1990b; Haslett et al., 2001b). This contrasts to the late Holocene when, under lower rates of sea-level rise, the intertidal surface was elevated within the tidal frame. Another consideration, is that through the Holocene, the tidal range increased (Austin, 1991), which in a hypertidal estuary would be expected to be relatively significant.

Sea-Level Influence on Initiation of Alluviation

Fluvial sediment transported through the Olway-Usk system is predominantly derived from the glaciated upland area in mid-Wales (for review, see Barclay, 1989). Haslett (2003) proposed a model (Fig. 3) suggesting that during the early Holocene sediment effectively bypassed the river valleys, via incised channels, to be delivered to the coast, where it was deposited. However, as sea level approached present levels during the mid-Holocene, drainage impedance promoted valley bottom-water logging, stimulating the formation of a thin and sporadic peat layer on the paleosurface. Peat samples at this junction have been radiocarbon dated from Goldcliff, near the mouth of the River Usk (Bell, 1995), and the Olway (site OLB3) and Pill Brook (site PB4) valleys (Haslett, 2003). Figure 4 shows that peat formed on the Mesolithic paleosurface at Goldcliff as the level of mean high water spring tide (MHWST) approached its maximum altitude, at the transition from the early Holocene phase of rapid sea-level rise to the mid- to late Holocene phase of a lower sea-level rise at around 6500 cal. yr B.P.

Of interest here, the peat sample from the Olway Valley, ~15 m higher in altitude and ~20 km upstream of Goldcliff, indicates virtually simultaneous surface-water logging. Haslett (2003) stated that this may be significant because site OLB3 may define the upstream limit of the "lower drainage system" of Schumm and Ethridge (1994) that responds directly to a base-level rise. Higher up at site PB4, peat formed ~1000 yr later and cannot easily be explained as a direct response to base-level rise. It is more likely that floodplain alluviation in the lower Olway Valley, brought about by a decrease in sediment bypassing of the valley, created a zone of drainage impedance that migrated upstream to affect its tributaries, such as the Pill Brook. Schumm (1993) demonstrated experimentally that while floodplain aggradation, in response to base-level rise, will occur in the lower valley, upstream erosion and incision may persist until sediment backfilling of the valley can occur (e.g., Harris, 1994). An indirect mechanism such as this, involving increased sediment availability coincident with progressive overbank sedimentation,

Geographical Province	**A** Early Holocene (pre-6500 yr B.P.)	**B** Mid-Holocene (after 6500 yr B.P.)	
Glaciated uplands of mid-Wales	sediment source	sediment source	
River valleys, e.g., Olway-Usk system	sediment bypass	sediment sink	
Severn Estuary and Levels	sediment sink	reduced sediment input	

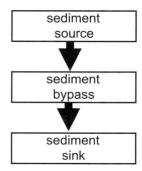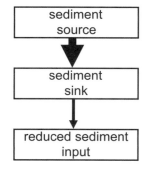

Figure 3. The changing function of the central river valleys of Gwent (e.g., the Olway-Usk Valleys), through the (A) early and (B) mid-Holocene. The dimensions of the arrows schematically represent relative amounts of sediment transfer (modified from Haslett, 2003).

was considered by Brown (1987) to have been responsible for much of the upstream sediment infill of the Severn River valley. Therefore, from 7 to 5 ka onward, valley function appears to switch from sediment bypass to sink with the onset of floodplain deposition, so reducing sediment delivery to the Severn Estuary (Haslett, 2003).

Archaeologically Dated Horizons

Up to ~3 m of reddish-brown sandy-silty-clayey alluvium overlies the sporadic Mesolithic-Neolithic peat layer in the Olway Valley, and it is largely devoid of organic remains, except for some occasional fragments of stratified wood. In order to establish datable horizons within the alluvium, in addition to radiocarbon dating wood, archaeological investigations have been undertaken near Gwernesney (site NIC of Haslett, 2005) and at the Olway-Usk Valley confluence near Usk (Cattle Bridge and Field Drain sites of Haslett, 2007) through the examination of excavated and natural exposures (Fig. 1), and dating has been achieved through artifact analysis and also the radiocarbon dating of a domestic animal bone.

Haslett (2005) employed an excavation strategy, similar to Haslett et al. (1998a), which investigated alluvium onlapping bedrock at the valley margin near Gwernesney. Here, archaeolog-

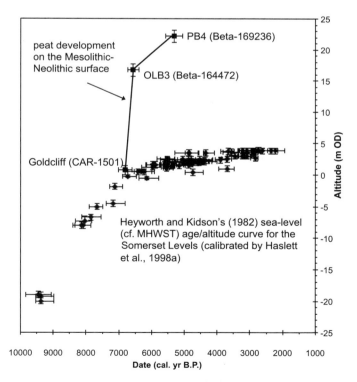

Figure 4. The relationship of ¹⁴C dates for peat initiation on the prehistoric buried land surface and regional relative sea-level rise. Sea-level information is derived from age/altitude data of Heyworth and Kidson (1982), calibrated by Haslett et al. (1998a). B.P.—before present (A.D. 1950); OD—Ordnance Datum, Newlyn (from Haslett, 2003).

ical material from valley-margin settlements was expected to be found, and were indeed found, stratified within the alluvium. The most significant find within the excavation was a coarse debris layer at a depth of 0.7–0.8 m within the alluvium that extended laterally out into the floodplain for ~40 m. Although this debris layer consists of remnants of a demolished medieval (thirteenth century) building, including building stone, roof and ridge tiles, and green-glazed pottery sherds, the deposition of the layer was dated by a radiocarbon date from a domestic animal bone lying on the surface of the layer (Table 1). Haslett (2007) also described a similar medieval coarse debris layer from near Usk, up to 0.9 m deep within the alluvium and extending ~60 m from the valley margin across the floodplain. These medieval debris layers occur elsewhere within the region and they have been interpreted as stone platforms and moated enclosures that may have been constructed to broaden the resource use of the floodplain environment, particularly in enabling livestock to utilize predrained wetlands (Aberg, 1978; Locock, 1998, 2000; Locock and Lawler, 2000). Such layers are, therefore, useful time horizons for dating valley-margin alluvial sequences.

Table 1 lists details of 11 dated horizons used in this paper, six of which are archaeologically derived. These are subdivided into broad Roman (A.D. 44–410), medieval (A.D. 1000–1500), and modern (A.D. 1750–2000) age groups. Of these, there is one dated Roman horizon (mean depth in the alluvium = 1.125 m, mean age = A.D. 123), two medieval horizons (mean depth = 0.833 m, mean age = A.D. 1293), and three modern period horizons (mean depth = 0.285 m, mean age = A.D. 1916). The two stratified wood samples provided new radiocarbon dates reported in this paper (Table 1). Sample OLB1 was collected by augering on the bank of the Olway Brook 10 m southwest of OLB3 (Fig. 1). Sample PB4:2.8–3.2 m was collected from a natural bank exposure on the Pill Brook (Fig. 1). Both were dated using standard radiometric technique.

The dates available are biased toward the historic period (i.e., past 2000 yr) and the Mesolithic–Early Neolithic. There is a clear lack of dated material from the intervening period, which should be sought in future studies to expand the database presented here. Potential to do this exists in that scattered Neolithic artifacts that have been recovered from surfaces on the sides of the Olway and Usk Valleys (Fig. 1; Peterson and Pollard, 2004), as has, to a lesser extent, Bronze Age (Hamilton, 2004) and pre–Roman Iron Age (Howell and Pollard, 2004) material. It is likely that artifacts from these periods are stratified within alluvium, but that sites await discovery.

Floodplain Sedimentation Rates and Volumes

Utilizing radiocarbon dates derived from peat and wood, combined with archaeologically dated horizons, I constructed age-depth plots for the Olway Valley alluvium and also the Pill Brook, but based on fewer dates (Fig. 5). The overall sedimentation rate for the Holocene alluvium of the Olway Valley is 0.44 ± 0.02 mm yr⁻¹, which is lower than the mean of 1.4 mm yr⁻¹ for

TABLE 1. DETAILS OF RADIOCARBON AND ARCHAEOLOGICALLY DATED HORIZONS WITHIN THE FLOODPLAIN ALLUVIUM OF THE OLWAY VALLEY

Site	Age group	Sample	Material	Dating method	Date	Source
Goldcliff	Mesolithic	"Mesolithic site"	Fenwood peat	^{14}C, CAR-1501	5920 ± 80 yr B.P.; cal. yr 5060–4660 B.C.	Bell (1995); Bell and Neumann (1997)
Olway Brook	Modern	NIC: 0.00–0.38 m	Pottery	Archaeological	A.D. 1850–2000	Haslett (2005)
	Modern	Cattle Bridge: 0.28–0.45 m	Artifacts	Archaeological	A.D. 1920	Haslett (2007)
	Modern	Field Drain: 0.2–0.4 m	Artifacts	Archaeological	A.D. 1900 ± 30	Haslett (2007)
	Medieval	NIC: 0.7–0.8 m	Bone	^{14}C, Beta-169461	390 ± 50 yr B.P.; cal. yr A.D. 1430–1640	Haslett (2005)
	Medieval	Field Drain: 0.6–0.95 m	Artifacts	Archaeological	A.D. 1250 ± 50	Haslett (2007)
	Medieval	OLB1: 103–116 cm	Wood	^{14}C, Beta-164471	960 ± 40 yr B.P.; cal. yr A.D. 1010–1180	This paper
	Roman	NIC: 0.9–1.35 m	Pottery	Archaeological	A.D. 50–200	Haslett (2005)
	Mesolithic	OLB3: 280–295 cm	Clayey peat	^{14}C, Beta-164472	5760 ± 80 yr B.P.; cal. yr 4780–4450 B.C.	Haslett (2003)
Pill Brook	Medieval	PB4: 2.68–3 m	Wood	^{14}C, Beta-169235	1050 ± 60 yr B.P.; cal. yr A.D. 880–1140	This paper
	Neolithic	PB4: 383–392 cm	Woody peat	^{14}C, Beta-169236	4600 ± 80 yr B.P.; cal. yr 3620–3090 B.C.	Haslett (2003)

lower Severn Valley alluvium (Brown, 1987); however, both these figures fall within the 0.2–10 mm yr^{-1} range of modeled average alluvial sedimentation rates for periods over 500 yr (Bridge and Leeder, 1979). Within this overall rate, there is considerable variation between dated horizons (Fig. 5); relatively low mean sedimentation rates of 0.37 mm yr^{-1} between Mesolithic and Roman horizons appear to continue, probably little changed, up to the medieval period. Subsequently, however, mean sedimentation appears to increase significantly to ~1 mm yr^{-1} to the modern period, thereafter increasing considerably to around 10 mm yr^{-1}. Such an increase is not unusual in Europe, as was shown, for example, by Rommens et al. (2006), who also documented a tenfold increase in alluvial sedimentation over the past 1000 yr in Belgium.

The post-medieval increase in sedimentation, as seen in the Severn Valley (Brown, 1991), is likely to have been due to human activity, especially intensification in agriculture, firstly deforestation and later widespread ploughing. Indeed, within the predominantly rural catchment of the Olway Valley, landscape paintings by Joshua Gosselin (Mitchell, 2003) from the early nineteenth century (1805) were examined by Haslett (2005) and show the Olway floodplain to be undrained, and fields on the valley sides supporting pasture and orchards, with no evidence of ploughing. Twentieth-century agricultural practices became more diverse here and included cereal growing and root crop cultivation, requiring ploughing in preparation for sowing, both on the valley sides and bottom. Therefore, the tenfold increase in sedimentation during the modern period may reflect the advent of widespread ploughing within the catchment since 1805.

By applying these sedimentation rates to the lower Olway and Usk Valleys, it is possible to estimate the volume of sediment accumulated through the Holocene for this system. For the estimation, based on topographic and geotechnical surveys, the lower Olway and Usk Valleys are measured to have a length of 7.25 and 15.5 km and a mean width of 0.54 and 0.877 km, respectively, and a combined area of 17.5 km^2, with a standard 3 m depth of alluvium. During prehistory, beginning in the Mesolithic, ca. 6500 cal. yr B.P., alluvium accumulated at 6.47 × 10^6 m^3 k.y.$^{-1}$, totaling 3.28 × 10^7 m^3 by the Roman period. The volume accumulated between the Roman and medieval periods is estimated to be 5.11 × 10^6 m^3, but this increased significantly to 9.59 × 10^6 m^3 through the shorter interval between the medieval to modern periods. The Modern period, spanning around a fifth/sixth of the previous interval, accumulated over half the equivalent volume at 4.99 × 10^6 m^3 under high sedimentation rates.

One of the consequences of such alluvial sedimentation and volume accumulation is that the floodplain environment has extended vertically and laterally, onlapping pre-Holocene geology. Settlements established in such areas would have witnessed encroaching alluvium through time, exacerbating flooding as the floodplain surface was elevated. Therefore, areas settled some time ago may have become progressively more vulnerable to riverine flooding. An example of this is the town of Usk, which was originally constructed on a raised area of glaciofluvial gravels

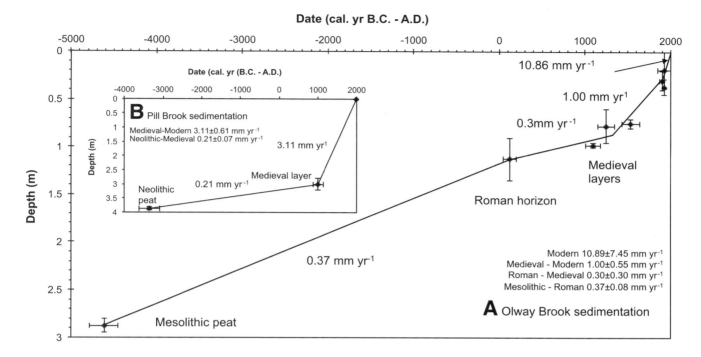

Figure 5. Floodplain alluvium sedimentation in the (A) Olway Valley and (B) Pill Brook and details of sedimentation rates.

and bedrock as the Roman fortress of *Burrium* occupied between ca. A.D. 49 and 74 (Manning, 1981). Mein (1986) did not consider the area to have been occupied by the native Welsh, due to flooding problems, after the Roman's left, but this is unlikely as the floodplain surface would have been around 1 m lower than present, affording greater accommodation space for flood waters. Indeed, shortly after the Norman conquest in A.D. 1066, Usk was reestablished as a fortress town, and an extensive Norman settlement was constructed on the remaining raised gravels and bedrock, an unlikely decision if flooding were a regular occurrence at the time. However, flooding has become a problem in more recent years, with the last major flood occurring in 1979 and resulting in the temporary evacuation of many inhabitants and the subsequent construction of a flood prevention scheme during the 1980s.

Relationship to Coastal Sediment Flux in the Severn Estuary

It has been discussed already herein that the rise of Holocene sea level and its attainment of near present levels ~6500 yr ago probably resulted in the impedance of rivers flowing into the Severn Estuary, with a subsequent raising of water levels, water logging of the ground surface (peat formation), avulsion, floodplain initiation, and minerogenic alluvial deposition. Through system feedback, this would have resulted in a reduction of fine sediment reaching the coast and an increase in sediment storage in the developing floodplains. It is expected that this would influence the distribution of sediments within the estuary and coastal evolution.

Using this investigation as a representative case study for all fluvial input into the Severn Estuary during the Holocene, it is possible to evaluate previous sediment budget estimates for the Severn Estuary system. Allen (1990a), based on available sea-level data, proposed that sediment began to accumulate in the Severn Estuary Levels around 8500 yr B.P. The extent of the Severn Estuary Levels was estimated by Allen (1990a) to be 840 km^2 and with an average thickness of the Holocene coastal fine sediment infill of 10 m. Using a dry bulk density of 1.35 tons m^{-3}, he estimated that ~1.13 × 10^{10} t of fine sediment are present and has accumulated since 8500 yr B.P. If the amount of sediment in the present water body and the fine sediment deposits in the active estuary (see previous) are added to this figure, then a total of 1.16 × 10^{10} t of fine sediment is present in the entire Holocene Severn Estuary system (Allen, 1990a). Allen (1990a) attempted to estimate the fine sediment contribution to the Severn Estuary from rivers and intra-estuarine bedrock erosion through the Holocene (past 8500 yr), but using current rates of fluvial input achieved a figure of 2.07 × 10^{10} t, which is far in excess of that observed. Accepting that the current rate is likely to be greater than the average Holocene rate due to human activity in the catchment, he somewhat arbitrarily took 50% of the current rate as a more realistic figure, yielding a contribution of 1.04 × 10^{10} t.

The present study now allows for an independent estimate of fluvial contribution by using the Olway-Usk system as a proxy for fluvial input from the entire Severn basin. If the data are nondimensionalized and percentage thickness is used, it is possible to compare alluvial sedimentation with coastal stratigraphic accumulation of fine sediments in the estuary. Figure 6 shows this comparison, and there is a clear indication that over 60% of coastal minerogenic sedimentation occurred in the early Holocene (10–7 ka: 30% of the period), when sediment was bypassing the river valleys, and that the onset of alluvial floodplain sedimentation coincided with a major reduction in fine sediment deposition within the estuary and, indeed, ensuing peat formation. As discussed already, it is likely that as sea-level approached present levels, it initiated drainage impedance, peat formation, and floodplain deposition, but the permanent decrease in fluvial input into the estuary thereafter may, coupled with a reduction in the rate of sea-level rise (or a fall), favor peat growth over minerogenic deposition within the estuary.

In order to estimate the variation in the amount of fluvial sediment input into the estuary through the Holocene (past 8500 yr), we need to accept that the current annual rate of fluvial input is related to the rate of floodplain sedimentation and that they covary in proportion to one another. Figure 5 indicates that alluvial sedimentation began around 6500 cal. yr B.P. and remained remarkably consistent until the medieval period, when there was a significant increase to the present. Therefore, for simplicity (and, in fact, the data do not allow much more), floodplain sedimentation may be divided into Mesolithic–medieval and medieval–present rates. The Mesolithic–medieval alluvial rate is around 31% that of the post-medieval rate and would equate to a fluvial input into the estuary of 5.91×10^5 t yr^{-1}. It is important now to estimate the proportion of total fluvial sediment load deposited in

overbank floodplain deposits and the remainder that contribute to the fluvial input of the estuary. Sediment budget studies exist that enable an estimation to be made. For example, Phillips (1989), in a study of 10 catchments, established that between 29% and 93% of fluvial sediment is stored in floodplain deposits. However, in Britain, similar conveyance studies have indicated a lower range between 23% and 50% (Walling and Quine, 1993; Owens et al., 1999; Walling et al., 1999). Because the present study involves a long time period, and is attempting to extend a generalization from one tributary of the Severn Estuary to the entire basin, the median of these British extremes is used here, i.e., 36.5%.

Prior to floodplain initiation around 6500 yr B.P., 9.32×10^5 t yr^{-1} of fluvial sediment were bypassing the river valleys and entering directly into the Severn Estuary, totaling 1.76×10^9 t over the period. It is likely that this relatively high supply rate (compared to the Mesolithic–medieval period) enabled intertidal surfaces to keep pace with increasing accommodation space provided by relatively rapid sea-level rise during the early Holocene. Interestingly, the summed total of fluvial inputs to the Severn Estuary since 8500 yr B.P., with a steady contribution from bedrock erosion based on present rates, yields 1.13×10^{10} t, which corresponds precisely with Allen's (1990a) estimate of Holocene fine sediment stored in the Severn Estuary Levels. This suggests that the estimations presented here for fluvial input to the Severn Estuary are relatively robust and that the method of using one tributary catchment as a proxy for basinwide contributions may not be unreasonable.

One outstanding question concerns the fate of excess fluvial sediment during the mid-Holocene (i.e., the ~63.5% not stored in floodplain alluvium) when the coastal stratigraphic sequence was dominated by peat formation. Haslett et al. (2001a) demonstrated that mid-Holocene peat layers thin, split, and disappear toward

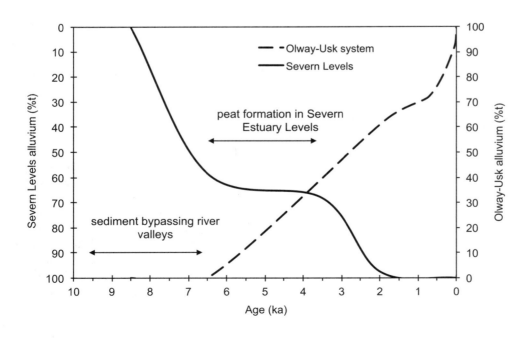

Figure 6. Nondimensional (percentage) accumulation of floodplain alluvium in the Olway-Usk Valley system versus fine sediment accumulation in the coastal wetlands of the Severn Estuary Levels.

areas where minerogenic deposition continued, but, with some exceptions, the majority of these areas probably were located offshore the present coastline and, therefore, have been eroded during the late Holocene. It is likely that a belt of minerogenic deposition fringed the more landward peat-forming environments at this time. The subsequent erosion of this belt, upon either renewed sea-level rise and/or an increase in coastal erosion, released the fine sediment that contributed to late Holocene minerogenic sedimentation that overwhelmed the peat environments. It is possible then, if not likely, that most of the mid-Holocene fluvial sediment introduced into the evolving Severn Estuary is currently stored in late Holocene coastal wetland sequences.

CONCLUSIONS

This study employed geoarchaeological techniques in developing a chronology for alluvial floodplain sedimentation since around 6500 yr B.P. in the Olway-Usk Valley system, a tributary of the Severn Estuary in southwest Britain, a major coastal feature with the second highest tidal range in the world. Stratified archaeological and radiocarbon dated horizons have allowed the onset of deposition to be dated, and rates and volumes of fine sediment accumulation to be established. The results indicate:

1. Floodplain deposition was initiated around 6500 yr B.P., coincident with the approach of relative sea level to present levels. This is likely to have impeded river drainage, water logged the ground surface, created sporadic peat-forming environments in the river valleys, and stimulated overbank deposition of alluvium.

2. Approximately 0.44 ± 0.02 mm yr^{-1} of fine sediment have accumulated in the valley system over the past 6500 yr, but this includes a dramatic increase in accumulation to 10 mm yr^{-1} within the modern period, probably due to human activity, especially the advent of widespread ploughing of agricultural land in the catchment since the beginning of the nineteenth century. A total volume of 5.25×10^7 m^3 of fine alluvial sediment has been stored within the Olway-Usk valley system since 6500 yr B.P., which equates to 7.09×10^7 t of sediment.

3. These results present an opportunity to examine the accuracy of estimates of Holocene fluvial inputs into the Severn Estuary through using Olway-Usk Valley floodplain accumulation as a proxy for total fluvial input. This modeling estimates that the combined sediment contribution from rivers and intra-estuarine bedrock erosion since marine inundation first occurred in the estuary around 8500 yr B.P. is 1.13×10^{10} t. This corresponds precisely to a previously estimated amount of Holocene sediment lying beneath the Severn Estuary Levels (Allen, 1990a). These independent estimates give confidence to our understanding of the sediment dynamics in the Severn Estuary through the Holocene, especially regarding the contribution from fluvial sources.

ACKNOWLEDGMENTS

This research was funded by Bath Spa University. Mary Holmes processed samples for geochemical analysis.

REFERENCES CITED

Aberg, F.A., ed., 1978, Medieval Moated Sites: Council for British Archaeology Research Report No. 17.

Allen, J.R.L., 1990a, The Severn Estuary in southwest Britain: Its retreat under marine transgression, and fine-sediment regime: Sedimentary Geology, v. 66, p. 13–28, doi:10.1016/0037-0738(90)90003-C.

Allen, J.R.L., 1990b, Salt-marsh growth and stratification: A numerical model with special reference to the Severn Estuary, southwest Britain: Marine Geology, v. 95, p. 77–96, doi:10.1016/0025-3227(90)90042-I.

Allen, J.R.L., 2001a, The Severn Estuary Levels in the later Quaternary: A brief history: Proceedings of the Cotteswold Naturalists' Field Club, v. 42, p. 48–63.

Allen, J.R.L., 2001b, Late Quaternary stratigraphy in the Gwent Levels (southeast Wales): The subsurface evidence: Proceedings of the Geologists' Association, v. 112, p. 289–315.

Allen, J.R.L., and Haslett, S.K., 2002, Buried salt-marsh edges and tide-level cycles in the mid-Holocene of the Caldicot Level (Gwent), South Wales, UK: The Holocene, v. 12, p. 303–324, doi:10.1191/0959683602hl537rp.

Allen, J.R.L., and Haslett, S.K., 2006, Granulometric characterization and evaluation of annually banded mid-Holocene estuarine silts, Welsh Severn Estuary (UK): Coastal change, sea level and climate: Quaternary Science Reviews, v. 25, p. 1418–1446, doi:10.1016/j.quascirev.2005.12.009.

Allen, J.R.L., and Haslett, S.K., 2007, The Holocene estuarine sequence at Redwick, Welsh Severn Estuary Levels: The character and role of silts: Proceedings of the Geologists' Association, v. 118, p. 157–174.

Allen, J.R.L., Haslett, S.K., and Rinkel, B.E., 2006, Holocene tidal palaeochannels, Severn Estuary Levels, UK: A search for granulometric and foraminiferal criteria: Proceedings of the Geologists' Association, v. 117, p. 329–344.

Ashley, G.M., and Sheridan, R.E., 1994, Depositional model for valley fills on a passive continental margin, *in* Dalrymple, R.W., Boyd, R., and Zaitlin, B.A., eds., Incised-Valley Systems: Origin and Sedimentary Sequences: SEPM (Society for Sedimentary Geology) Special Publication 51, p. 285–301.

Austin, R.M., 1991, Modelling Holocene tides on the NW European continental shelf: Terra Nova, v. 3, p. 276–288, doi:10.1111/j.1365-3121.1991.tb00145.x.

Autin, W.J., and Aslan, A., 2001, Alluvial pedogenesis in Pleistocene and Holocene Mississippi River deposits: Effects of relative sea-level change: Geological Society of America Bulletin, v. 113, p. 1456–1466, doi:10.1130/0016-7606(2001)113<1456:APIPAH>2.0.CO;2.

Barclay, W.J., 1989, Geology of the South Wales Coalfield: Part II. The Country around Abergavenny (3rd ed.): British Geological Survey Memoir 232, 147 p.

Belknap, D.F., Kraft, J.C., and Dunn, R.K., 1994, Transgressive valley-fill lithosomes: Delaware and Maine, *in* Dalrymple, R.W., Boyd, R., and Zaitlin, B.A., eds., Incised-Valley Systems: Origin and Sedimentary Sequences: SEPM (Society for Sedimentary Geology) Special Publication 51, p. 303–320.

Bell, M., 1995, Field survey and excavation at Goldcliff, Gwent 1994: Archaeology in the Severn Estuary, v. 5, p. 115–144, 157–167.

Bell, M., and Neumann, H., 1997, Prehistoric archaeology and environments in the Severn Estuary: World Archaeology, v. 29, p. 95–113, doi:10.1080/00438243.1997.9980365.

Blum, M.D., and Aslan, A., 2006, Signatures of climate vs. sea-level change within incised valley-fill successions: Quaternary examples from Texas Gulf Coast: Sedimentary Geology, v. 190, p. 177–211, doi:10.1016/j.sedgeo.2006.05.024.

Bowen, D.Q., 1999, Wales, *in* Bowen, D.Q., ed., A Revised Correlation of Quaternary Deposits in the British Isles: Geological Society of London Special Report 23, p. 79–90.

Bridge, J.S., and Leeder, M.R., 1979, A simulation model of alluvial stratigraphy: Sedimentology, v. 26, p. 617–644, doi:10.1111/j.1365-3091.1979.tb00935.x.

Brown, A.G., 1987, Holocene floodplain sedimentation and channel response of the lower River Severn, United Kingdom: Zeitschrift für Geomorphologie N. F., v. 31, p. 293–310.

Brown, A.G., 1991, Hydrogeomorphology and palaeoecology of the Severn Basin during the last 15,000 years: Orders of change in a maritime catchment, *in* Gregory, K.J., Starkel, L., and Thornes, J.B., eds., Fluvial Processes in the Temperate Zone during the Last 15,000 Years: Chichester, Wiley, p. 147–169.

Collins, M.B., 1987, Sediment transport in the Bristol Channel: Proceedings of the Geologists' Association, v. 98, p. 367–383.

Esker, D., Eberli, G.P., and McNeill, D.F., 1998, The structural and sedimentological controls on the reoccupation of Quaternary incised valleys, Belize southern lagoon: American Association of Petroleum Geologists Bulletin, v. 82, p. 2075–2109.

Findlay, D.C., Colborne, G.J.N., Cope, D.W., Harrod, T.R., Hogan, D.V., and Staines, S.J., 1984, Soils and Their Use in South West England: Soil Survey of England and Wales Bulletin 14, 419 p.

George, T.N., 1956, The Namurian Usk anticline: Proceedings of the Geologists' Association, v. 66, p. 297–316.

Hamilton, M.A., 2004, The Bronze Age, *in* Aldhouse-Green, M., and Howell, R., eds., The Gwent County History: Volume 1. Gwent in Prehistory and Early History: Cardiff, University of Wales Press, p. 84–110.

Harris, P.T., 1994, Incised valleys and backstepping deltaic deposits in a foreland-basin setting, Torres Strait and Gulf of Papua, Australia, *in* Dalrymple, R.W., Boyd, R., and Zaitlin, B.A., eds., Incised-Valley Systems: Origin and Sedimentary Sequences: SEPM (Society for Sedimentary Geology) Special Publication 51, p. 97–108.

Haslett, S.K., 1990, Magnetic survey of a monchiquite intrusion in central Gwent: Geological Magazine, v. 127, p. 591–592, doi:10.1017/S001675680001548X.

Haslett, S.K., 1992, Petrology of a monchiquite from the Welsh Borderlands: Mercian Geologist, v. 13, p. 43–46.

Haslett, S.K., 1998, Biostratigraphic synthesis of vertebrate and plant occurrences in the Lower Old Red Sandstone (Siluro-Devonian) of southern Gwent, Wales, UK: Neues Jahrbuch für Geologie und Paläontologie, Monatshefte, v. 1998, p. 182–192.

Haslett, S.K., 2003, Early to mid-Holocene (Mesolithic-Neolithic) development of the Olway Valley (central Gwent, UK) and its archaeological potential: The Monmouthshire Antiquary (Proceedings of the Monmouthshire Antiquarian Association), v. 19, p. 3–19.

Haslett, S.K., 2005, Holocene floodplain sediments and associated archaeology of the Olway Valley (Gwent, UK): An excavation report. The Monmouthshire Antiquary (Proceedings of the Monmouthshire Antiquarian Association), v. 21, p. 5–20.

Haslett, S.K., 2006, Topographic variation of an estuarine salt marsh: Northwick Warth (Severn Estuary, UK): Bath Spa University Occasional Papers in Geography 3, p. 1–17.

Haslett, S.K., 2007, Archaeologically-dated horizons in Olway Valley floodplain alluvium at Usk (Gwent, UK): The Monmouthshire Antiquary (Proceedings of the Monmouthshire Antiquarian Association), v. 23, p. 3–11.

Haslett, S.K., 2008, Coastal Systems (2nd ed.): London, Routledge, 240 p.

Haslett, S.K., and Davies, P., 2002, Holocene lithostratigraphy and coastal change in the Somerset Levels: Evidence from Nyland Hill, Axe Valley, Somerset: Bath Spa University College Occasional Papers in Geography 2, p. 37–43.

Haslett, S.K., Davies, P., Curr, R.H.F., Davies, C.F.C., Kennington, K., Kings, C.P., and Margetts, A.J., 1998a, Evaluating late-Holocene relative sea-level change in the Somerset Levels, southwest Britain: The Holocene, v. 8, p. 197–207, doi:10.1191/095968398669499299.

Haslett, S.K., Davies, P., and Strawbridge, F., 1998b, Reconstructing Holocene sea-level change in the Severn Estuary and Somerset Levels: The foraminifera connection: Archaeology in the Severn Estuary, v. 8 (for 1997), p. 29–40.

Haslett, S.K., Howard, K.L., Margetts, A.J., and Davies, P., 2001a, Holocene stratigraphy and evolution of the northern coastal plain of the Somerset Levels, UK: Proceedings of the Cotteswold Naturalists' Field Club, v. 42, p. 78–88.

Haslett, S.K., Davies, P., Davies, C.F.C., Margetts, A.J., Scotney, K.H., Thorpe, D.J., and Williams, H.O., 2001b, The changing estuarine environment in relation to Holocene sea-level and the archaeological implications: Archaeology of the Severn Estuary, v. 11 (for 2000), p. 35–53.

Haslett, S.K., Davies, P., Eales, C.P., Vowles, E.M., and Williams, H.O., 2006, Variability in the Holocene lithostratigraphy of the Somerset Levels, UK, *in* Hunt, C.O., and Haslett, S.K., eds., The Quaternary of Somerset: Field Guide: Cambridge, Quaternary Research Association, p. 44–52 (refs p. 205–236).

Hawkins, A.B., 1971a, The Late Weichselian and Flandrian transgression of South West Britain: Quaternaria, v. 14, p. 115–130.

Hawkins, A.B., 1971b, Sea level changes around South-West England: Colston Papers, v. 23, p. 67–87.

Heyworth, A., and Kidson, C., 1982, Sea-level changes in southwest England and Wales: Proceedings of the Geologists' Association, v. 93, p. 91–111.

Hori, K., Saito, Y., Zhao, Q.H., and Wang, P.X., 2002, Evolution of coastal depositional systems of the Changjiang (Yangtze) River in response to late Pleistocene–Holocene sea-level changes: Journal of Sedimentary Research, v. 72, p. 884–897, doi:10.1306/052002720884.

Howell, R., and Pollard, J., 2004, The Iron Age: Settlement and material culture, *in* Aldhouse-Green, M., and Howell, R., eds., The Gwent County History: Volume 1. Gwent in Prehistory and Early History: Cardiff, University of Wales Press, p. 140–177.

Kidson, C., and Heyworth, A., 1973, The Flandrian sea-level rise in the Bristol Channel: Proceedings of the Ussher Society, v. 2, p. 565–584.

Kidson, C., and Heyworth, A., 1976, The Quaternary deposits of the Somerset Levels: Quarterly Journal of Engineering Geology, v. 9, p. 217–235, doi:10.1144/GSL.QJEG.1976.009.03.05.

Knox, J.C., 2006, Floodplain sedimentation in the Upper Mississippi Valley: Natural versus human: Geomorphology, v. 79, p. 286–310, doi:10.1016/j.geomorph.2006.06.031.

Locock, M., 1998, Rockingham Farm, Avonmouth, 1993–1997: Moated enclosures on the north Avon Levels: Archaeology in the Severn Estuary, v. 8 (for 1997), p. 83–88.

Locock, M., 2000, Cabot Park, Avonmouth, Bristol: Excavations on later Bronze Age and Medieval sites at Kites Corner and Moorend Farm, 1999: Archaeology in the Severn Estuary, v. 10 (for 1999), p. 125–128.

Locock, M., and Lawler, M., 2000, Moated enclosures on the north Avon Level: Survey and excavation at Rockingham Farm, Avonmouth, 1993–1997: Transactions of the Bristol and Gloucestershire Archaeological Society, v. 118, p. 93–122.

Long, A.J., Scaife, R.G., and Edwards, R.J., 2000, Stratigraphic architecture, relative sea-level, and models of estuary development in southern England: New data from Southampton Water, *in* Pye, K., and Allen, J.R.L., eds., Coastal and Estuarine Environments: Sedimentology, Geomorphology and Geoarchaeology: Geological Society of London Special Publication 175, p. 253–279.

Manning, W.H., 1981, Report on the Excavations at Usk, 1965–1976: The Fortress Excavation 1968–1971: Cardiff, University of Wales Press, 225 p.

Mein, A.G., 1986, Norman Usk: The Birth of a Town: Usk, A.G. Mein, 128 p.

Mitchell, J., 2003, Joshua Gosselin in Monmouthshire: The Monmouthshire Antiquary (Proceedings of the Monmouthshire Antiquarian Association), v. 19, p. 87–112.

Owens, P.N., Walling, D.E., and Leeks, G.J.L., 1999, Deposition and storage of fine-grained sediment within the main channel system of the River Tweed, Scotland: Earth Surface Processes and Landforms, v. 24, p. 1061–1076, doi:10.1002/(SICI)1096-9837(199911)24:12<1061::AID-ESP35>3.0.CO;2-Y.

Parker, W.R., and Kirby, R., 1982, Sources and transport patterns of sediment in the inner Bristol Channel and Severn Estuary, *in* Institution of Civil Engineers, ed., Severn Barrage: London, Thomas Telford, p. 181–194.

Peterson, R., and Pollard, J., 2004, The Neolithic: The first farming societies, *in* Aldhouse-Green, M., and Howell, R., eds., The Gwent County History: Volume 1. Gwent in Prehistory and Early History: Cardiff, University of Wales Press, p. 56–83.

Phillips, J.D., 1989, Fluvial sediment storage in wetlands: Water Resources Bulletin, v. 25, p. 867–873.

Phillips, J.D., 2003, Alluvial storage and the long-term stability of sediment yields: Basin Research, v. 15, p. 153–163, doi:10.1046/j.1365-2117.2003.00204.x.

Phillips, J.D., and Slattery, M.C., 2006, Sediment storage, sea level, and sediment delivery to the ocean by coastal plain rivers: Progress in Physical Geography, v. 30, p. 513–530, doi:10.1191/0309133306pp494ra.

Rippon, S., 1996, The Gwent Levels: The Evolution of a Wetland Landscape: York, Council for British Archaeology Research Report 105, 148 p.

Rippon, S., 1997, The Severn Estuary: Landscape Evolution and Wetland Reclamation: Leicester, Leicester University Press, 318 p.

Rommens, T., Verstraeten, G., Bogman, P., Peeters, I., Poesen, J., Govers, G., van Rompaey, A., and Lang, A., 2006, Holocene alluvial sediment storage in a small river catchment in the loess area of central Belgium: Geomorphology, v. 77, no. 1–2, p. 187–201, doi:10.1016/j.geomorph.2006.01.028.

Rustomji, P., Olley, J., and Chappell, J., 2006, Holocene valley aggradation driven by river mouth progradation: Examples from Australia: Earth Surface Processes and Landforms, v. 31, p. 1510–1524, doi:10.1002/esp.1359.

Schumm, S.A., 1993, River response to baselevel change: Implications for sequence stratigraphy: The Journal of Geology, v. 101, p. 279–294, doi:10.1086/648221.

Schumm, S.A., and Ethridge, F.G., 1994, Origin, evolution and morphology of fluvial valleys, *in* Dalrymple, R.W., Boyd, R., and Zaitlin, B.A., eds., Incised-Valley Systems: Origin and Sedimentary Sequences: SEPM (Society for Sedimentary Geology) Special Publication 51, p. 11–27.

Severn Tidal Power Group, 1989, Severn Barrage Project: Detailed Report (Volumes 1–4): Department of Energy, UK.

Soil Mechanics Ltd, 1966, Site Investigation for Proposed Newport-Worcester Trunk Road (Raglan to Newport Section) and Usk Link, Monmouthshire: London, Soil Mechanics Ltd.

Stouthamer, E., and Berendsen, H.J.A., 2001, Avulsion frequency, avulsion duration, and interavulsion period of Holocene channel belts in the Rhine-Meuse Delta, the Netherlands: Journal of Sedimentary Research, v. 71, p. 589–598, doi:10.1306/112100710589.

Thorne, J., 1994, Constraints on riverine valley incision and the response to sea-level change based on fluid mechanics, *in* Dalrymple, R.W., Boyd, R., and Zaitlin, B.A., eds., Incised-Valley Systems: Origin and Sedimentary Sequences: SEPM (Society for Sedimentary Geology) Special Publication 51, p. 30–43.

van Heijst, M.W.I.M., and Postma, G., 2001, Fluvial response to sea-level changes: A quantitative analogue, experimental approach: Basin Research, v. 13, p. 269–292, doi:10.1046/j.1365-2117.2001.00149.x.

Walling, D.E., and Quine, T.A., 1993, Using Chernobyl-derived fallout radionuclides to investigate the role of downstream conveyance losses in the suspended sediment budget of the River Severn, United Kingdom: Physical Geography, v. 14, p. 239–253.

Walling, D.E., Owens, P.N., and Leeks, G.J.L., 1999, Rates of contemporary overbank sedimentation and sediment storage on the floodplains of the main channel systems of the Yorkshire Ouse and River Tweed, UK: Hydrological Processes, v. 13, p. 993–1009, doi:10.1002/(SICI)1099-1085(199905)13:7<993::AID-HYP786>3.0.CO;2-C.

Welch, F.B.A., and Trotter, F.M., 1961, Geology of the Country around Monmouth and Chepstow: Geological Survey of Great Britain Memoirs, Sheets 233 and 250, 164 p.

Wilkinson, K.N., Scaife, R.G., and Sidell, E.J., 2000, Environmental and sea-level changes in London from 10,500 BP to the present: A case study from Silvertown: Proceedings of the Geologists' Association, v. 111, p. 41–54.

Williams, G.J., 1968, The buried channel and superficial deposits of the Lower Usk, and their correlation with similar features in the Lower Severn: Proceedings of the Geologists' Association, v. 79, p. 325–348.

Zaitlin, B.A., Dalrymple, R.W., and Boyd, R., 1994, The stratigraphic organization of incised-valley systems associated with relative sea-level change, *in* Dalrymple, R.W., Boyd, R., and Zaitlin, B.A., eds., Incised-Valley Systems: Origin and Sedimentary Sequences: SEPM (Society for Sedimentary Geology) Special Publication 51, p. 45–60.

MANUSCRIPT ACCEPTED BY THE SOCIETY 3 AUGUST 2010

The Geological Society of America
Special Paper 476
2011

Environmental change and evidence for Archaic and Woodland floodplain occupation along the lower Nottawasaga River, southern Ontario, Canada

Mary J. Thornbush*

Oxford University Centre for the Environment, University of Oxford, Dyson Perrins Building, South Parks Road, Oxford, OX1 3QY, UK

Joseph R. Desloges†

Department of Geography, University of Toronto, 100 St. George Street, Room 5047, Toronto, Ontario, M5S 3G3, Canada

ABSTRACT

This study investigates environmental change as a context for the location of occupation in campsites along the lower Nottawasaga River in southern Ontario, Canada. Evidence of Archaic and Woodland period campsites presents a difficult scenario for archaeological interpretation. Did Archaic cultures prefer to occupy higher ground, such as on the Edenvale moraine (206 m above sea level [a.s.l.]), or lower areas within river valleys, such as on the floodplain (181 m a.s.l.)? The aim of this study is to disentangle the evidence from a geoarchaeological perspective, considering cultural sites cross-temporally in their physical setting of a river floodplain in the Great Lakes region. We used geoarchaeological methods and methodologies, including soil-sediment analysis, sedimentological profiling of cutbanks and cores, topographic profiling in the field, river morphometric and hydrometric measurements using various techniques, ground-penetrating radar (GPR), and conceptual modeling. Results indicate that the Edenvale moraine, which topographically confines the channel and floodplain in the study area, may have led to catastrophic stripping of the floodplain during drainage of glacial lakes, causing the Nottawasaga River to downcut into the Edenvale moraine. This occurred following a period of floodplain stability, when natural and cultural deposits would have been preserved and buried in confined sections of the floodplain that are currently being vertically accreted. Any model that considers accretion style, such as the preservation-exposure model presented here, should be interpreted within the context of the environmental history of the area, since accretion style varies temporally and spatially at the river-reach scale.

*Current address: Lakehead University, Orillia Campus, Heritage Place, 1 Colborne Street West, Orillia, Ontario, L3V 7X5, Canada; mthornbu@lakeheadu.ca.
†desloges@geog.utoronto.ca.

Thornbush, M.J., and Desloges, J.R., 2011, Environmental change and evidence for Archaic and Woodland floodplain occupation along the lower Nottawasaga River, southern Ontario, Canada, *in* Brown, A.G., Basell, L.S., and Butzer, K.W., eds., Geoarchaeology, Climate Change, and Sustainability: Geological Society of America Special Paper 476, p. 105–116, doi:10.1130/2011.2476(09). For permission to copy, contact editing@geosociety.org. © 2011 The Geological Society of America. All rights reserved.

INTRODUCTION

Alluvial geoarchaeological research is relevant from a framework of archaeological interpretation and has been conducted, for instance, for the Princess Point Complex in southwestern Ontario (e.g., Walker et al., 1997; Crawford et al., 1998). Other researchers have employed geologic perspectives in their understanding of southern Ontario archaeology (e.g., Karrow, 1994), considering landscape features such as shorelines, for instance, to track Paleoindian sites (e.g., Storck, 1982, 1984). Further research of this nature is necessary so that artifacts can be understood from a geoarchaeological perspective as context-specific deposits susceptible to postdepositional taphonomic processes (e.g., Shackley, 1978; Hanson, 1980; Butzer, 1982; Hiscock, 1985; Stein, 1987). A geoarchaeological approach is particularly necessary for interpretations of archaeological sites that can be affected through erosion or burial because of their small size and location, as on floodplains.

The lack of alluvial geoarchaeological research on floodplain development and dynamics in southern Ontario is a major shortcoming in literature focused on the differentiation of natural versus cultural signatures in the archaeological record. In his book on alluvial geoarchaeology, Brown (1997) addressed the issue of negative evidence, where natural site destruction and invisibility are mostly controlled by rates and processes of floodplain development. Lateral channel migration associated with sideways erosion at cutbanks and the lateral accretion of sediments naturally destroy contextual evidence and rework cultural deposits at rates of floodplain erosion-deposition cycles. At the lower Vyrnwy River in Wales, for instance, Lewin (1992) attributed lateral channel migration associated with bars, cutoffs, and oxbow lakes in a meandering river as naturally destructive of cultural remains, whereas the overbank deposition of alluvial sediments preserves archaeological information, although it may be rendered invisible by burial. Moreover, the lack of Paleoindian and Early and Middle Archaic cultural remains in lowland alluvial deposits near the Little Missouri River in the western North Dakota Badlands was ascribed to natural site destruction rather than human avoidance of floodplains (Waters and Kuehn, 1996).

The current study is a contribution toward geoarchaeological interpretations of campsites in southern Ontario. More specifically, the central aim of this paper is to examine the archaeological evidence (campsites) located in an alluvial setting on the lower Nottawasaga River in southern Ontario in order to disentangle the possible effects of burial and postdepositional disturbance that may be affecting the archaeological record. Several geoarchaeological methods and methodologies are employed in this type of research, including (1) the analysis of soils and sediments; (2) section stratigraphy; (3) flood hydrology; (4) ground-penetrating radar (GPR); and (5) conceptual modeling. The latter is particularly important in assisting archaeologists who are working in floodplain environments to understand their findings in a particular context of floodplain erosion and accretion. This understanding, it is hoped, will help to identify where the cultural record has been altered or even distorted by landscape development.

STUDY AREA

The study area in Simcoe County, Ontario, extends 16 km upstream from just downstream of Jack's Lake southeast to the town of Edenvale (based on Ontario Surveys and Mapping, 1986). The downstream boundary in this reach is ~14 km along the river channel of the lower Nottawasaga River from the outlet in the south portion of Georgian Bay as part of Lake Huron (Fig. 1), and its boundary at the furthest point upstream is ~30 km from the outlet. This is a low-gradient terrain situated in an area of former glacial-lake bottoms.

In the study area, the Nottawasaga River cuts into a clay plain at Edenvale, works into the till plain of the Edenvale moraine, and emerges relatively unconfined into a sand plain near New Flos, before reentering into a clay plain near Jack's Lake (based on Chapman and Putnam, 1984). As shown in Figure 1, local relief in the study area is ~30 m, much of which is between the Edenvale moraine (210 m above sea level [a.s.l.]) and Jack's Lake (180 m a.s.l.). Burwasser and Ford (1974) showed that bedrock elevations range from 107 to 152 m a.s.l. The total drift thickness in this section varies between 103 m at the Edenvale moraine to 28 m outside it. There is one terrace contiguous with the valley wall on both sides, and it contains Pleistocene glaciolacustrine clays and eolian sand deposits (cf. Burwasser and Cairns, 1974). Although generally classified as a small sand-bed stream, where it cuts through till and kame moraine in its upper reaches, the riverbed consists of coarse gravel and cobbles, becoming sandy in reaches of glaciolacustrine deposits (Chandler and Kostaschuk, 1994).

Prehistoric human occupation at the lower Nottawasaga River has been subject to some investigation, even though studies have focused on sections of the Nottawasaga River downstream of the study area (e.g., Cooke, 1993; Garrad, 1993; P. Cooke, 2000, personal commun.). Based on archaeological evidence, O'Brien (1975) speculated that the earliest human presence in the study area was associated with lagoon shore camps found at Wasaga Beach (Georgian Bay shoreline) and the Edenvale moraine some 5500 yr ago in the Archaic cultural period. Later, substantial campsites during the Middle Woodland period appear to have been located in greater numbers upriver in the lower course (e.g., downstream of the study area), away from the river mouth.

Fitzgerald (1985) provided a postglacial history of the Minesing Basin that encompasses the various glacial lakes in the Edenvale area (see his figure 2, p. 135), which has been summarized as shoreline positions/elevations in Figure 1. Lake Algonquin occupied the study area ~10,600–11,000 yr B.P., leaving well-developed scarps and beaches outside of the study area. Lake Wyebridge also produced well-developed shoreline features, and its lowering to a less-well-defined Lake Penetang level left the Edenvale moraine emergent, creating Lake Minesing. The Nottawasaga River downcut through the Edenvale moraine during this time as Lake Minesing lagged behind in its drainage

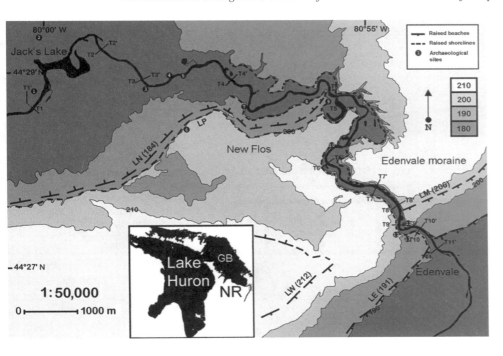

Figure 1. Map of the study area at the lower Nottawasaga River, Simcoe County, Ontario, Canada, showing transects (T1 through T11), archaeological sites (presented numerically between 1 and 13 and outlined in Tables 2 and 3), and abandoned shoreline features (after Fitzgerald, 1985; Lewis and Anderson, 1985), including glacial Lakes Wyebridge (LW), Penetang (LP), Minesing (LM), Edenvale (LE), and Nipissing (LN), with respective elevations in brackets, where available (based on figure 2 *in* Fitzgerald, 1985, p. 135; Lewis and Anderson, 1985). Georgian Bay (GB) and the Nottawasaga River (NR) are represented in the inset map. River flow is to the northwest into Georgian Bay. The Edenvale moraine forms the high-elevation ridge trending southwest-northeast. Elevation contours are in m above sea level (a.s.l.).

into Georgian Bay. The gradient of the Nottawasaga River was reduced through the Edenvale moraine during the high water of the Nipissing phase and caused the Minesing Basin to flood, creating Lake Edenvale (between 4000 and 6000 yr B.P.), which had a slightly higher water level than the Nipissing phase elevations in Lake Huron. As the level of the Nipissing phase dropped, the gradient of the Nottawasaga River through the Edenvale moraine increased.

The levels of the Great Lakes have fluctuated due to climate and postglacial drainage changes, including isostatic rebound (tilting up to the northeast; Fitzgerald, 1985), e.g., low-water stages during the Early Archaic (8000–10,000 yr B.P.) period and Middle Archaic up until the Nipissing high-water stage (ca. 5500 yr B.P.), and essentially modern lake levels from the Late Archaic (2800–4500 yr B.P.) to the present day (see figure 4-1 *in* Ellis et al., 1998). These factors have implications for the archaeological record. If, as O'Brien (1975) believed, the earliest people to inhabit the study area appeared in the late Middle Archaic (some 5500 yr B.P.), then this corresponds with the timing of the high-water stage of the Nipissing phase in the Huron Basin. The attraction of this area at a high-water postglacial stage would be the advantage of the Edenvale moraine over areas both south and north of the moraine. Archaic campsites should appear at higher elevations than later cultural remains (after O'Brien, 1975), such as Woodland cultures, which would have been deposited at a time when lake levels were retreating and lower-elevation floodplains began final development.

Figure 2 summarizes the postglacial retreat of lake levels largely based on Fitzgerald's (1985) reconstruction of raised shoreline locations. Two glacial lake elevations are not defined in the study area, namely Lake Penetang and Lake Nipissing,

because of weak evidence for shoreline positions. However, Lewis and Anderson (1985) suggested that the Nipissing phase was at an elevation of 184 m a.s.l. The much higher elevation for glacial Lake Algonquin is included for comparison at an elevation of 242 m a.s.l. (even though its shorelines appear outside of the study area to the east and south). Cultural periods are based on O'Brien's (1975) categories of 7000–3000 yr B.P. for Archaic sites, 3000–1200 yr B.P. for Middle Woodland sites, and 1200–300 yr B.P. for Late Woodland sites. More recently, Ellis et al. (1998) redefined these cultural periods to Early Archaic 10,000–8000 yr B.P., Middle Archaic 8000–4500 yr B.P., and Late Archaic 4500 yr–2800 B.P. Paleoindian sites date from the Late Archaic to 11,000 yr B.P., following deglaciation in the study area some 12,000 yr B.P. (Fitzgerald, 1985).

METHODS

A topographically centered field analysis was necessary in this study to understand lake levels in the context of the peopling of the area. Different topographic sections were investigated in the field component of the research, including 11 transects (T1–T11 in Fig. 1) distributed in reaches where the floodplain was confined within the Edenvale moraine (T5–T10; the area depicted in Fig. 3A) and in unconfined sections (T1–T4 and T11 in Fig. 1; as at the Edenvale gauge appearing in Fig. 3B). These transects were established through survey perpendicular to flow on the modern floodplain in the study area, spaced at intervals between 0.5 and 3.4 km. The purpose of this planform perspective of analysis was to understand downstream characteristics of the floodplain and river channel. It is an essential part of the spatial analysis used in the interpretation of the results.

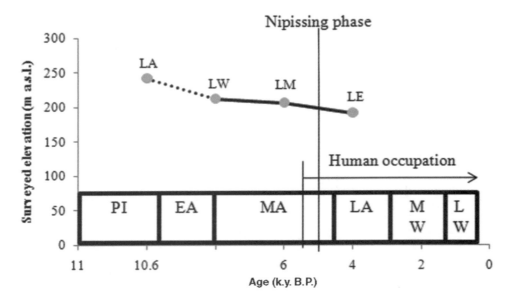

Figure 2. Chronology of shoreline elevations based on surveys in Fitzgerald (1985, figure 2, p. 135) of Lake Algonquin (LA) outside the study area, Lake Wyebridge (LW), Lake Minesing (LM), and Lake Edenvale (LE), including the Nipissing phase from 5000 yr B.P. Also denoted are cultural periods according to O'Brien (1975) for the Late Woodland (LW), Middle Woodland (MW), and Archaic cultural periods; and Ellis et al. (1998) for earlier cultural periods, including a breakdown of the Archaic into Late Archaic (LA), Middle Archaic (MA), and Early Archaic (EA), plus Paleoindian (PI). Human occupation is indicated since ca. 5500 yr B.P. (after O'Brien, 1975).

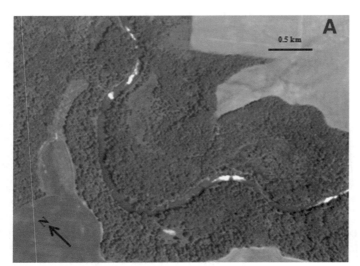

Figure 3. Photographs of the study area, including (A) the Edenvale moraine within a confined reach, as seen through Google Earth; and (B) the hydrometric gauge below Edenvale within the unconfined area upstream of the Edenvale moraine.

In addition to a planform investigation, floodplain stratigraphy was also examined through coring (using an Oakfield auger) and at cutbanks, including two that were prominent at the time of survey and were excavated on the left banks at unconfined T3 and at confined T7. GPR also assisted the sedimentological analysis and for mapping floodplain thickness and stratigraphy (cf. Davis and Annan, 1989). Shallow geophysics proved to be a practical methodology to investigate alluvial sediments (cf. Froese et al., 2005). Ékes and Hickin (2001), for example, applied GPR at Cheekye Fan, southwestern British Columbia, Canada, where alluvial-fan sediments were imaged to a depth of >40 m using 50 MHz antennas; 10 radar facies were derived from over 27 km of radar data. The technique has been most successfully applied to sandy, gravelly, and organic-rich fluvial, deltaic, and beach deposits, and it operates relatively poorly on muddy sediments with a high clay or saline water content because of signal attenuation where conductivity is high (Jol and Smith, 1991). GPR provides high-quality data of quartz-rich, nonclayey sand, and gravel deposits, even in water-saturated conditions. The most versatile antenna center frequency is 100 MHz, since there is a trade-off between penetration depth and resolution (Davis and Annan, 1989). Whereas 50 MHz antennas, for instance, allow for deeper penetration, 200 MHz antennas permit higher resolution for shallow penetration. The antennas used in this study had a center frequency of 50 and 100 MHz, and a couple of results for the former are reported here (taken at T2 and T6), since it portrays longer-term sediment change on the floodplain. PulseEKKO IV (V4.2) software was used to process the GPR profiles.

In addition to floodplain deposits, it was useful to examine the active channel morphology at each transect to establish conditions of flow and sediment discharge. Channel width was measured at frequent intervals using 1989 aerial photography, and an echosounder (200 kHz) mounted on an inflatable watercraft was used to define streambed shape, thalweg depth, and channel cross-sectional area. This technique was applied at all transect locations within ~2 m of each riverbank and as close as possible (±5 m) to the ground survey. Water-surface slope measurements were taken with a Sokkia SET48 total station utilizing measurement points near unconfined T1, at T4 and T11, as well as at confined T8 and T9. Using available hydrometric data and the measured slopes, it was possible to estimate reach-specific stream power, where unit stream power $\omega = \gamma QS/w$ (γ is the specific weight of water; Q is specified stream discharge level [often bankfull]; S is water surface gradient; and w is channel width; see Knighton, 1998).

The laboratory component of the analysis focused on examining soil and sediment properties, mainly through analyses of particle size and organic matter content. Particle size analysis was performed in the laboratory after Folk (1968) for 15 cutbank samples, which were manually extracted from cutbanks using a trowel. Because there were no clasts ≥2 mm (gravel or larger), coarse-fraction samples, 2000–63 μm (−1.00–4.00φ) in size, were oven dried for at least 4 h at 100 °C (after Gardner, 1965). They were granulated using a mortar and pestle and then dry sieved for 15 min at 0.50φ increments. The Wentworth scale was used to define size categories, and the percentile-intercept method was used to acquire median grain size (after Folk, 1966). For the fine fraction (<63 μm), a Micromeritics SediGraph 5100 Particle Size Analysis System (V3.07) was used. This method required a silt-clay dry weight of ~2.5 g dispersed in a solution of 0.05% $Na(PO_3)_6$ in distilled water. All samples were heated to ~35 °C in an ultrasonic bath for 1 min immediately preceding the analysis. A differential thermal analysis technique, or loss on ignition (LOI), was used (after Dean, 1974) on 3–5 g of sample in batches of 25 lidded crucibles, in order to quantitatively measure organic matter and carbonate content in each sample. Notably, for both particle size and LOI analyses, samples were selected to represent all distinct strata in cutbank samples.

The archaeology for this study relies on surveys performed by O'Brien in the 1970s (namely, 1974 and 1975). Her work has been incorporated into the archaeological sites database of the Ministry of Citizenship, Culture and Recreation, which provides a basis for the location of archaeological sites. Detailed field checking was not possible, but the database, in general, has proven reliable, and the studies cited here were thorough. For these reasons, the findings already contained in the archaeological database are the source of information pertaining to human occupation in the study area. The cross-disciplinary approach (cf. Butzer, 2008) here revisits the archaeological work as a means of bringing an understanding of landscape development to archaeology (specifically, the location of sites), and to consider whether sites have retained their locational integrity and are indeed diagnostic of prehistoric human occupation patterns.

RESULTS

Samples extracted from a 175-cm-deep cutbank, visible on the left bank at unconfined T3 (Fig. 4A), show a generally fining-upward stratigraphic sequence with a wide range of median particle diameters (D_{50}) between 270 and 5 μm (medium sand to very fine silt). The unconfined cutbank consists mostly of sand, except for a clay-rich layer at a depth of 115 cm and some evidence of greater fining (with more silt and clay) within the top 27 cm. Strata within this cutbank are mostly unlaminated massive sands, although the basal unit exposed during excavation below ~160 cm appears to be rippled medium-fine sand. Organic matter ranges between 0% and almost 4%, and is high at a depth of 115 cm in the clay-rich layer, where $CaCO_3$ is greatest (55%).

Further upstream, near confined T7, a 120-cm-deep cutbank also on the left bank exposes massive sands with lamination present to a depth of ~74 cm (Fig. 4B). An erosional surface (unconformity) is evident between 90 and 94 cm in the profile immediately above a buried A-horizon (Ah) soil from ~94 to 104 cm. At 94 cm depth, the buried soil is a very dark grayish brown (10YR 3/2, moist) granular sandy loam with 4% organic matter and 7% $CaCO_3$. Whole sediments coarsen upward slightly, with a narrow range of D_{50} between 125 and 83 μm (very fine sand). Sand predominates, and clay is minimal throughout. Organic matter is greatest in the buried soil layer, and $CaCO_3$ is more abundant (between 11% and 13%) in the sediments just above and toward the surface. This contrasts significantly with the much lower, almost absent, $CaCO_3$ content in the upper profile at T3 (see Fig. 4A).

The GPR profile for the left bank of unconfined T2 shows what may be a buried channel ~4 m in depth some 21 m away from the active channel (Fig. 5A). The thalweg depth of the buried channel roughly corresponds with the echosounder results for the active channel thalweg depth of 3.3 m sampled along the same transect. This shows lateral movement of the channel and vertical stability. A GPR profile in a confined section of the river at T6 is shown in Figure 5B. The profile was taken over the frozen river surface and shows mostly horizontal to shallow channelward-dipping reflectors, suggesting mainly vertical accretion over time beneath the active channel with no strong evidence of recent lateral movement of the channel.

Hydrometric data appear in Table 1. Estimates of the average channel width in unconfined sections are 40 ± 5.4 m and 36 ± 5.1 m in confined sections, compared to 38 ± 5.4 m average channel width across all transects. Echosounder profiles show that the channel is generally deepest in confined sections (e.g., T8 at 4.5 m) and shallowest in unconfined reaches (e.g., T3 at 2.9 m). Unconfined conditions generally lead to higher width-to-depth ratios. Average cross-sectional areas are not significantly different, at ~154 m^2 in unconfined sections and 158 m^2 in confined sections.

At the hydrometric gauge below Edenvale (see Fig. 3A), bankfull flow (Q_b approximated by the median annual flood of Q_2) is 92.4 m^3 s^{-1} (based on 61 yr of flow between 1949 and 2006 at Baxter from Environment Canada HYDAT). Using respective measured average regional channel slopes of 0.00072 and 0.02615 (see Table 1), ω averages between ~16 ± 2 W m^{-2} in unconfined sections and 665 ± 89 W m^{-2} in confined sections.

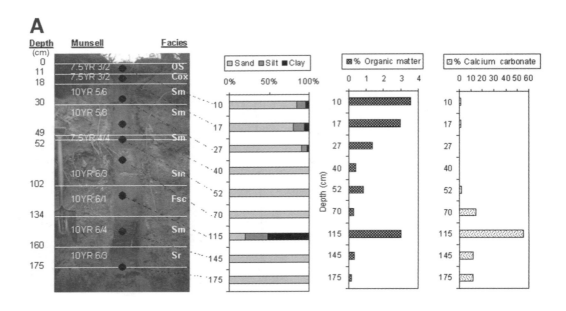

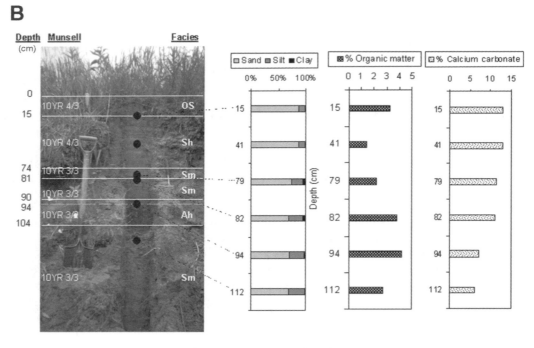

Figure 4. (A) Moist Munsell colors and facies stratigraphy, particle size, organic matter, and carbonate content of unconfined cutbank at T3 (on the left bank). Facies abbreviations are after Miall (1977): OS—occupational surface; Cox—oxidized C-horizon soil; Sm—massive sand; Fsc—massive silt, mud, organics; Sr—rippled sand. (B) Moist Munsell colors and facies stratigraphy, particle size, organic matter, and carbonate content of confined cutbank near T7 (on the left bank). Facies abbreviations are after Miall (1977): OS—occupational surface; Sh—horizontally laminated sand; Sm—massive sand; Ah—A-horizon soil.

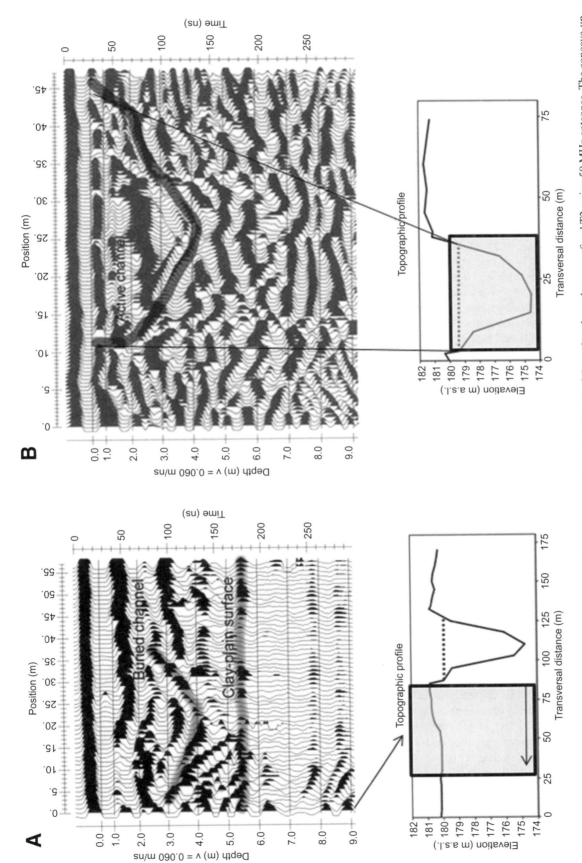

Figure 5. (A) Ground-penetrating radar (GPR) cross-profile (looking downstream) from the left bank of the active channel at unconfined T2, using 50 MHz antennas. The concave-up reflectors represent a buried channel (with several infilling events), with a thalweg depth over 4 m at ~21 m from the active channel and ~1.5 m above a signal refusal layer of thick lake-plain clays. (B) GPR cross-profile at confined T6 (looking upstream), taken with 50 MHz antennas, across the active channel surveyed in the winter over the ice-covered river. Vertical accretion sequences are visible in the floodplain reflectors. The concave-up reflectors of the riverbed show an approximate thalweg depth of ~4 m.

TABLE 1. CHANNEL MORPHOMETRY AND STREAMFLOW, WITH AVERAGE VALUES FOR EACH OF THE TRANSECTS

Transect	Width (m)	Depth (m)	Width:Depth (m m^{-1})	Cross-sectional area (m^2)	Velocity (m s^{-1})	Slope (m m^{-1})	ω (W m^{-2})
1	45	3.1	14.3	162	0.57	0.00072	14
2	45	3.3	13.6	173	0.53	0.00072	14
3	38	2.9	12.9	119	0.78	0.00072	17
4	41	4.3	9.6	184	0.50	0.00072	16
5	45	4.0	11.2	192	0.48	0.02615	526
6	35	4.4	7.9	169	0.55	0.02615	676
7	36	3.8	9.4	143	0.65	0.02615	658
8	33	4.5	7.4	134	0.69	0.02615	717
9	30	4.0	7.5	136	0.68	0.02615	789
10	38	4.1	9.2	172	0.54	0.02615	623
11	32	3.7	8.6	133	0.69	0.00072	20

Note: Shaded transects are located where the floodplain is confined.

At the peak flood of 267 m^3 s^{-1} in each of the two reach types, ω likely exceeds 1000 W m^{-2} and 50 W m^{-2}, respectively (flood-stage flow widths are difficult to estimate).

The Ministry of Citizenship, Culture, and Recreation archaeological sites database shows a total of 13 sites with Borden designations of BcGx and BcHa (Table 2). All sites, except BcHa-38, have artifact-based estimations of cultural period affiliation (see Table 2). The artifacts being used include varieties of ceramics (e.g., coiled, dentate); tools such as stemmed projectile points, scrapers, and adzes; and the appearance of faunal (mammal) remains (see Table 2). All are surface collections of campsites with varying sizes, spanning an elevation between 181 and 206 m a.s.l. (Table 3), inside and outside the Edenvale moraine in the study area. According to O'Brien (1974), there are seven known floodplain sites (BcGx-4, BcGx-5, BcGx-6, BcGx-8, BcGx-10, BcGx-11, and BcGx-13). Overall, (Middle) Woodland sites are found in unconfined sections in the study area, whereas Archaic sites (with the possible exception of BcGx-7) are located in confined sections.

DISCUSSION

The rippled sand layer in the unconfined cutbank at T3 (see Fig. 4A), all in a generally fining-upward sequence, suggests that lateral accretion is important in unconfined sections. As conveyed previously, however, Miall (1992) attributed the appearance of very small ripples amid massive laminated fines to a vertically accreted facies. Because it is not readily apparent to what depth the rippled sands extend, this evidence alone does not provide any strong support for lateral accretion through this section. The GPR profile at T2 (see Fig. 5A), in an unconfined section, on the other hand, provides much stronger support for long-term lateral migration of the channel, including burial of an older channel.

Light-dark banding in the cutbank near confined T7 (see Fig. 4B) suggests seasonal flooding during the time span above ~74 cm. Generally, the decreasing silt content and marginally increasing sand content in this uppermost recent deposit may be indicative of more energetic floods or processes linked with natural levee development in the confined section. Horizontally lami-

nated layers are also evident elsewhere in confined sections, such as near the left bank at T6, where there is a levee with a maximum height of ~1 m, and on the right bank at T9, where there is levee and backwater sedimentation. The absence of thicker sandy units with strong cross-bedding coupled with a high frequency of thinner and finer laminations indicate that deposition from overbank flows is a dominant process in confined sections. This affirms observations (e.g., Pizzuto, 1987) of overbank sedimentation, where coarse sediment settles along channel margins in levees, and finer sediments are diffused outward to distal sites in the floodplain. The radar profile at T6 (Fig. 5B) further conveys the idea that vertical accretion may be more dominant where there is confinement. These findings are in agreement with other floodplain research for vertically accreted systems, showing coarser near-channel sedimentation with levee development (e.g., Marriott, 1992; Lewin, 1996; Kalicki, 2000). Walker et al. (1997), for instance, showed that buried soils at the Grand Banks site in the lower Grand River, southern Ontario, Canada, were indicative of dominant vertical accretion processes and very stable channel positions during the Holocene.

The 1.5 order of magnitude higher stream powers and lateral confinement of the river channel through the Edenvale moraine led to floodplain erosion, where accreted sediments can be locally stripped off the floodplain surface and then reaccreted. Nanson (1986) suggested that this is a dominant mechanism in some confined floodplains in Australia, where high-energy channels that are laterally stable and gradually accreting are susceptible to episodes of erosion and catastrophic stripping during extreme floods. This is a plausible mechanism in sections of the modern floodplain surface, where there is confinement by the Edenvale moraine. Nanson and Croke (1992) suggested that rivers with ω of 300–1000 W m^{-2} are in the very high-energy class, with less-cohesive floodplains and confined vertical accretion. Although these typify a disequilibrium floodplain in the classification, it is difficult to positively distinguish whether confined sections are responding to recent environmental change (e.g., greater flood magnitude in response to climatic change; cf. Knox, 1993) with relatively recent accretion, or if the floodplain sediments are much older in origin, as, in this case, related to disequilibrium

TABLE 2. ARCHAEOLOGICAL SITES IN THE STUDY AREA (COMPILED FROM THE ONTARIO ARCHAEOLOGICAL SITES DATABASE)

Site	Borden designation	Site name	Artifact(s)	Cultural period(s)
1	BcHa-38	Jack Lake	2 chert	N.D.
2	BcHa-36	Klondike Park	34 ceramics, 2 lithics (scraper), 1 faunal	Middle Woodland (Nottawasaga)
3	BcGx-6	Fisherman	17 ceramics, 3 lithics, 7 faunal (calcined bone, clamshell)	Middle, Late Woodland (Nottawasaga)
4	BcGx-5	Dominici	2 ceramics, 5 lithics (scraper), 1 faunal	Middle Woodland (Saugeen)
5	BcGx-4	Bridge	14 ceramics, 1 lithic (scraper), 1 faunal	Middle Woodland (Saugeen)
6	BcGx-7	Pebble Bridge	1 lithic (point)	Archaic/Middle Woodland
7	BcGx-8	New Flos	8 ceramics, 5 chert, 16 miscellaneous lithics, 4 bones	Middle Woodland, early Late Woodland
8	BcGx-9	Edenvale 1	1 chert flake, 3 bones	Archaic
9	BcGx-14	Edenvale 6	1 adze, 3 miscellaneous lithics	Archaic
10	BcGx-10	Edenvale 2	1 chert flake, 1 quartz flake, 2 miscellaneous lithics	Archaic
11	BcGx-11	Edenvale 3	35 chert, 3 miscellaneous lithics, 3 bones	Archaic
12	BcGx-13	Edenvale 5	6 chert, 8 miscellaneous lithics	Archaic
13	BcGx-12	Edenvale 4	23 chert, 2 ground stones, 1 miscellaneous lithic, 2 bones	Archaic

Note: Shaded sites appear where the floodplain is confined. N.D.—not determined.

TABLE 3. LOCATION AND CONDITION OF ARCHAEOLOGICAL SITES

Site	Borden designation	Site name	Geomorphic location	Elevation (m a.s.l.)	Condition
1	BcHa-38	Jack Lake	N.D.	182	Destroyed
2	BcHa-36	Klondike Park	N.D.	N.D.	Destroyed
3	BcGx-6	Fisherman	Floodplain (left side)	183	Intact, some erosion
4	BcGx-5	Dominici	Floodplain (right bank)	181	Partially gardened
5	BcGx-4	Bridge	Floodplain (left bank)	181	Eroding into river, very little left
6	BcGx-7	Pebble Bridge	N.D.	183	Destroyed (in garden)
7	BcGx-8	New Flos	Floodplain (left bank)	183	Fair (ploughed)
8	BcGx-9	Edenvale 1	Floodplain (left side)	185	Disturbed (ploughing, blowouts, trails)
9	BcGx-14	Edenvale 6	Floodplain (left side)	189	Poor/fair (some undisturbed areas)
10	BcGx-10	Edenvale 2	Floodplain (left bank)	206	Ploughed
11	BcGx-11	Edenvale 3	Floodplain (right bank)	198	Ploughed
12	BcGx-13	Edenvale 5	Floodplain (left bank)	198	Ploughed
13	BcGx-12	Edenvale 4	Floodplain (left bank)	191	Ploughed

Note: Shaded sites appear where the floodplain is confined. N.D.—not determined.

from glacial-lake drainage events and ongoing isostatic develeling (cf. Renwick, 1992). However, the appearance of an unconformity on the buried soil in the cutbank near T7 (see Fig. 4B) suggests that some sediment stripping has occurred in confined sections, so the floodplain was stable until the buried soil developed and then possibly was stripped more recently from instability likely linked with the draining of Lake Edenvale during the Nipissing phase.

Archaic sites, which O'Brien (1975) dated between 7000 and 3000 yr B.P. (representing cultural complexes of the Middle to Late Archaic period), appear in confined sections as surface deposits. Woodland sites are visible in unconfined sections downstream, including Middle Woodland sites (from ca. 1800 yr B.P.). O'Brien (1975) identified what may be Late Woodland sites also on the floodplain surface. These surface collections suggest that little burial has occurred, even in vertically accreted confined sections of the floodplain, where Archaic remains can be found. It is possible that Archaic sites (which O'Brien identified as floodplain sites; see Table 3) have not been disturbed, except by major flood events, because of the long-term lateral stability of the channel and limited post–Nipissing-phase erosion of the floodplain. It is puzzling, however, that younger sites, such as from the Woodland period, are not located in confined sections. A consideration of the archaeological findings in an environmental context of floodplain accretion style and stability is one possible interpretative approach.

A conceptual model of exposure and preservation of natural and cultural materials in the modern floodplain is presented in Figure 6. As a generalized model, the exposure-preservation model shows three distinct possible environmental sequences in decreasing order of stability (from vertical accretion to lateral accretion to vertical stripping). Vertically accreted floodplains have the least exposure and the greatest preservation. Sections T7 and T8 in the confines of the Edenvale moraine are good examples. Laterally accreted floodplains have good selective exposure, but evidence may be destroyed by lateral channel migration. Sections T1–T4 downstream of the moraine are good examples. Exposure is generally greatest, and in situ preservation poorest, where floodplains are stripped. T7 in the moraine reach shows this well. This model is useful for application in archaeological studies considering floodplain stability, such as Crawford et al.'s (1998) study of the Grand River in confined reaches with river gradient controlled by base level in Lake Erie. A period of stability at the Grand Banks site in the lower Grand River occurred at 3100 yr B.P. (uncalibrated), similar to that of the lower Humber River in Toronto, Ontario (Weninger and McAndrews, 1989), which is when Lake Edenvale would have been draining. Stability of the lower Nottawasaga River along with a reduction of river gradient can also be inferred.

Archaeological sites in the study area may have been disturbed by fluvial erosion and might be missing small and light artifacts such as beads, bone fragments, and microdebitage. However, based on current hydrometric measurements, most artifacts >2 mm in the high overbank (levee-dominated) environment could not have been easily transported by Nottawasaga River flows (cf. Hjulström, 1935). Artifacts that O'Brien (1975) reported at these sites are too large for river entrainment and, hence, long-distance transport. At the unconfined Bridge site (BcGx-4), for example, O'Brien spotted a mostly intact vessel found in the right riverbank, indicating that larger Woodland artifacts are in situ and have likely not been washed downstream from confined sections. Although transport disturbance may vary

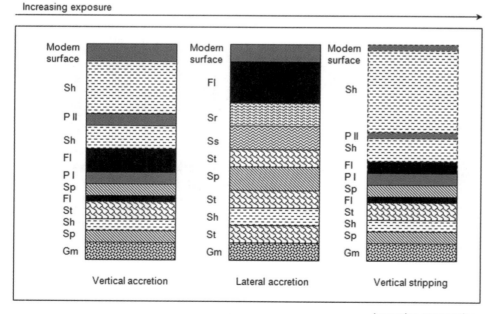

Figure 6. Exposure-preservation model: exposure and preservation of natural and cultural particles and deposits on the modern floodplain. Facies abbreviations are after Miall (1977): Sh—horizontally laminated sand; P—buried soil; Fl—fine laminated sand, silt, mud; Sp—planar cross-bedded sand; St—trough cross-bedded sand; Gm—massive gravel; Sr—rippled sand; Ss—cross-stratified sand.

with increased stream competence (e.g., with increasing flood-flow magnitude; cf. Olsen et al., 1997), ω in unconfined sections is at the lower end of 10–60 W m^{-2}, typifying medium-to-low, noncohesive floodplains (cf. Nanson and Croke, 1992).

After the Edenvale moraine became emergent with the lowering of Lake Wyebridge to Lake Penetang (see Fig. 1), the river began to downcut into the moraine, steepening the gradient of the river and eroding the moraine at the outlet of Lake Minesing (Fitzgerald, 1985). The draining of this lake would have left behind ponds or swamps that would have affected human occupation of the floodplain. With the rising of the Nipissing phase in the Georgian Bay Basin, river gradient through the Edenvale moraine would have been reduced, creating Lake Edenvale, which occupied the Minesing Basin at a slightly higher level than Lake Nipissing (Fitzgerald, 1985). When the level of the Nipissing phase dropped to the present level of Georgian Bay, the gradient of the Nottawasaga River increased through the Edenvale moraine, draining the Minesing Basin. Periods of increased river gradient (steepening) would have destabilized the floodplain, stripping away evidence of human occupation.

Even though the floodplain stratigraphy model in Figure 6 provides a useful context for exposure-preservation probabilities, it cannot be readily applied without recognition of Holocene fluvial-hydrologic change. From early Holocene to late Holocene intervals, isostatic uplift rates have declined, sediment supply from the upper watershed has also declined (except for a post–1800 A.D. flux related to forest clearance), and there have been moderate to subtle hydrologic changes from the mid-Holocene warm period to the later Holocene Neoglacial period of cooler, drier, and more stable conditions (McFadden et al., 2005). The formation and then drainage of Lake Edenvale in the Minesing Basin were probably of particular importance in floodplain development. Jackson et al. (2000), for instance, found a similar influence of fluctuating glacial lake levels impacting Paleoindian sites in the eastern Great Lakes. The buried soil in the confined cutbank near T7 (see Fig. 4B) denotes the general preservation of vertically accreted deposits, even though it contains evidence of a likely unconformity above it, indicating the likelihood of erosion following a period of stability. Currently, there are no dates available to constrain the timing of this unconformity in our study.

CONCLUSIONS

Unconfined sections in the lower Nottawasaga River show evidence for lateral accretion and vertical stability. Extensive lateral migration is possible in these low-gradient, low-energy, former lake-bottom settings. The strongest indicators of lateral accretion in unconfined sections of the lower Nottawasaga River include generally fining-upward stratigraphic sequences and buried channels. The floodplain in confined reaches shows the importance of vertical accretion. Alluvial fining away from the active channel, laminated sediments where there is strong levee development, and evidence for buried soils support this. The potential for catastrophic stripping of the floodplain in confined reaches is

related to dramatic increases in stream power as the average local gradient increases significantly dramatically through the Edenvale moraine, coupled with a narrower channel. The coarsening-upward alluvial sequences and sandy laminations in near-channel levees indicate more energetic high-magnitude floods through the Edenvale moraine. Although the evidence for catastrophic stripping through the confined section is not unequivocal, an erosional surface above the buried soil suggests that this was possible at some time in the past.

This research shows that landscape change is linked with climatically forced environmental change, which, in the Great Lakes region, is contingent upon past lake levels. Following drainage of highstand glacial lake phases, channel gradients in the Nottawasaga River stabilized sometime after 5500 yr B.P., leading to floodplain development. This corresponds roughly with the timing of occupation within the study area. Invisibility does not explain why Archaic sites are exposed in confined sections of the floodplain and Woodland sites are visible downstream in unconfined sections. The key to correctly interpreting the archaeological evidence in this study area may not be cultural, but rather a product of past climate and environmental change associated with fluctuating lake levels and changing modes of deposition in floodplains. This is most likely the case for all major rivers valleys draining from peninsular southern Ontario into the lower Great Lakes.

ACKNOWLEDGMENTS

This research was supported by a Natural Sciences and Engineering Research Council of Canada grant to J.R. Desloges. Thanks are due to K. Buckeridge, K.R. Hodder, A. Stewart, and M. Church for field assistance; various property owners, including N. and E. DeGorter, for access; W.K.E. Martin for laboratory assistance; and J. Werner for technical support. Thanks also to W.C. Mahaney and M.A. Latta for feedback; G.W. Crawford and D.G. Smith for suggestions; R. von Bitter and R.M. O'Brien at the Ministry of Citizenship, Culture, and Recreation for maps and other information on archaeological sites; and C. Garrad as well as D. Burritt, B.C. Wesson, C. Jones, and M. Dodd at the Nottawasaga Valley Conservation Authority for materials, including reports.

REFERENCES CITED

Brown, A.G., 1997, Alluvial Geoarchaeology: Floodplain Archaeology and Environmental Change: Cambridge, UK, Cambridge University Press, 377 p.

Burwasser, G.J., and Cairns, B.D., 1974, Quaternary Geology of the Barrie Area (Western Half), Southern Ontario: Ottawa, Ontario Division of Mines Geological Series Preliminary Map P.978, scale 1:50,000, 1 sheet.

Burwasser, G.J., and Ford, M.J., 1974, Bedrock Topography of the Barrie Area, Southern Ontario: Ottawa, Ontario Division of Mines Bedrock Topography Series Preliminary Map P.979, scale 1:50,000, 1 sheet.

Butzer, K.W., 1982, Archaeology as Human Ecology: Method and Theory for a Contextual Approach: New York, Cambridge University Press, 364 p.

Butzer, K.W., 2008, Challenges for a cross-disciplinary geoarchaeology: The intersection between environmental history and geomorphology: Geomorphology, v. 101, p. 402–411, doi:10.1016/j.geomorph.2008.07.007.

Chandler, T.J., and Kostaschuk, R.A., 1994, Test of selected bed-material load transport models: Nottawasaga River, Ontario: Canadian Journal of Civil Engineering, v. 21, p. 770–777, doi:10.1139/l94-083.

Chapman, L.J., and Putnam, D.F., 1984, Physiography of the south-central portion of southern Ontario: Ottawa, Ontario Department of Mines and Northern Affairs Map 2226, scale 1:253,440, 1 sheet.

Cooke, P., 1993, Site updates: Lower Nottawasaga River, 1992: Annual Archaeological Report, Ontario, v. 4, p. 2–3.

Crawford, G.W., Smith, D.G., Desloges, J.R., and Davis, A.M., 1998, Floodplains and agricultural origins: A case study in south-central Ontario, Canada: Journal of Field Archaeology, v. 25, p. 123–137, doi:10.2307/530574.

Davis, J.L., and Annan, A.P., 1989, Ground-penetrating radar for high-resolution mapping of soil and rock stratigraphy: Geophysical Prospecting, v. 37, p. 531–551, doi:10.1111/j.1365-2478.1989.tb02221.x.

Dean, W.E., Jr., 1974, Determination of carbonate and organic matter in calcareous sediments and sedimentary rocks by loss on ignition: Comparison with other methods: Journal of Sedimentary Petrology, v. 44, p. 242–248.

Ékes, C., and Hickin, E.J., 2001, Ground penetrating radar facies of the paraglacial Cheekye Fan, southwestern British Columbia, Canada: Sedimentary Geology, v. 143, p. 199–217, doi:10.1016/S0037-0738(01)00059-8.

Ellis, C.J., Kenyon, I.T., and Spence, M.W., 1998, The Archaic, *in* Ellis, C.J., and Ferris, N., eds., The Archaeology of Southern Ontario to A.D. 1650: Newboro, Adams Heritage Consultants, Occasional Publications of the London Chapter, Ontario Archaeological Society, no. 5, p. 65–124.

Fitzgerald, W.D., 1985, Postglacial history of the Minesing Basin, Ontario, *in* Karrow, P.F., and Calkin, P.E., eds., Quaternary Evolution of the Great Lakes: Geological Association of Canada Special Paper 30, p. 133–146.

Folk, R.L., 1966, A review of grain-size parameters: Sedimentology, v. 6, p. 73–93, doi:10.1111/j.1365-3091.1966.tb01572.x.

Folk, R.L., 1968, Petrology of Sedimentary Rocks: Austin, Hemphill's, 170 p.

Froese, D.G., Smith, D.G., and Clement, D.T., 2005, Characterizing large river history with shallow geophysics: Middle Yukon River, Yukon Territory and Alaska: Geomorphology, v. 67, p. 391–406, doi:10.1016/j.geomorph.2004.11.011.

Gardner, W.H., 1965, Water content, *in* Black, C.A., ed., Methods of Soil Analysis, Part 1: Madison, Wisconsin, American Society of Agronomy, p. 82–127.

Garrad, C., 1993, Archaeological investigations in the Petun area 1992: Annual Archaeological Report, Ontario, v. 4, p. 8–11.

Hanson, C.B., 1980, Fluvial taphonomic processes: Models and experiments, *in* Behrensmeyer, A.K., and Hill, A.P., eds., Fossils in the Making: Vertebrate Taphonomy and Paleoecology: Chicago, University of Chicago Press, p. 156–181.

Hiscock, P., 1985, The need for a taphonomic perspective in stone artefact analysis: Queensland Archaeological Research, v. 2, p. 82–95.

Hjulström, F., 1935, Studies of the morphological activity of rivers as illustrated by the River Fyris: Bulletin of the Geological Institute of the University of Uppsala, v. 25, p. 221–527.

Jackson, L.J., Ellis, C., Morgan, A.V., and McAndrews, J.H., 2000, Glacial lake levels and eastern Great Lakes Palaeo-Indians: Geoarchaeology: International Journal (Toronto, Ontario), v. 15, p. 415–440.

Jol, H.M., and Smith, D.G., 1991, Ground-penetrating radar of northern lacustrine deltas: Canadian Journal of Earth Sciences, v. 28, p. 1939–1947.

Kalicki, T., 2000, Grain size of the overbank deposits as carriers of paleogeographical information: Quaternary International, v. 72, p. 107–114, doi:10.1016/S1040-6182(00)00026-4.

Karrow, P.F., 1994, Geomorphology and glacial history: The archaeological implications of Quaternary geology, *in* MacDonald, R.I., ed., Great Lakes Archaeology and Aleoecology: Exploring Interdisciplinary Initiatives for the Nineties: Waterloo, Ontario, The Quaternary Sciences Institute, University of Waterloo, p. 219–235.

Knighton, D., 1998, Fluvial Forms and Processes: A New Perspective: Toronto, Oxford University Press Canada, 383 p.

Knox, J.C., 1993, Large increases in flood magnitude in response to modest changes in climate: Nature, v. 361, p. 430–432, doi:10.1038/361430a0.

Lewin, J., 1992, Alluvial sedimentation style and archaeological sites: The lower Vyrnwy, Wales, *in* Needham, S., and Macklin, M.G., eds., Alluvial Archaeology in Britain: Oxford, Oxbow Books, p. 103–109.

Lewin, J., 1996, Floodplain construction and erosion, *in* Petts, G., and Calow, P., eds., River Flows and Channel Forms: Selected Extracts from the Rivers Handbook: Cambridge, UK, Blackwell Science, p. 203–220.

Lewis, C.F.M., and Anderson, T.W., 1985, Postglacial lake levels in the Huron Basin: Comparative uplift histories of basins and sills in a rebounding glacial marginal depression, *in* Karrow, P.F., and Calkin, P.E., eds., Quaternary Evolution of the Great Lakes: Geological Association of Canada Special Paper 30, p. 147–148.

Marriott, S., 1992, Textural analysis and modelling of a flood deposit: River Severn, U.K.: Earth Surface Processes and Landforms, v. 17, p. 687–697, doi:10.1002/esp.3290170705.

McFadden, M.A., Patterson, W.P., Mullins, H.T., and Anderson, W.T., 2005, Multi-proxy approach to long- and short-term Holocene climate-change: Evidence from eastern Lake Ontario: Journal of Paleolimnology, v. 33, p. 371–391, doi:10.1007/s10933-004-7634-5.

Miall, A.D., 1977, A review of the braided-river depositional environment: Earth-Science Reviews, v. 13, p. 1–62, doi:10.1016/0012-8252(77)90055-1.

Miall, A.D., 1992, Alluvial deposits, *in* Walker, R.G., and James, N.P., eds., Facies Models: Response to Sea Level Change: Stittsville, Geological Association of Canada, p. 119–142.

Nanson, G.C., 1986, Episodes of vertical accretion and catastrophic stripping: A model of disequilibrium flood-plain development: Geological Society of America Bulletin, v. 97, p. 1467–1475, doi:10.1130/0016-7606(1986)97<1467:EOVAAC>2.0.CO;2.

Nanson, G.C., and Croke, J.C., 1992, A genetic classification of floodplains: Geomorphology, v. 4, p. 459–486, doi:10.1016/0169-555X(92)90039-Q.

O'Brien, R.M., 1974, Survey of Wasaga Beach: Toronto, Ministry of Citizenship, Culture, and Recreation, several p.

O'Brien, R.M., 1975, Archaeological Survey of Wasaga Beach, 1974: Toronto, Ministry of Citizenship, Culture, and Recreation, 101 p.

Olsen, D.S., Whitaker, A.C., and Potts, D.F., 1997, Assessing stream channel stability thresholds using flow competence estimates at bankfull stage: Journal of the American Water Resources Association, v. 33, p. 1197–1207, doi:10.1111/j.1752-1688.1997.tb03546.x.

Ontario Surveys and Mapping, 1986, Barrie, Ontario: Ottawa, Department of Energy, Mines and Resources Map of the National Topographic System Number 31 D/5, scale 1:50,000, 1 sheet.

Pizzuto, J.E., 1987, Sediment diffusion during overbank flows: Sedimentology, v. 34, p. 301–317, doi:10.1111/j.1365-3091.1987.tb00779.x.

Renwick, W.H., 1992, Equilibrium, disequilibrium, and nonequilibrium landforms in the landscape: Geomorphology, v. 5, p. 265–276, doi:10.1016/0169-555X(92)90008-C.

Shackley, M.L., 1978, The behaviour of artefacts as sedimentary particles in a fluviatile environment: Archaeometry, v. 20, p. 55–61, doi:10.1111/j.1475-4754.1978.tb00212.x.

Stein, J.K., 1987, Deposits for archaeologists: Advances in Archaeological Method and Theory, v. 11, p. 337–395.

Storck, P.L., 1982, Palaeo-Indian settlement patterns associated with the strandline of glacial Lake Algonquin in south central Ontario: Canadian Journal of Archaeology, v. 6, p. 1–31.

Storck, P.L., 1984, Research into the Paleo-Indian occupations of Ontario: A review: Ontario Archaeology, v. 41, p. 3–28.

Walker, I.J., Desloges, J.R., Crawford, G.W., and Smith, D.G., 1997, Floodplain formation processes and archaeological implications at the Grand Banks site, lower Grand River, southern Ontario: Geoarchaeology, v. 12, p. 865–887, doi:10.1002/(SICI)1520-6548(199712)12:8<865::AID-GEA3>3.0.CO;2-3.

Waters, M.R., and Kuehn, D.D., 1996, The geoarchaeology of place: The effect of geological processes on the preservation and interpretation of the archaeological record: American Antiquity, v. 61, p. 483–497, doi:10.2307/281836.

Weninger, J.M., and McAndrews, J.H., 1989, Late Holocene aggradation in the lower Humber River valley, Toronto, Ontario: Canadian Journal of Earth Sciences, v. 26, p. 1842–1849.

MANUSCRIPT ACCEPTED BY THE SOCIETY 3 AUGUST 2010

The Geological Society of America
Special Paper 476
2011

Geoarchaeology and archaeological landscapes in the Till River valley, northern England

David G. Passmore*

School of Geography, Politics, and Sociology, University of Newcastle upon Tyne, Newcastle upon Tyne, NE1 7RU, UK

Clive Waddington

Archaeological Research Services Ltd., Angel House, Portland Square, Bakewell, Derbyshire, DE45 1HB, UK

Tim van der Schriek

School of Geography, Politics, and Sociology, University of Newcastle upon Tyne, Newcastle upon Tyne, NE1 7RU, UK

Basil Davis

Atmosphere Regolith Vegetation (ARVE), École Polytechnique Fédérale de Lausanne, Lausanne, Switzerland

Emma Tetlow

Headland Archaeology (UK) Ltd., 13 Jane St., Edinburgh, EH6 5HE, UK

David Smith

Institute of Archaeology and Antiquity, University of Birmingham, Edgbaston, Birmingham, B15 2TT, UK

Jacqui Cotton

Environment Agency, Rivers House, 21 Park Square South, Leeds, LS1 2QG, UK

ABSTRACT

This paper presents an overview of the Till-Tweed project, an Aggregates Levy Sustainability Fund–sponsored geoarchaeological assessment of archaeological and paleoenvironmental records in a major northern UK river basin. The project methodology employed a suite of geomorphological, paleoecological, and archaeological techniques to identify, define, and delimit landform, sediment, and archaeological associations over 358 km² of the Till and lower Tweed Valleys. These associations were integrated in a geographic information system (GIS), establishing a baseline audit of the heritage resource that is driving the development of both heritage management and research frameworks in these river valley settings.

Particular attention is paid to the new perspectives on landscape development, land use, and settlement that are being derived from analysis of associations between landforms, paleoenvironmental records, and enhanced archaeological data sets. The utility of this approach is illustrated by a case study of the Breamish–Till River at

*d.g.passmore@ncl.ac.uk

Passmore, D.G., Waddington, C., van der Schriek, T., Davis, B., Tetlow, E., Smith, D., and Cotton, J., 2011, Geoarchaeology and archaeological landscapes in the Till River valley, northern England, *in* Brown, A.G., Basell, L.S., and Butzer, K.W., eds., Geoarchaeology, Climate Change, and Sustainability: Geological Society of America Special Paper 476, p. 117–133, doi:10.1130/2011.2476(10). For permission to copy, contact editing@geosociety.org. © 2011 The Geological Society of America. All rights reserved.

New Bewick, near Powburn, Northumberland. This landscape exhibits a wide range of documented archaeological records, including upstanding monuments, crop marks, and lithic scatters, as well as the potential for alluvial burial of remains that have yet to be discovered. Elements of particular interest are extensive areas of terraced sand and gravel associated with late Devensian deglaciation that are shown to host persistent, multiperiod occupation dating from the Mesolithic period. Numerous infilled kettle holes in these surfaces offer the prospect of long paleoenvironmental records, while paleochannel fills preserved on the adjacent Holocene alluvial valley floor have been shown to locally date from the fourth millennium B.C. and have yielded paleoecological evidence of episodic Anglo-Saxon and later woodland clearance, pastoral activities, and cereal cultivation in the immediate vicinity of the archaeological sites.

We conclude that the integration of these geoarchaeological data sets into a GIS platform not only brings clear practical benefits to heritage managers and developers, but constitutes a valuable research tool by permitting more sophisticated and systematic analyses of links between the modern landscape, the environmental record, and the archaeological data set.

INTRODUCTION

Geoarchaeological techniques and approaches are widely recognized as enabling syntheses of landscape development and the archaeological record (e.g., Waters, 1992, 2000; Needham and Macklin, 1992; Stafford, 1995; Brown, 1997; Howard and Macklin, 1999; French, 2002; Howard et al., 2003; Macklin et al., 2003), and hence also the development of frameworks that may aid the prospection, understanding, and management of archaeological resources (e.g., Gardner and Donahue, 1985; Olivier, 1996; Pryor et al., 1985; French and Wait, 1988; French et al., 1992; Hayes and Lane, 1992; Lane, 1993; Allen et al., 1997; Passmore et al., 2002; Howard et al., 2008). In general, however, the collaboration between earth science and archaeological communities is rarely integrated from the outset of a project. In the UK, for example, there are relatively few published examples of studies that attempt to systematically define landform and archaeological associations for river valley floors, and yet these settings are liable to have experienced considerable environmental change since the last glacial episode.

Recently, however, the advent of the English Heritage Aggregates Levy Sustainability Fund (ALSF) program in the UK (www.english-heritage.org.uk/ALSF) has provided a major impetus for geoarchaeological assessment of England's valley floors (Brown, 2009). Introduced in 2002, the program's core objectives include developing the capacity to manage aggregate extraction landscapes into the future. This has required multidisciplinary evaluations of the character, scale, and distribution of archaeological and paleoenvironmental records in localities with significant deposits of Quaternary sands and gravels. Accordingly, geoarchaeological concepts and techniques have been widely adopted in ALSF-funded investigations in many of the country's major river basins (e.g., Knight and Howard, 2004; Howard, 2005; Brown, 2009).

The valley floors of the rivers Till (called the Breamish in its upper reaches) and lower Tweed contain the largest expanse of late Pleistocene and Holocene sand and gravel deposits in northeast England. These deposits host a regionally and nationally important archaeological record, especially in the Milfield Basin (e.g., Hope-Taylor, 1977; Harding, 1981; Waddington, 1999), although comparatively little is known about early settlement chronology in the wider area (e.g., Burgess, 1984; Waddington, 1999). Indeed, there has been very little previous archaeological work done in the lower Tweed valley or the reaches of the Till between the Milfield Basin and the Breamish valley, despite the considerable archive of crop mark sites known from aerial photography of this region. Large-scale investigations of late Quaternary landforms (Clapperton, 1970, 1971a, 1971b) and soils (Payton, 1980, 1988, 1992) in the Breamish-Till catchment provide a broad geomorphological framework for this area, but detailed paleoenvironmental investigations of Holocene sediment sequences have been limited to localized alluvial sites in the Milfield Basin (Borek, 1975; Tipping, 1998; Passmore et al., 2002), the Breamish valley (Tipping, 1992, 1994), and Lower Tweed (Passmore et al., 2006). Beyond these subreaches, however, there has been little published paleoenvironmental work in the study area that serves to inform the development of archaeological research and resource management frameworks.

Ongoing, planned, and potential aggregate extraction in the Till-Tweed catchment thus presents a serious threat to the archaeological and paleoenvironmental record of catchment sand and gravel deposits. Accordingly, the Till-Tweed project has built on the success of the earlier Milfield Basin project (Passmore et al., 2002) and has sought to (1) assess the extent, age, and character of landscapes associated with deglaciation and Holocene environmental change in the study basin, (2) enhance understanding of the chronology and patterns of past human activity on the sand and gravel terraces of the study area, (3) develop an archaeological resource evaluation and management guidance framework for the Till-Tweed study area, and (4) provide a basis for driving forward research and educational opportunities. The development of a management framework and planning guidance for the Till-Tweed catchment has been described by Passmore et al. (2006) and is fully documented by Passmore and Waddington (2009). In this paper, we focus on the research implications of the project by outlining the methodology adopted for landscape analysis, and, using a case study reach of the Breamish-Till valley at New Bewick, near Powburn, Northumberland, we illustrate the ways in which the combination of archaeological and paleoenvironmental techniques is enabling a more coherent and informed appreciation of landscape development and human activity.

PHYSIOGRAPHY, GEOLOGY, AND QUATERNARY HISTORY OF THE TILL-TWEED STUDY AREA

The gravel-bed Till River is the second largest tributary of the Tweed River, with a catchment area of 650 km², and it joins the Tweed at Tweedmill, 4 km downstream of Coldstream (Fig. 1). Upper reaches of the Till (called the Breamish above Bewick Mill; Fig. 1) drain the rounded upland domes of the southern and southeast Cheviot Hills, which reach a maximum elevation of 815 m above sea level (asl). The catchment of the Till River is predominantly rural, and modern land use is closely related to altitude, relief, and the underlying geology. Over half of the basin lies above 300 m asl and is characterized by moorland, conifer plantations, and rough pasture. Middle and lower reaches of the Till, by contrast, are dominated by gently undulating relief that supports arable cultivation and improved pasture. The underlying pre-Quaternary geology of the Till valley is of Devonian and Carboniferous age. The rounded domes of the Cheviot Hills are formed by a complex of Devonian volcanic rocks predominantly composed of ashes, pyroclasts, and andesitic lavas and a later Devonian granite intrusion. To the east of the Cheviots, the landscape is dominated by a pair of gently curving escarpments with west-facing craggy ridges formed by Carboniferous Fell Sandstones. Intervening broad vales are underlain by Carboniferous cementstones. Soil cover in the region includes well-drained brown earths in many of the lowland settings, gleys on intermediate slopes, and podzols and peats in upland locations (Payton, 1980).

The Cheviot–Lower Tweed region has a long record of Quaternary research, although a secure chronological framework is lacking (Douglas, 1991; Lunn, 2004). Investigations of regional Quaternary stratigraphies remain reliant on morphostratigraphic analysis of landform-sediment assemblages that are provisionally dated by analogy to independently dated sequences from other upland regions of the British Isles (Harrison, 2002). On this basis, surviving landform-sediment assemblages of glacial origin are generally regarded as dating to the late Devensian. During the Last Glacial Maximum, most of the Cheviot–Lower Tweed area was probably overrun by ice flows originating from the Southern Uplands and Solway Firth to the west, and much of the area is mantled with a variable thickness of till. Two extensive areas of glaciofluvial sand and gravel have received particular attention: a northerly complex stretching between Cornhill in the Tweed valley around the northern flank of the Cheviots, and to the south between Wooler and the Breamish valley at Powburn (Fig. 2). These hummocky landscapes consist of ice-contact and proglacial features including eskers, kames, kettle holes, and terraced

outwash associated with downwasting and retreating ice at the end of the Dimlington Stadial (Clapperton, 1970, 1971a, 1971b; Douglas, 1991; Lunn, 2004). Glaciolacustrine deposits are also locally present in the valley of the Breamish-Till. These deposits, together with extensive and complex systems of meltwater channels on the northern and eastern flanks of the Cheviot Hills, have been described in detail by Clapperton (1970, 1971a, 1971b).

Methodology

The Till-Tweed Project encompasses some 560 km² of the middle and lower Breamish–Till valley downstream of Ingram and the lower reaches of the Tweed River between Coldstream and the A1 road crossing 5 km upstream of the river mouth at Berwick (Fig. 1). Details of the archaeological and paleoenvironmental techniques are summarized in Table 1. Archaeological investigations have adopted two principal techniques. First, a program of aerial photograph transcription and interpretation (following the National Mapping Programme format and standards developed for archaeological site records in England by English Heritage) has recorded, in total, 254 new sites (both upstanding and buried), as well as enhancing the records for 218 existing sites. Second, a program of field-walking and test-pitting has been implemented across a range of contrasting geological, geomorphological, and topographical settings. Field selection has been contingent upon the plowing schedule and, following the results of earlier work in the region (Waddington, 1999), focused in particular on glaciofluvial and fluvial sand and gravel terraces. The field-walking program yielded a total of 2142 stone artifacts, together with 30 fragments of pottery, and all find spots were point-referenced with a total station and the field boundaries surveyed so that field plots could be related to the Ordnance Survey (OS) grid.

The primary requirement for the development of a landform element classification for the project was a geomorphological map of the Till-Tweed landscape. Mapping and delimitation of landform assemblages in the study area were greatly facilitated by LiDAR (light detection and ranging; e.g., Challis, 2006) data of the valley floor topography at a vertical resolution of ±20 cm. This technique enabled a complete geomorphological mapping survey of valley floor landforms throughout the survey area within the time frame of the project. Mapping was also informed by analysis of historic and modern OS topographic coverages and published geological maps of the region, and a program of field visits. Mapping sought to identify all major valley floor landform assemblages of glacial, glaciofluvial, and fluvial origin. Particular attention was focused on fluvial valley floor environments where mapping sought to delimit terrace scarps, flood basins, and paleochannels. For parts of the study block that were located outside the LiDAR coverage, mapping was undertaken at a lower resolution equivalent to the scale of landform-sediment assemblages differentiated by drift geology maps. In these areas, we prioritized the identification of kettle holes and larger enclosed basins (which have the potential to preserve organic-rich sediment

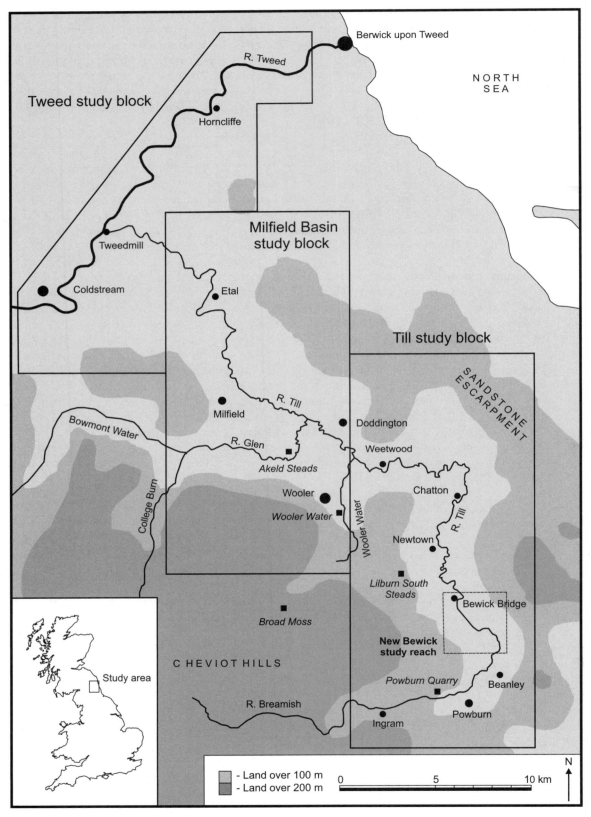

Figure 1. Map of the Till River and Lower Tweed River basins, showing relief, location of study blocks, and sites mentioned in text.

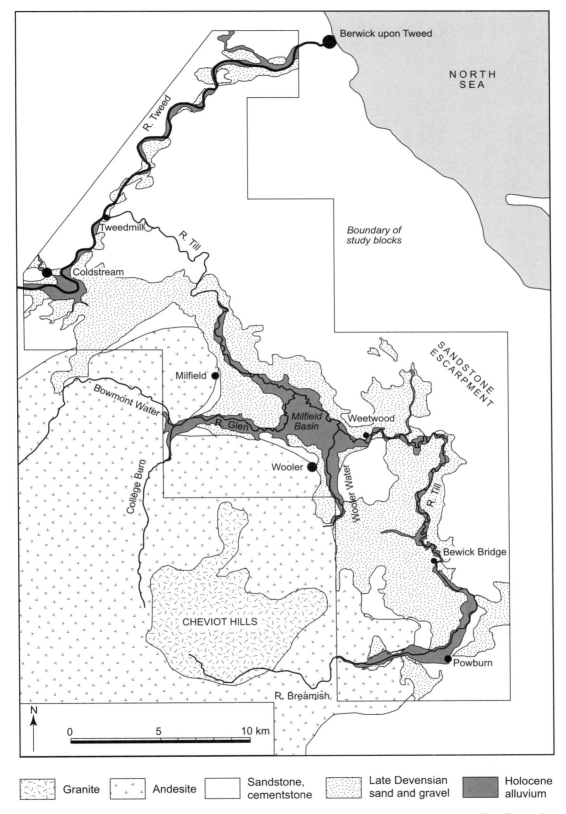

Figure 2. Simplified pre-Quaternary geology and Quaternary deposits in the study area; areas of late Devensian sand and gravel include ice-contact meltwater, glaciofluvial deposits, and glaciodeltaic deposits and are mapped in the study blocks only.

TABLE 1. SUMMARY OF ARCHAEOLOGICAL AND GEOARCHAEOLOGICAL METHODS EMPLOYED BY THE TILL-TWEED PROJECT

	Technique	Data sources and fieldwork	Description and notes
Archaeological methods			
1.	Aerial photograph transcription	Oblique aerial photographs from the Museum of Antiquities (Newcastle) and the National Monument Record	Mapping of cropmarks, soil marks, and paleoenvironmental features over ~350 km². Interpretation and hardcopy/digital transcription at 1:10,000 scale.
2.	Field-walking	35 fields with a combined area of 391.4 hectares were field-walked	Fields line-walked at 5 m intervals giving ~40% coverage (assuming walkers inspect the ground 1 m either side of themselves; cf. Tolan-Smith, 1997). All find spots were point referenced to Ordnance Survey coordinates with a total station. Fields were also mapped by slope unit (morphometric mapping) so that each find spot could be ascribed to a slope unit (cf. Waddington, 1999; Passmore and Waddington, 2009).
Geoarchaeological methods			
3.	Geomorphological mapping	LiDAR coverage of 358 km² of the valley floors; Geological (1:50,000) and Ordnance Survey (1:10,000) maps; field survey	LiDAR (light detection and ranging) flights and data preparation commissioned from the Environment Agency; unfiltered data with 2 m horizontal spacing and a vertical resolution of ±0.2 m were rendered as digital elevation models in a GIS (ArcGIS) and used as the basis for geomorphological mapping; for further details, see text.
4.	Sediment logging/coring	Aggregate quarry and riverbank sections where available; sediment coring	Sediment cores extracted using hand-operated augers that permitted recovery of continuous cores. All cores/sections were logged for color, texture, bedding structures, and inclusions; organic-rich sedimentary sequences were sampled as continuous bodies and removed intact to the laboratory for storage and subsampling.
5.	Paleoecological analysis	Subsampled organic-rich sediments from (4)	
	(a) Pollen		(1) Assessment of pollen preservation and content was undertaken on all organic-rich sediment units recovered during the coring program; (2) full analysis of organic-rich sediments was conducted in 10 selected sediment cores. Sample preparation followed standard laboratory techniques (Moore et al., 1989). For full pollen analysis, counts of up to 500 land pollen grains were undertaken for each level.
	(b) Plant macrofossils		Subsamples were prepared following standard techniques (Dickson, 1970; Watts, 1978; Birks, 1980); samples were weighed and then sieved through a 125 µm mesh, with the remaining contents transferred to a beaker containing distilled water. These were scanned with a low-power binocular microscope, and all identifiable botanical remains were extracted and identified using modern published reference material. Plant macrofossil data were interpreted via comparison with published data of vegetation communities (Rodwell, 1992; 1995; Stace, 1997).
	(c) Insect fauna		Subsamples were processed using the standard method of paraffin flotation (Kenward et al., 1980). Identification of insects followed the system for rapid "scanning" of insect faunas (Kenward et al., 1986).
6.	¹⁴C dating	A program of ¹⁴C analyses was developed in collaboration with the English Heritage Scientific Dating team	In total, 24 samples were submitted for accelerator mass spectrometry/radiometric dating. All dates quoted in the text (unless stated otherwise) are calibrated date ranges (95% confidence intervals) calculated by the maximum intercept method (Stuiver and Reimer, 1986), using the program OxCal v. 3.5 (Bronk Ramsey, 1995, 1998, 2001) and the INTCAL98 data set (Stuiver et al., 1998).

sequences), and have not yet attempted to produce detailed maps of individual kames, eskers, and other ice-contact, glaciofluvial, and subglacial landforms.

Six subreaches of the Breamish-Till and Lower Tweed valleys that are representative of the range of valley floor environments in the study area were selected for detailed sedimentological, paleo-ecological, and geochronological investigations (Passmore et al., 2006; Passmore and Waddington, 2009). In this paper, we focus on a study site located in the middle reaches of the Breamish-Till valley at New Bewick. At each site, sediment sequences representative of discrete fluvial valley floor units were investigated by examination of quarry faces and river bank sections (where available) and sediment coring (Table 1). Attention focused in particular on flood basin and paleochannel deposits, which form the most likely context for preservation of organic materials suitable for ^{14}C and paleoecological analyses. A program of ^{14}C analyses was developed with the aim of establishing (1) a model of valley floor evolution that may be related to archaeological periods and their likely preservation and/or burial potential, and (2) the maximum ages of pollen, plant macrofossil, and insect assemblages recovered from selected sediment sequences.

Paleoecological analyses were undertaken to evaluate the potential of recorded sediment sequences for yielding information on Holocene valley floor environments. A factor of particular interest here is the potential for these sediments to yield "off-site" records of human activity (e.g., woodland clearance, cereal cultivation), which renders them as an archaeological resource. Indeed, paleochannel fills offer potentially high-resolution records of environmental change that are proximal to areas of former settlement and subsistence activity (Fyfe et al., 2003). Accordingly, all fine-grained organic-rich sediment sequences recovered and stored were assessed for content and preservation of (1) pollen, (2) plant macrofossils, and (3) insect fauna. In the following discussion, it should be noted that the plant macrofossil and insect fauna analyses were undertaken in order to establish the potential of selected sites (and by implication other similar depositional environments) for yielding paleoenvironmental information. Furthermore, in order to achieve adequate sample sizes, it was frequently necessary to combine material spanning depositional thicknesses in excess of 5–10 cm, and hence the temporal and contextual resolution of the assessment is typically less than that achieved by pollen analysis. Accordingly, the analyses should be regarded as giving only a provisional assessment of species assemblages.

HOLOCENE ALLUVIAL HISTORY OF THE BREAMISH-TILL RIVER AT NEW BEWICK

The study reach described here spans a 4 km stretch of the middle reaches of the Breamish-Till River between New Bewick and Bewick Bridge (Figs. 1 and 3); within this stretch of the river, the Breamish is renamed the Till below Bewick Mill (Fig. 3). To the east of the Breamish-Till, the study reach is overlooked by a glacially streamlined Carboniferous sandstone escarpment with localized drift cover and prominent bare-rock crags (Fig. 3). Infilling the valley floor, there is an extensive assemblage of depositional landforms associated with the late Devensian deglaciation of the area, and which locally rise up to 40 m above the present floodplain. These deposits have been described by Clapperton (1970, 1971a, 1971b) and consist of sand and gravel deposited as ice-contact meltwater deposits and inset glaciofluvial and glaciodeltaic outwash terraces (Fig. 3). Other features that are present on the west-facing flanks of the escarpment are large fan-shaped landforms infilling the lower parts of small tributary gullies; these are provisionally interpreted as late Devensian alluvial fans (Fig. 3). Meltwater-derived terraces locally feature kettle holes (Fig. 3), and where local drainage has been impeded, these depressions have developed persistent small lakes, ponds, and wetlands with associated organic-rich sediment sequences. Previous studies at Lilburn South Steads, 4 km northwest of New Bewick (Fig. 1), have proven that such sites may have accumulated sediments to depths of 14 m; at Lilburn, sedimentation was found to have started prior to ca. 13,400 cal yr B.C. (Jones et al., 2000) and potentially spans the entire Holocene period.

Holocene alluvial deposits infill the valley floor of the Breamish throughout this area and are typically inset at least 5 m below late Devensian deposits (Figs. 3 and 4). The alluvial valley floor has a maximum width of 1 km in an alluvial basin upstream of New Bewick, but downstream of the basin, it occupies a relatively confined trench that is typically narrower than 0.5 km (Fig. 3). A low-relief floodplain terrace flanks the Breamish in the wider alluvial settings and locally features sinuous paleochannels (Figs. 3 and 4). Valley floor relief is generally not pronounced and features no distinctive alluvial terrace scarps that delimit alluvial surfaces of differing age (Fig. 4). The present floodplain is up to 50 m wide and located between nineteenth-century embankments, up to 1.5 m below the low-relief terrace surface (Fig. 4). Nineteenth-century canalization of a 1.5 km reach of the Breamish between New Bewick and Bewick Bridge has also necessitated artificial cutoff of several meander loops (Fig. 3).

Three well-defined paleochannels and flanking terrace deposits have been cored immediately upstream of Bewick Bridge (Figs. 3 and 4). Channel-fill deposits at this site consist of up to 2.4 m of peaty clay-silt overlying inorganic sands and basal channel-bed gravels; adjacent terrace sediments are largely inorganic fining-upward sands and sandy silts, between 0.9 and 2 m thick, overlying sandy gravel (Fig. 4). Provisional age control for channel abandonment is provided by ^{14}C samples taken at or near the base of the infill sequences (Fig. 4; Table 2). The smallest and most northerly paleochannel of the group was cored at BT5, where a peat sample between 160–170 cm in depth gave a date of cal A.D. 390–600 (SUERC-1159; Fig. 4; Table 2). To the south of this channel, the middle paleomeander of the group was cored at site BT10 and yielded a peat sample between 95 and 110 cm in depth that dates to cal A.D. 680–940 (SUERC-1160; Fig. 4; Table 2). The final paleomeander of the group appears

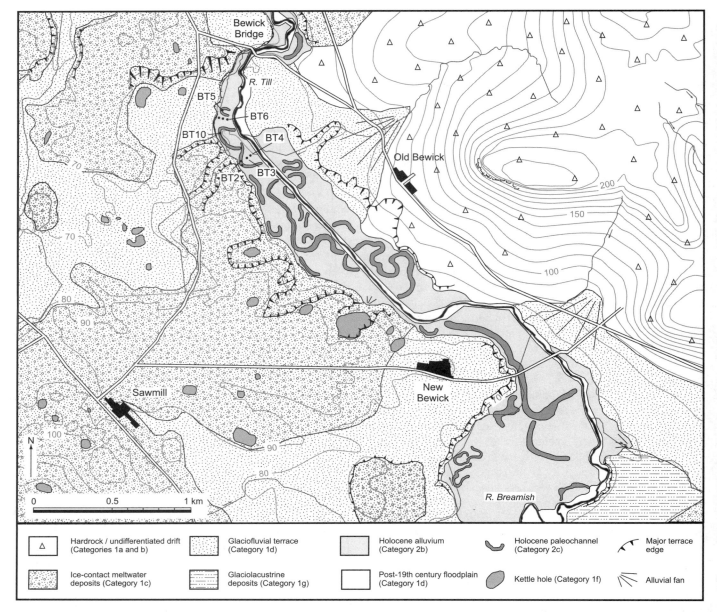

Figure 3. Geomorphological map of the valley floor and Fell Sandstone escarpment at New Bewick (Breamish-Till River) showing major paleochannels, kettle holes, terrace edges, and sediment core locations.

to truncate the southerly limb of the BT10 channel; here, a peat sample at a depth of 200–214 cm at site BT2 gave a date of cal A.D. 900–1160 (SUERC-1158; Fig. 4; Table 2), which confirms the morphostratigraphic evidence of a younger age for this channel. In combination, these paleochannels demonstrate localized shifts of the meandering gravel-bed Breamish channel during the first and early second millennium A.D. There is no evidence of scroll-bar formation on the terrace surface inside the paleomeanders, and hence channel shifts were probably accomplished by avulsion during one or more flood events. Avulsion occurred in the context of a vertically stable channel bed eleva-

tion although overbank sedimentation of fine-grained alluvium will have aggraded the floodplain terrace surface during this period. The analyzed dates for the paleochannel deposits therefore suggest that the greater part of the valley floor at Bewick Bridge dates from the Roman period onward, and that locally there is a lateral age zonation of the valley floor (although it is also acknowledged that paleochannels of an earlier date may survive in wider parts of the valley floor). The initiation of valley fill sedimentation in the study reach is currently undated, but it is assumed that alluviation began shortly after late-glacial incision of the valley floor.

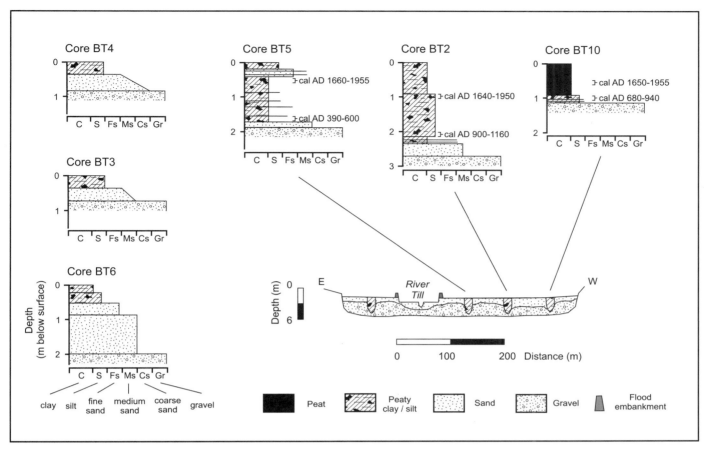

Figure 4. Schematic cross profile and sediment logs for the Holocene alluvial valley floor at Bewick Bridge.

TABLE 2. ¹⁴C DATES AND CALIBRATION DETAILS FROM PALEOCHANNEL CORES AT NEW BEWICK, BREAMISH-TILL RIVER

Laboratory code	Sedimentary sequence	Sample depth (cm below surface)	Sample	Material	^{13}C (‰)	Radiocarbon age (yr B.P.)	Calibrated date (95% confidence)
SUERC-1158	BT2	200–214	BTcd-1	Peat, humic acid	−29.5	1015 ± 40	cal A.D. 900–1150
OxA-15049	BT2	97	BTcd-1(2)	*Carex* sp., seeds	−25.9	229 ± 28	cal A.D. 1640–1950
SUERC-1159	BT5	160–170	BTcd-2	Peat, humic acid	−28.4	1585 ± 40	cal A.D. 390–570
OxA-15050	BT5	43	BTcd-2(2)	*Carex* sp., seeds	−25.9	171 ± 28	cal A.D. 1660–1955
SUERC-1160	BT10	95–110	BTcd-3	Peat, humic acid	−29.3	1220 ± 40	cal A.D. 670–940
OxA-15051	BT10	65	BTcd-3(2)	*Carex* sp., seeds	−27.1	182 ± 27	cal A.D. 1650–1955

ARCHAEOLOGY OF THE TILL VALLEY AT NEW BEWICK

A rich, mixed-age assemblage of earthworks, archaeological crop marks, and artifact scatters in the study area testifies to long-term occupation of the valley floor and its immediate surroundings (Fig. 5). Some of the more prominent monuments have been described by earlier workers, notably an unusual Iron Age "spectacle"-type hill fort at Old Bewick with flanking Roman-British enclosures (Charlton, 1935; Jobey, 1965) (Fig. 5) that are sited on the sandstone escarpment and command panoramic views across the valley to the Cheviots and, on the undulating glaciofluvial landscape to the west of New Bewick, a complex of sunken-featured buildings of Grübenhauser-type that constitute an Anglo-Saxon settlement or industrial site (Gates and O'Brien, 1988; Fig. 5). However, aerial photograph analysis in this project represents the first attempt to systematically identify and describe the full range of crop marks and earthworks in the Till-Tweed study area. In the New Bewick study reach, this has revealed prehistoric and early historic archaeology to be well represented by crop marks on the undulating late Devensian sand and gravel terraces on the western

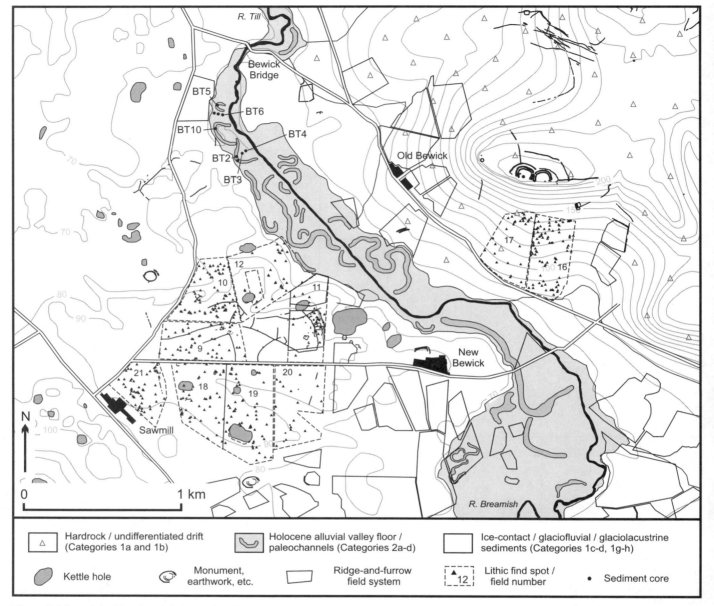

Figure 5. Map of the New Bewick–Bewick Bridge study reach showing location of archaeological earthworks and crop marks, lithic find spots, and selected landform elements. Also shown are the locations of sediment cores mentioned in the text.

side of the Breamish-Till. These include probable Bronze Age ring-ditches and numerous prehistoric and Roman-British pit alignments and enclosures (Fig. 5). It is also interesting to note that a large kettle hole (which presently contains standing water) in field 12 appears to lie immediately adjacent to an access point of a former (crop mark) field system (Fig. 5). It is possible, therefore, that these boundaries formed part of a stock-control system that utilized the pond for stock watering. This field system could date from the late prehistoric period through to the early medieval; further precision is only possible with recourse to excavation.

The archaeological record has been supplemented at New Bewick by field-walking of eight large fields that yielded lithics dating from the Mesolithic, Neolithic, and Early Bronze Age periods (Fig. 5). Mesolithic material was found across the entire area, suggesting that hunter-gatherer groups found local hillslopes and free-draining terraces close to the river to be attractive for settlement and subsistence activity. Neolithic and Bronze Age material, including end scrapers and a barbed and tanged arrowhead, was recovered from fields 9, 11, 12, 18, 19, 20, and 21, and this is likely to relate to crop mark evidence for a group of pit features visible on aerial photographs clustered around field 9

(Fig. 5). Much of the lithic material occurs in close proximity to kettle hole depressions in fields 12, 18, and 19 that are likely to have supported contemporary ponds or wetlands (Fig. 5).

Large-scale arable cultivation during the medieval and post-medieval period is attested by extensive areas of ridge-and-furrow throughout the study reach, including the Holocene alluvial valley floor, where they constitute the only archaeology recorded to date (Fig. 5).

PALEOECOLOGY OF CHANNEL-FILL DEPOSITS

A full description of paleoecological data was presented by Passmore and Waddington (2009); here, we present summaries of pollen assemblages and plant macrofossil and insect remains for cores BT5 (Fig. 6), BT10 (Fig. 7), and BT2 (Fig. 8). In combination, these records span much of the period between the fourth century A.D. and the nineteenth century. Pollen assemblages in all three sediment sequences at Bewick Bridge suggest that, for much of the past 1600 yr or so, drier parts of the floodplain and adjacent glaciofluvial land surfaces have supported low levels of woodland cover in a largely open grassland landscape, and that the landscape was probably extensively deforested by the later medieval period. The woodland composition is similar at all three sites, being composed mainly of hazel, oak, and, on wetter parts of the floodplain, stands of alder, while an increase in pine pollen in the upper part of each sequence is consistent with the eighteenth century and later expansion of pine plantations. Gramineae dominate the herbaceous taxa at all sites, but there is also a significant presence of disturbance indicators such as Liguliflorae, *Plantago* sp., and Chenopodiaceae. These may, at least in part, reflect natural environmental disturbance associated with flooding, but the frequent presence of cereal-type pollen also points to localized and episodic arable cultivation from at least as early as cal A.D. 680–940 (BT10; Fig. 7), and subsequently around cal A.D. 900–1160 (BT2; Fig. 8). A local presence of grassland and pasture on the valley floor is also evidenced by the insect fauna assemblages. Local paleochannel wetland conditions are indicated by quite significant levels of Cyperaceae, and the lower levels of all channel fills feature relatively high counts of floodplain alder. This would suggest permanently damp conditions and may indicate a hydroseral succession to reed swamp associated with shallowing of floodplain ponds due to infilling and declining flood frequency. Plant macrofossils also testify to the existence of local floodplain ponds and wetland/marsh habitats in paleochannel depressions.

DISCUSSION: LANDFORM, SEDIMENT, AND ARCHAEOLOGICAL ASSOCIATIONS IN THE BREAMISH-TILL VALLEY

The primary aim of the Till-Tweed project has been to establish a heritage management framework and planning guidance for the study area (Passmore et al., 2006; Passmore and Waddington, 2009), and this has been articulated by compiling the complete project data set in a GIS with accompanying maps and documentation (Waddington and Passmore, 2005). Investigations at New Bewick show that these formerly glaciated landscapes and postglacial valley floors present differing scenarios for the visibility and preservation of archaeological records. Accordingly, a range of evaluation techniques is required in order to understand the past history of settlement and land use in these valley settings, as well as to identify the location of surviving remains in advance of any development. In the light of the ongoing and future threat to archaeological resources posed by aggregate extraction, particular attention has focused on the late Devensian sand and gravel terraces that extend across much of the valley floor; here, archaeological field-walking has demonstrated that plow soils may contain good evidence for Stone Age activity in the form of lithic scatters, while crop mark data derived from analysis of aerial photographs reveal numerous buried features dating from the Neolithic through to the Early medieval period (Fig. 5). In the drift-mantled and craggy upland landscape to the east of the Breamish-Till River, aerial photography topographic survey and field-walking have been used to identify and record upstanding monuments, rock art, and, on the west-facing hillslopes, more evidence of Mesolithic and Neolithic artifact scatters.

A combination of aerial photography and LiDAR survey has also identified widespread survival of low-relief ridge and furrow field systems of medieval and later age, including on Holocene alluvial surfaces, where they constitute the only recorded archaeological features. The apparent absence of prehistoric archaeology on the surface of the Holocene alluvial valley floor is likely to reflect, at least in part, a tendency of prehistoric cultures to avoid major settlement activity in flood-prone contexts (although subsistence and ritual activities may have been intimately linked with watercourses and wetland habitats, e.g., Evans, 1992; Needham and Macklin, 1992; Brown, 1997). It is also recognized that the combination of limited plowing and relatively poorly drained alluvial soils is not conducive to detection of crop marks or artifact scatters; indeed, no alluvial fields at New Bewick were available for field walking during the duration of this project. To these considerations, we must add the possibility of archaeology being buried beneath alluvium, allied with localized reworking of older Holocene parts of the valley floor by meander migration and avulsion, which results in a preservation bias toward younger Holocene deposits (cf. Lewin and Macklin, 2003) and their associated archaeology. In this relatively confined alluvial valley floor, it is perhaps not surprising that the dated paleochannels are relatively young, being respectively abandoned shortly before ca. cal A.D. 390–600, cal A.D. 680–940, and cal A.D. 900–1160. A full analysis of the chronology and character of valley floor development lies beyond the scope of this paper, but here we note that the medieval period (especially the eleventh and twelfth centuries) was associated with channel changes and river instability in several other parts of the Till-Tweed catchment (Passmore et al., 2006; Passmore and Waddington, 2009) and has parallels in catchments elsewhere in Britain (e.g., Passmore and Macklin, 2000; Howard, 2005; Macklin et al., 2005; Chiverrell,

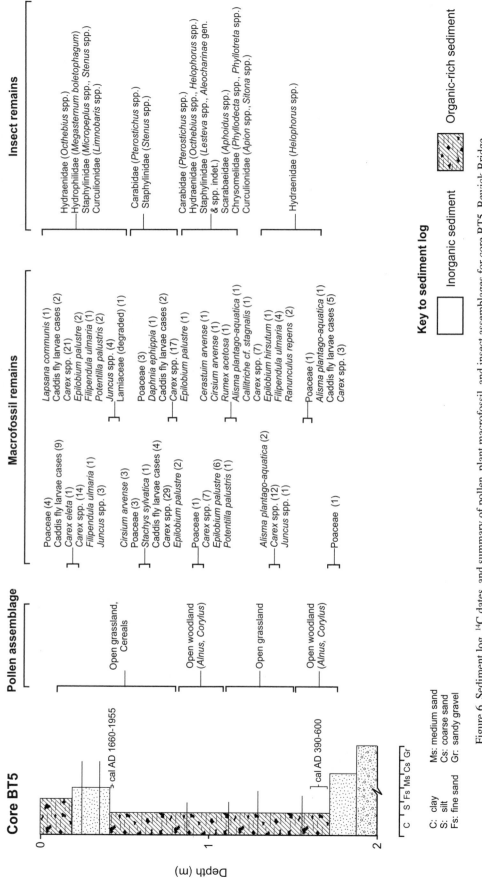

Figure 6. Sediment log, ^{14}C dates, and summary of pollen, plant macrofossil, and insect assemblages for core BT5, Bewick Bridge.

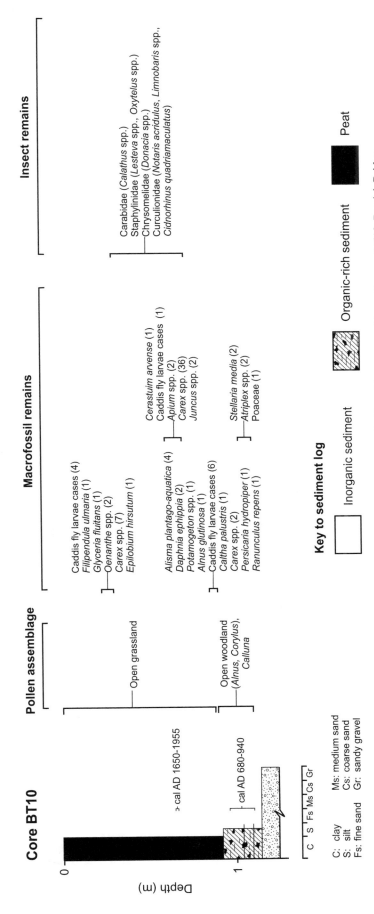

Figure 7. Sediment log, ^{14}C dates, and summary of pollen, plant macrofossil, and insect assemblages for core BT10, Bewick Bridge.

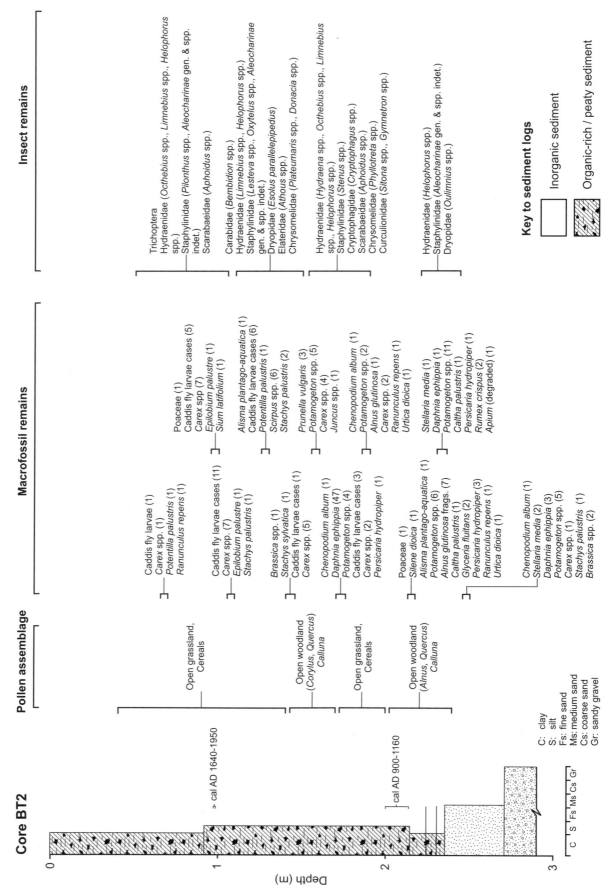

Figure 8. Sediment log, ^{14}C dates, and summary of pollen, plant macrofossil, and insect assemblages for core BT2, Bewick Bridge.

2006; Brown, 2008) and Europe (e.g., Macklin et al., 2006; Starkel et al., 2006; Thorndycraft and Benito, 2006; Hoffmann et al., 2008). Relatively high rates of fluvial activity during the tenth–fifteenth centuries A.D. (often termed the Medieval Warm Period) are likely to have been promoted by a catchment-wide agricultural expansion, attested in the Breamish valley upstream of New Bewick by extensive medieval ridge and furrow field systems (Passmore and Waddington, 2009), coupled with changes in flood frequency and magnitude associated with climate change (e.g., Rumsby and Macklin, 1996; Ogilvie and Farmer, 1997).

In addition to potentially harboring archaeological material typically associated with wetland environments, paleochannels (this study) and infilled kettle-hole deposits (Jones et al., 2000) have been shown to yield paleoecological data for valley floor localities that are highly complementary to the archaeological record. By comparison with published pollen diagrams recovered from regional upland peat bogs and mires (Davies and Turner, 1979; Tipping, 1996; Young, 2004), the paleoecological sequences available from upland paleochannel fills tend to span shorter time spans (here less than ~1400 yr) and are subject to particular taphonomic challenges presented by the depositional environment (e.g., Brown, 1997). They are nevertheless receiving increasing attention from geoarchaeologists (e.g., Moores et al., 1999; Fyfe et al., 2003; Knight and Howard, 2004), not least because they offer insights into environmental settings and land-use activities in the immediate vicinity of settlement foci on and near valley floors. Dated channel fills at New Bewick, for example, are currently confined to the period during and after the fourth century A.D., but their paleoecological records indicate that local communities had been actively engaged in episodic woodland clearance and arable cultivation since at least the early part of the first millennium A.D., and well before the medieval and later expansion of cereal production that is reflected in the extensive areas of extant ridge and furrow. This record of early historic land-use and subsistence activity is derived from sediment sequences that are located less than 500 m to the east of a probable Anglo-Saxon settlement site on the adjacent ice-contact meltwater and outwash terraces (Fig. 5).

In combination, geoarchaeological and archaeological surveys and analysis conducted in the Breamish-Till valley can therefore be shown to have greatly enhanced our understanding of landscape and settlement in this part of northern England. Thick sequences of sand and gravel deposited by downwasting ice sheets and meltwater during late Devensian deglaciation of the region are particularly well developed in the study area's valley floors, and these presently form upstanding hummocky and terraced landscapes that are intensively farmed and quarried for their high-quality aggregate. Glaciofluvial landscapes at New Bewick, in common with formerly glaciated valleys elsewhere in the Britain (e.g., Topping, 1992; Harding, 2000; Howard, 2005; Roberts, 2005) and Europe (e.g., Roberts, 1998; Boric, 2002; Davison et al., 2006), have long been recognized as being rich in archaeological remains, given their attractions for postglacial settlement. Work undertaken by the Till-Tweed project has shown,

however, that the valley floor of the Breamish-Till preserves a much greater range of archaeological and paleoenvironmental resources than have been hitherto appreciated and has established that the New Bewick reach, located only 6 km up-valley from the major prehistoric and early historic settlements of the Milfield Basin, functioned as an important local focus for settlement and associated subsistence activity throughout prehistoric and early historic times.

CONCLUSIONS

In common with much of the recent ALSF-sponsored geoarchaeological research in the sand and gravel landscapes of British valley floors (Brown, 2009), multidisciplinary approaches to the investigation of landform history, sediment sequences, and archaeological associations in the Till-Tweed study have established a baseline audit of the heritage resource that is driving the development of both management and research frameworks in these northern British river valley settings. The New Bewick case study demonstrates the linkages between particular landform types and the full range of documented archaeological records, including upstanding monuments, crop marks, and lithic scatters, as well as potential remains that have yet to be discovered. It also underlines the importance of assessing paleoenvironmental resources as a means of enhancing our understanding of past land-use activities. From a curatorial perspective, therefore, the project has enabled the development of archaeological evaluation and management guidelines that are tailored to specific environmental contexts throughout the Till-Tweed study area, and that explicitly recognize contrasting scenarios for the preservation and evaluation of archaeological and paleoenvironmental resources (Waddington and Passmore, 2005; Passmore et al., 2006; Passmore and Waddington, 2009).

Furthermore, the multidisciplinary methodology permits a more sophisticated and systematic analysis of links among the modern landscape, the environmental record, and the archaeological data set, and thereby yields new perspectives on landscape development, land use, and settlement. Work in the Breamish-Till valley underlines the attraction of valley floor sand and gravel landscapes associated with late Devensian deglaciation as areas of persistent, multiperiod occupation; it also suggests that at local scales, discrete landscape features (such as kettle-hole depressions) may have been incorporated in specific land-use activities. The earlier work of the Milfield Basin project (Passmore et al., 2002) has already been recognized in the recently completed North East Regional Research Agenda for the historic environment (Petts and Gerrard, 2006); it is anticipated that by promoting the integration of landscape development proposals with the objectives of regional research frameworks, the Till-Tweed project will help direct planners to the key questions concerning our understanding of the past. In the future, this should mean that there is a clear purpose behind archaeological and paleoenvironmental work that moves beyond the simple recording of remains for posterity.

ACKNOWLEDGMENTS

We would like to thank Jonathon Last for his support throughout the project, the many specialists who contributed their expertise, including Alex Bayliss, Tim Gates, and Lynda Yorke, and the many landowners and farmers who granted access to their land. This work was sponsored by English Heritage (Aggregates Levy Sustainability Fund) Project 3325.

REFERENCES CITED

Allen, T., Hey, G., and Miles, D., 1997, A line of time: Approaches to archaeology in the Upper and Middle Thames Valley, England: World Archaeology, v. 29, no. 1, p. 114–129, doi:10.1080/00438243.1997.9980366.

Birks, H.H., 1980, Plant macrofossils in Quaternary lake sediments: Archiv für Hydrobiologie, v. 15, p. 3–59.

Borek, M.J.E., 1975, Pollen Analysis and Vegetational History of the Akeld Basin [M.Sc. thesis]: Durham, University of Durham, 94 p.

Boric, D., 2002, The Lepenski Vir conundrum: Reinterpretation of the Mesolithic and Neolithic sequences in the Danube gorges: Antiquity, v. 76, p. 1026–1039.

Bronk Ramsey, C., 1995, Radiocarbon Calibration and Analysis of Stratigraphy: The OxCal Program: Radiocarbon, v. 37, p. 425–430.

Bronk Ramsey, C., 1998, Probability and dating: Radiocarbon, v. 40, p. 461–474.

Bronk Ramsey, C., 2001, Development of the radiocarbon calibration program: Radiocarbon, v. 43, p. 355–363.

Brown, A.G., 1997, Alluvial Geoarchaeology: Floodplain Archaeology and Environmental Change: Cambridge, UK, Cambridge University Press, 377 p.

Brown, A.G., 2008, Geoarchaeology, the four dimensional (4D) fluvial matrix and climatic causality: Geomorphology, v. 101, p. 278–297, doi:10.1016/j.geomorph.2008.05.021.

Brown, A.G., 2009, Aggregate-Related Archaeology: Past, Present and Future: King's Lynn, English Heritage/Heritage Marketing and Publications.

Burgess, C.B., 1984, The prehistoric settlement of Northumberland: A speculative survey, *in* Miket, R., and Burgess, C., eds., Between and Beyond the Walls: Essays on the Prehistory and History of North Britain in Honour of George Jobey: Edinburgh, John Donald, p. 126–175.

Challis, K., 2006, Airborne laser altimetry in alluviated landscapes: Archaeological Prospection, v. 13, no. 103–127.

Charlton, J., 1935, Report on a trial excavation at Old Bewick: Proceedings of the Society of Antiquaries of Newcastle, v. 6 (4th series), p. 252–256.

Chiverrell, R.C., 2006, Past and future perspectives upon landscape instability in Cumbria, northwest England: Regional Environmental Change, v. 6, p. 101–114, doi:10.1007/s10113-005-0005-6.

Clapperton, C.M., 1970, The evidence for a Cheviot ice cap: Transactions of the Institute of British Geographers, v. 29, p. 31–45.

Clapperton, C.M., 1971a, The location and origin of glacial meltwater phenomena in the eastern Cheviot Hills: Proceedings of the Yorkshire Geological Society, v. 38, no. 3, p. 361–380, doi:10.1144/pygs.38.3.361.

Clapperton, C.M., 1971b, The pattern of deglaciation in part of north Northumberland: Transactions of the Institute of British Geographers, v. 53, p. 67–78, doi:10.2307/621659.

Davies, G., and Turner, J., 1979, Pollen diagrams from Northumberland: The New Phytologist, v. 82, p. 783–804, doi:10.1111/j.1469-8137.1979.tb01673.x.

Davison, K., Dolukhanov, P., Sarson, G.R., and Shukurov, A., 2006, The role of waterways in the spread of the Neolithic: Journal of Archaeological Science, v. 33, p. 641–652, doi:10.1016/j.jas.2005.09.017.

Dickson, C.A., 1970, The study of plant macrofossils in British Quaternary deposits, *in* Walker, D., and West, R.G., eds., Studies in the Vegetational History of the British Isles: Cambridge, UK, Cambridge University Press, p. 233–255.

Douglas, T., 1991, Glacial deposits of Northumbria, *in* Ehlers, J., Gibbard, P.L., and Rose, J., eds., Glacial Deposits in Great Britain and Ireland: Rotterdam, the Netherlands, Balkema, p. 169–174.

Evans, J.G., 1992, River valley bottoms and archaeology in the Holocene, *in* Coles, B., ed., The Wetland Revolution in Prehistory: Exeter, The Prehistoric Society & WARP, p. 47–53.

French, C.A.I., 2002, Geoarchaeology in Action: Studies in Soil Micromorphology and Landscape Evolution: London, Routledge, 291 p.

French, C.A.I., and Wait, G.A., 1988, An Archaeological Survey of the Cambridgeshire River Gravels: Cambridge, Cambridgeshire County Council and Fenland Archaeological Trust, 127 p.

French, C.A.I., Macklin, M.G., and Passmore, D.G., 1992, Archaeology and palaeochannels in the Lower Welland and Nene valleys: Alluvial archaeology at the fen-edge, eastern England, *in* Needham, S., and Macklin, M.G., eds., Alluvial Archaeology in Britain: Oxford, UK, Oxbow Monograph 27, p. 169–176.

Fyfe, R.M., Brown, A.G., and Coles, B.J., 2003, Mesolithic to Bronze Age vegetation change and human activity in the Exe Valley, Devon, UK: Proceedings of the Prehistoric Society, v. 69, p. 161–181.

Gardner, G.D., and Donahue, J., 1985, The Little Platte drainage, Missouri: A model for locating temporal surfaces in a fluvial environment, *in* Stein, J.K., and Farrand, W.R., eds., Archaeological Sediments in Context: Orono, Maine, Center for the Study of Early Man, University of Maine, p. 69–89.

Gates, T., and O'Brien, C., 1988, Cropmarks at Milfield and New Bewick and the recognition of Grubenhäuser in Northumberland: Archaeologia Aeliana, v. 16 (5th series), p. 1–9.

Harding, A.F., 1981, Excavations in the prehistoric ritual complex near Milfield, Northumberland: Proceedings of the Prehistoric Society, v. 46, p. 87–135.

Harding, A.F., 2000, Henge monuments and landscape features in northern England: Monumentality and nature, *in* Ritchie, A., ed., Neolithic Orkney in Its European Context: Cambridge, UK, McDonald Institute for Archaeological Research, p. 267–274.

Harrison, S., 2002, Lithological variability of Quaternary slope deposits in the Cheviot Hills, UK: Proceedings of the Geologists' Association, v. 113, p. 121–138.

Hayes, P.P., and Lane, T.W., 1992, The Fenland Project No. 5: Lincolnshire Survey, the South-West Fens: Heritage Trust of Lincolnshire, East Anglian Archaeology Report 55, 265 p.

Hoffmann, T., Lang, A., and Dikau, R., 2008, Holocene river activity: Analysing ^{14}C-dated fluvial and colluvial sediments from Germany: Quaternary Science Reviews, v. 27, p. 2031–2040, doi:10.1016/j.quascirev.2008.06.014.

Hope-Taylor, B., 1977, Yeavering. An Anglo-British Centre of Early Northumbria: London, Her Majesty's Stationery Office, 412 p.

Howard, A.J., 2005, The contribution of geoarchaeology to understanding the environmental history and archaeological resources of the Trent Valley, U.K.: Geoarchaeology, v. 20, no. 2, p. 93–107, doi:10.1002/gea.20038.

Howard, A.J., and Macklin, M.G., 1999, A generic geomorphological approach to archaeological interpretation and prospection in British river valleys: A guide for archaeologists investigating Holocene landscapes: Antiquity, v. 73, p. 527–541.

Howard, A.J., Macklin, M.G., and Passmore, D.G., eds., 2003, Alluvial Archaeology in Europe: Rotterdam, the Netherlands, Swets, 313 p.

Howard, A.J., Brown, A.G., Carey, C.J., Challis, K., Cooper, L.P., Kincey, M., and Toms, P., 2008, Archaeological resource modelling in temperate river valleys: A case study from the Trent Valley, UK: Antiquity, v. 82, p. 1040–1054.

Jobey, G., 1965, Hill forts and settlements in Northumberland: Archaeologia Aeliana, v. 43 (4th series), p. 21–64.

Jones, R.L., Keen, D.H., and Robinson, J.E., 2000, Devensian Late Glacial and early Holocene floral and faunal records from NE Northumberland: Proceedings of the Yorkshire Geological Society, v. 53, p. 97–110.

Kenward, H.K., Hall, A.R., and Jones, A.K.G., 1980, A tested set of techniques for the extraction of plant and animal macrofossils from waterlogged archaeological deposits: Scientific Archaeology, v. 22, p. 3–15.

Kenward, H.K., Engleman, C., Robertson, A., and Large, F., 1986, Rapid scanning of urban archaeological deposits for insect remains: Circaea, v. 3, p. 163–172.

Knight, D., and Howard, A.J., 2004, Trent Valley Landscapes. The Archaeology of 500,000 Years of Change: King's Lynn, Heritage Marketing and Publications Ltd, 202 p.

Lane, T.W., 1993, The Fenland Project No. 8: Lincolnshire Survey, the Northern Fen Edge: Heritage Trust of Lincolnshire, East Anglian Archaeology Report 66, 130 p.

Lewin, J., and Macklin, M.G., 2003, Preservation potential for late Quaternary alluvium: Journal of Quaternary Science, v. 18, no. 2, p. 107–120, doi:10.1002/jqs.738.

Lunn, A.G., 2004, Northumberland: London, Harper Collins, 304 p.

Macklin, M.G., Howard, A.J., and Passmore, D.G., 2003, The condition of Holocene alluvial archaeology in the UK: Progress, constraints and opportunities, *in* Howard, A.J., Macklin, M.G., and Passmore, D.G., eds., Alluvial Archaeology in Europe: Rotterdam, the Netherlands, Swets, p. 3–14.

Macklin, M.G., Johnstone, E., and Lewin, J., 2005, Pervasive and long-term forcing of Holocene river instability and flooding in Great Britain by centennial-scale climate change: The Holocene, v. 15, no. 7, p. 937–943, doi:10.1191/0959683605hl867ft.

Macklin, M.G., Benito, G., Gregory, K.J., Johnstone, E., Lewin, J., Soja, R., Starkel, L., and Thorndycraft, V.R., 2006, Past hydrological events reflected in the Holocene fluvial record of Europe: Catena, v. 66, p. 145–154, doi:10.1016/j.catena.2005.07.015.

Moore, P.D., Webb, J.A., and Collinson, M.E., 1989, Pollen Analysis: Oxford, Blackwell, 216 p.

Moores, A., Passmore, D.G., and Stevenson, A.C., 1999, High-resolution palaeochannel records of Holocene valley floor environments in the North Tyne basin, northern England, *in* Brown, A.G., and Quine, T.A., eds., Fluvial Processes and Environmental Change: Chichester, Wiley, p. 283–310.

Needham, S., and Macklin, M.G., 1992, Alluvial Archaeology in Britain: Oxford, Oxbow Monograph 27, 277 p.

Ogilvie, A., and Farmer, G., 1997, Documenting the medieval climate, *in* Hulme, M., and Barrow, E., eds., Climates of the British Isles: London, Routledge, p. 112–133.

Olivier, A., 1996, Frameworks for Our Past: A Review of Research Frameworks, Strategies and Perceptions: London, English Heritage, 60 p.

Passmore, D.G., and Macklin, M.G., 2000, Late Holocene channel and floodplain development in a wandering gravel-bed river: The River South Tyne at Lambley, northern England: Earth Surface Processes and Landforms, v. 25, p. 1237–1256, doi:10.1002/1096-9837(200010)25:11<1237::AID-ESP134>3.0.CO;2-S.

Passmore, D.G., and Waddington, C., 2009, Managing Archaeological Landscapes: A Geoarchaeological Approach: Oxford, Oxbow Books, 400 p.

Passmore, D.G., Waddington, C., and Houghton, S., 2002, Geoarchaeology of the Milfield Basin, northern England; towards an integrated archaeological research and management framework: Journal of Archaeological Prospection, v. 9, p. 71–91, doi:10.1002/arp.184.

Passmore, D.G., Waddington, C., and van der Schriek, T., 2006, Enhancing the evaluation and management of river valley archaeology: Geoarchaeology in the Till-Tweed catchment: Northern England: Archaeological Prospection, v. 13, p. 269–281, doi:10.1002/arp.293.

Payton, R.W., 1980, Soils of the Milfield Plain, Northumberland: Proceedings of the North of England Soils Discussion Group, v. 16, p. 1–52.

Payton, R.W., 1988, The Characteristics and Genesis of Fragipans in British Soils [Ph.D. thesis]: Newcastle upon Tyne, Department of Soil Science, University of Newcastle upon Tyne, 298 p.

Payton, R.W., 1992, Fragipan formation in argillic brown earths (fragiadalfs) of the Milfield Plain, north-east England: Journal of Soil Science, v. 43, p. 621–644, doi:10.1111/j.1365-2389.1992.tb00164.x.

Petts, D., and Gerrard, C., 2006, Shared Visions: The North-East Regional Research Framework for the Historic Environment: Durham, Durham County Council, 120 p.

Pryor, F.M.M., French, C.A.I., Crowther, D., Gurney, D., Simpson, G., and Taylor, M., 1985, Archaeology and Environment in the Lower Welland Valley, Volume 1A: Cambridgeshire Archaeological Committee, East Anglian Archaeology Report 27, 243 p.

Roberts, I., ed., 2005, Ferrybridge Henge. The Ritual Landscape: Yorkshire Archaeology Volume 10: Leeds, West Yorkshire Archaeology Service, 278 p.

Roberts, N., 1998, The Holocene: An Environmental History (2nd ed.): Oxford, Blackwell, 316 p.

Rodwell, J.S., 1992, British Plant Communities: Volume 3. Grasslands and Montane Communities: Cambridge, UK, Cambridge University Press, 552 p.

Rodwell, J.S., 1995, British Plant Communities: Volume 4. Aquatic Communities, Swamps and Tall-Herb Fens: Cambridge, UK, Cambridge University Press, 296 p.

Rumsby, B.T., and Macklin, M.G., 1996, River response to the last neoglacial (the 'Little Ice Age') in northern, western and central Europe, *in* Branson, J., Brown, A.G., and Gregory, K.J., eds., Global Continental Changes: The Context of Palaeohydrology: Geological Society of London Special Publication 115, p. 217–233.

Stace, C., 1997, New Flora of the British Isles: Cambridge, UK, Cambridge University Press, 1130 p.

Stafford, C.R., 1995, Geoarchaeological perspectives on palaeolandscapes and regional subsurface archaeology: Journal of Archaeological Method and Theory, v. 2, no. 1, p. 69–104, doi:10.1007/BF02228435.

Starkel, L., Soja, R., and Michczyñska, D.J., 2006, Past hydrological events reflected in the Holocene history of Polish rivers: Catena, v. 66, p. 24–33, doi:10.1016/j.catena.2005.07.008.

Stuiver, M., and Reimer, P.J., 1986, A computer program for radiocarbon age calculation: Radiocarbon, v. 28, p. 1022–1030.

Stuiver, M., Reimer, P.J., Bard, E., Beck, J.W., Burr, G.S., Hughen, K.A., Kromer, B., McCormac, G., van der Plicht, J., and Spurk, M., 1998, INTCAL98 radiocarbon age calibration, 24,000–0 cal BP: Radiocarbon, v. 40, p. 1041–1083.

Thorndycraft, V.R., and Benito, G., 2006, Late Holocene fluvial chronology of Spain: The role of climatic variability and human impact: Catena, v. 66, p. 34–41, doi:10.1016/j.catena.2005.07.007.

Tipping, R., 1992, The determination of cause in the generation of major prehistoric valley fills in the Cheviot Hills, Anglo-Scottish border, *in* Needham, S., and Macklin, M.G., eds., Alluvial Archaeology in Britain: Oxford, Oxbow Monograph 27, p. 111–121.

Tipping, R., 1994, Akeld Steads and the evolution of the Milfield Plain, *in* Harrison, S., and Tipping, R.M., eds., The Geomorphology and Late Quaternary Evolution of the Cheviot Hills: London, British Geomorphological Research Group, p. 80–87.

Tipping, R., 1996, The Neolithic Landscapes of the Cheviot Hills and Hinterland: Palaeoenvironmental Evidence: Northern Archaeology, 13/14, Special edition: Neolithic Studies in No-Man's Land: Papers on the Neolithic of Northern England from the Trent to the Tweed: Newcastle upon Tyne, Northumberland Archaeological Group, p. 17–33.

Tipping, R., 1998, The chronology of late Quaternary fluvial activity in part of the Milfield Basin, north east England: Earth Surface Processes and Landforms, v. 23, no. 9, p. 845–856, doi:10.1002/(SICI)1096-9837(199809)23:9<845::AID-ESP902>3.0.CO;2-9.

Tolan-Smith, C., 1997, The Stone Age landscape: The contribution of fieldwalking, *in* Tolan-Smith, C., ed., Landscape Archaeology in Tynedale: Newcastle upon Tyne, University of Newcastle upon Tyne, p. 79–89.

Topping, P., 1992, The Penrith henges: A survey by the Royal Commission on the Historical Monuments of England: Proceedings of the Prehistoric Society, v. 58, p. 249–264.

Waddington, C., 1999, A Landscape Archaeological Study of the Mesolithic-Neolithic in the Milfield Basin, Northumberland: Oxford, British Archaeological Reports, British Series 291, 237 p.

Waddington, C., and Passmore, D.G., 2005, Planning for the Future. Historic Environment Guidance for the Till-Tweed Valleys, Northumberland, UK: London, English Heritage, 22 p.

Waters, M.R., 1992, Principles of Geoarchaeology: A North American Perspective: Tucson, University of Arizona Press, 398 p.

Waters, M.R., 2000, Alluvial stratigraphy and geoarchaeology in the American Southwest: Geoarchaeology, v. 15, no. 6, p. 537–557, doi:10.1002/1520-6548(200008)15:6<537::AID-GEA5>3.0.CO;2-E.

Watts, W.A., 1978, Plant macrofossils and Quaternary palaeoecology, *in* Walker, D., and Guppy, J.C., eds., Biology and Quaternary Environments: Canberra, Australian Academy of Science, p. 53–67.

Young, R., 2004, Peat, pollen and people; palaeoenvironmental reconstruction in Northumberland National Park, *in* Frodsham, P., ed., Archaeology in Northumberland National Park: Council for British Archaeology (CBA) Research Report 136, p. 156–170.

Manuscript Accepted by the Society 3 August 2010

The Geological Society of America
Special Paper 476
2011

Holocene channel changes and geoarchaeology of the Exe River, Devon, UK, and the floodplain paradox

Jenny A. Bennett
School of Geography, University of Exeter, Exeter, EX4 1RJ, UK

Antony G. Brown
Palaeoecology Laboratory, University of Southampton (PLUS), and School of Geography, University of Southampton, Highfields Campus, Southampton, SO17 1BJ, UK

Jean-Luc Schwenninger
Research Laboratory for Archaeology and the History of Art, University of Oxford, Dyson Perrins Building, South Parks Road, Oxford, OX1 3QY, UK

Edward J. Rhodes
Department of Environmental and Geographical Sciences, Manchester Metropolitan University, Chester Street, Manchester, M1 5GD, UK

ABSTRACT

Underlying all archaeological investigations in riverine environments, there needs to be as full an understanding as possible of the history of the fluvial system in question because fluvial history influences taphonomy and archaeology. Detailed investigation of five sites on the Holocene floodplain of the Exe River, southwest England, has extended our knowledge of channel change and fluvial sedimentation in this area. New dating from optically stimulated luminescence (OSL) has been combined with previous radiocarbon dates from the Upper and Lower Exe, and the resulting chronology is in approximate agreement with the phases of fluvial change described from southern Britain that appear to relate to Holocene climate shifts. Over the mid–late Holocene, avulsion and reoccupation of former channels have occurred, while in historic time, channel systems have been relatively stable, with some oscillation around channel bars or islands. The recognition of this change in channel behavior in the very late Holocene at a classic site has solved what had been a "floodplain paradox"—a contradiction between the rates of historical channel lateral migration and archaeology found on, and in, UK floodplains. The reoccupation of former channels allows lateral deposits to be stacked and is part of floodplain aggradation by overbank and bed sedimentation. This has significant implications for the preservation of archaeological material, including artifacts. Mesolithic artifacts have been found on the valley floors within the Exe catchment; their preservation has, to a large extent, been controlled by the style of Late Glacial and Holocene floodplain development.

Bennett, J.A., Brown, A.G., Schwenninger, J.-L., and Rhodes, E.J., 2011, Holocene channel changes and geoarchaeology of the Exe River, Devon, UK, and the floodplain paradox, *in* Brown, A.G., Basell, L.S., and Butzer, K.W., eds., Geoarchaeology, Climate Change, and Sustainability: Geological Society of America Special Paper 476, p. 135–152, doi:10.1130/2011.2476(11). For permission to copy, contact editing@geosociety.org. © 2011 The Geological Society of America. All rights reserved.

INTRODUCTION, AIMS, AND BACKGROUND

Fluvial contexts are disproportionately important in archaeology due to the preservation potential of fluvial deposits and the universal attractiveness of floodplains for human activities. However, it has not always been possible to reconcile the archaeological record of Holocene river valleys with their geomorphological styles and rates of change. In some cases, this has caused an apparent contradiction with the geomorphological record because the geomorphology indicates that the entire floodplain is only a few centuries old, but archaeological remains located on the floodplain are of much greater antiquity, i.e., the "floodplain paradox" of the title. The aim of the study described here was to reconcile the archaeological data and geomorphological evolution of a floodplain in the light of changing climate and land use. Recent technological advances, including the common use of direct-sediment dating methods, have greatly advanced the potential contribution of fluvial geomorphology to archaeological studies of human-environment interactions (Brown, 2008). Stone tools are commonly found in fluvial sands and gravels and account for a large proportion of the Paleolithic material that is known in Britain (Wymer, 1999). Although the record of Paleolithic materials is strongly biased by aggregate extraction, a recent study in southwest England (Palaeolithic Rivers of South-West Britain project, PRoSWEB) has erected the first chronology for terrace-derived lithics in this area (see Hosfield et al., 2006; Brown et al., 2007; Toms et al., 2008; Brown et al., 2010). Although this study is confined to late Pleistocene and Holocene fluvial deposits, they are still geoarchaeologically important for two reasons. First, much of the UK late Upper Paleolithic and Mesolithic record is found within fluvial deposits and on alluvial surfaces, and second, many of the taphonomically important processes (such as terrace formation) that can be observed more easily in the Pleistocene also operated during the earlier Holocene. During this period, there was also a bias toward rivers and floodplains by hunter-gatherer-forager-fishers due to their requirements for water, the utilization of aquatic plants and fish, and ease of hunting (e.g., ambush hunting), as well as easier access through forested landscapes.

The Exe River in Devon is a lowland river draining the uplands of Exmoor, the Blackdown Hills, and parts of Dartmoor (Fig. 1). It has a catchment of 1532 km^2 and flows over predominantly impervious bedrock, which, along with high precipitation in the headwaters, can result in high flood discharge and a flashy response to heavy rainfall (Walling and Moorhead, 1987). The river valley consists of a series of bedrock-related basins and constrictions, with the most extensive channel change seen in the basins, although channel-restricted channel change has also occurred in the constricted reaches. The whole catchment was beyond the limits of maximum glaciation in southern Britain, and a "staircase" of terrace deposits has been preserved, with eight terrace levels recognized and mapped by the British Geological Survey (BGS) (Edwards and Scrivener, 1999). The upper five terraces are separated altitudinally from each other, while the

three lower terraces (BGS terraces 1–3) are inset 1–3 m above the modern floodplain in the middle reaches but plunge below the modern floodplain in the estuarine zone. Downstream, these terraces grade to a series of submerged buried valleys (Durrance, 1969, 1980; Cullingford, 1982).

Despite an historical absence of large-scale and commercial aggregate extraction (due to there being hard-rock sources in the region), Paleolithic lithic material has been recovered from the terraces in the Exeter area (Pickard, 1933) through development and chance finds. At present, there are no known late Upper Paleolithic sites within gravels, the nearest being from fluvial gravels at Doniford in Somerset, but there is a strong representation of the Mesolithic. This includes Mesolithic microliths within gravels found at Exebridge (Fyfe, 2000) and on low terraces in the Culm Valley (N. Whitehouse, 2004, personal commun.), a tributary of the Exe that drains the Blackdown Hills, which host many scatters of later Mesolithic material (Berridge, 1985; Roberts, 2000). The probability of the Exe Valley having been a long-distance route as early as the Mesolithic is supported by the presence of a 1.6 ha site at Hawkcombe Head on Exmoor where many flint microliths of late Mesolithic type have been discovered in recent excavations (Riley and Wilson-North, 2001). This site is located on the interfluve of the Exe catchment with the Bristol Channel and has been interpreted as a summer hunting camp. In addition, several Mesolithic flakes from the Tiverton area are held in the Tiverton Museum and the Royal Albert Memorial Museum, Exeter, and many Mesolithic flint finds have been recorded from the Netherexe Basin in the Lower Exe valley (Silvester et al., 1987).

There are also over 20 Neolithic or early Bronze Age barrows and a large cursus in the Lower Exe valley recorded in the East Devon List of Scheduled Ancient Monuments. A Bronze Age barrow cemetery is known from Upton Pyne (Fox, 1969), and at least one barrow is known from the valley floor terrace in the Netherexe Basin at Brampford Speke (Devon County Council Sites and Monuments Record site 29676). Other human activities affecting the river valley and sedimentation are mining and forest clearance. There has been active mining on Exmoor for copper, lead, and iron since the Iron Age, and there is recently published evidence of Roman mining at Anstey's Combe (Brown et al., 2009), and probably at Roman Lode on Exmoor, as well as widespread evidence of eighteenth-century workings (Atkinson, 1997). Studies of vegetation change in the Upper Exe by Fyfe et al. (2003a, 2003b) have documented changes in both climate and human activity over the Late Glacial to Holocene period.

One of the few studies of fluvial change in the basin was undertaken by Hooke (1977) in the Brampford Speke area. Tithe maps and nineteenth-century Ordnance Survey maps were used to trace riverbank changes and erosion over the last 200 yr. Additional evidence for historic channel change is shown by the changes in bridge sites and in areas where the parish boundaries follow paleochannels rather than the present-day main channel. Hooke's study led to this location being one of the first Sites of Special Scientific Importance (SSSIs) scheduled on geomorphological grounds (Gregory, 1997).

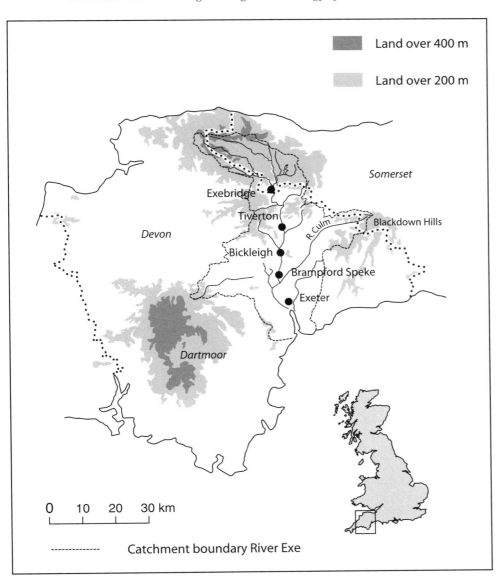

Figure 1. The Exe catchment, southwest England, and the locations of the sites described in this chapter.

METHODS AND SITES

Our study involved detailed geomorphological mapping from field survey and aerial photographs, the logging of sections and exposures, borehole information where available, and sediment dating in order to compare geomorphological evolution with the local archaeological record. Dating of river terrace material has been mainly done with optically stimulated luminescence (OSL) because the bulk of the fluvial deposits in the valley do not contain organic material. However, some radiocarbon dates have been obtained from organic channel fills on terrace surfaces at Exebridge (Fyfe, 2000) and in the Exeter area by the Exeter Archaeology Unit, and these were also incorporated into this study. Five study reaches were selected where exposures or mapping suggested the availability of dateable material (organics or suitable fine-grained clastic sediments) and where sampled

would be representative of the entire valley. The reaches are, from north to south: Exebridge, Tiverton, Bickleigh, Brampford Speke, and the Exeter City Basin (Fig. 1). The geomorphological mapping of the terrace deposits and paleochannels was undertaken at a scale of 1:2500, and valley cross sections were augered and surveyed using differential global positioning system (GPS) or a Total Station. Aerial photographs were used initially to plot the paleochannels, which were later confirmed and added to by surveying on the ground. British Geological Survey maps (BGS) (1:50,000 scale) of the Exeter area (Sheet 325), Tiverton (Sheet 310), and Dulverton (Sheet 294) were used as bedrock base maps, and in the Exeter area, detailed BGS mapping of the terrace deposits was also used. For the other sites, the less-detailed BGS mapping of terrace material was supplemented by further fieldwork. The relative heights and field relationships of these features were then used to establish a relative chronology of events on the valley floor at each site or reach. In several sites, cross sections through paleochannels are exposed in the present river banks and serve as indicators of the routes of abandoned channels. Because very little organic material has been preserved within the terrace deposits or the surface channel fill, the silts were sampled for dating purposes using OSL.

OSL dating provides an estimate of the time elapsed since luminescent minerals, such as quartz or feldspar, were last exposed to sunlight (Aitken, 1998; Duller, 2008; Huntley et al., 1985). Light-shielded grains may accumulate charge from the effects of the environmental radiation flux to which they are exposed, and the dose received by the sample can be measured using the luminescence signal. A burial age estimate is obtained by dividing the paleodose by the environmental dose rate. OSL dating of sedimentary quartz has become a well-established technique (Duller, 2004; Lian and Roberts, 2006), and recent applications demonstrate the potential of optical dating for securing chronological frameworks in fluvial depositional environments (Arnold et al., 2007; Briant et al., 2006, 2009; Colls et al., 2001; Folz et al., 2001; Fuchs et al., 2005; Rodnight et al., 2006; Rowland et al., 2005).

Luminescence Methodology

Luminescence dating was based on quartz grains extracted from samples collected in 2003 and 2004 from test pits and natural sections. Sample preparation took place under low-intensity safe-lighting provided by filtered sodium lamps (emitting at 588 nm). Laboratory procedures were designed to yield clean, sand-sized (180–250 μm) grains of quartz for optical dating according to standard preparation methods, including wet sieving, HCl acid digestion, heavy liquid flotation (sodium polytungstate), and etching in 68% HF acid to dissolve feldspars and to clean and remove the outer alpha-dosed layer of quartz grains. The latter residual grains were resieved to the original grain size range and mounted as multigrain monolayers of ~3 mm diameter (e.g., less than 200 grains) onto new 10 mm aluminum discs using a silicone oil adhesive. OSL measurements were conducted using automated Risø instruments (Bøtter-Jensen, 1988, 1997; Bøtter-Jensen et al., 2000) and were based on conventional single-aliquot regeneration (SAR) measurement protocols (Murray and Wintle, 2000; Wintle and Murray, 2006). Paleodose estimates were obtained using up to 12 repeat measurements for each sample. Optical stimulation for single aliquots was provided by clusters of blue-light-emitting diodes (42 Nichia 470Δ20 nm), providing a sample stimulation power of ~32–36 mW cm^{-2}. Natural and regenerative doses were preheated at 240 °C for 10 s, and the fixed test doses (which are used to correct for any sensitivity changes) were preheated at a reduced temperature of 220 °C for 10 s before optical stimulation. The absence of infrared-sensitive minerals (e.g., feldspars) was checked and confirmed using an infrared bleach provided by a solid-state laser diode (830Δ10 nm; 1 W cm^{-2}) at 50 °C for 100 s before blue-light stimulation. The ultraviolet OSL emission at ~370 nm was detected using an Elec-

tron Tubes Ltd. 9235Q, a photomultiplier tube fitted with a blue-green–sensitive bi-alkali photocathode, and Hoya U-340 glass filters. Laboratory doses used for constructing dose response curves were calculated using a calibrated ^{90}Sr/^{90}Y beta source housed within the reader.

The environmental gamma and beta components of the dose rate result from the decay of K and the radioactive decay series of natural U and Th within the sediment. A portable gamma-ray spectrometer (Ortec Micronomad multichannel analyzer equipped with a NaI [Tl] scintillator crystal) was employed in a 4π-geometry and calibrated against the Oxford calibration blocks (Rhodes and Schwenninger, 2007). These on-site measurements provided direct estimation of the in situ environmental gamma radiation field (~30 cm radius sphere of the sampling location). Except for samples X1550, X1555, and X1556, the beta dose rate was derived from the measured concentrations of parent isotopes by either neutron activation analysis or inductively coupled plasma–mass spectroscopy (ICP-MS) using a lithium metaborate/tetraborate fusion. For the former three samples, the dose rate was based solely on the gamma-ray spectrometer measurements. Concentrations of radioisotopes were converted to dose rates according to attenuation factors proposed by Adamiec and Aitken (1998), using corrections for grain size (Mejdahl, 1979) and water content (Zimmerman, 1971).

The cosmic-ray dose was calculated according to Prescott and Hutton (1994), taking into account the thickness and density of the overburden, as well as the geomagnetic latitude and altitude of the sites. The past water content of the sediments may at times have deviated from the modern field values, but the present moisture contents are considered to represent the best approximation of the average water content of the samples throughout their burial history.

Paleodoses were determined from the first 2 s of OSL, using the final 10 s as background. Dose-response curves were fitted using a weighted linear fitting procedure based on the propagation of all measurement errors. A systematic laboratory reproducibility uncertainty of 2% was added (in quadrature) to each OSL measurement error to account for uncertainties in the calibration of the beta source. The results of the OSL dating are presented in Table 1. The characteristics of the observed luminescence signals were typical of quartz and consistent with requirements for application of the SAR protocol (recycling ratios close to unity and low thermal transfer), and only rare and low levels of infrared stimulated luminescence (IRSL) signal were recorded. However, samples X2172 and X2173 showed a relatively high degree of scatter between repeat measurements on different aliquots. This may be indicative of incomplete bleaching of the sediment at the time of deposition, with some grains having retained a residual signal from a previous event. Heterogeneous bleaching can be a serious problem in the dating of fluvial sediments (Murray et al., 1995; Olley et al., 1998), and in order to minimize the risk of overestimating the true burial date of the sediment, only the lowest paleodose estimates were used to calculate the OSL age estimates (Rhodes, 2007). The

TABLE 1. OPTICALLY STIMULATED LUMINESCENCE DATING RESULTS FROM EXE CATCHMENT
(SAMPLES X1550, 1555, 1556 COLLECTED AND ANALYZED BY E.J. RHODES)

Location	Field code	Lab. code	Depth (cm)	Paleodose (Gy)	Dose rate (Gy/k.y.)	Age (yr before 2009)
Brampford Speke	EXE04-01	X2172	120	0.91 ± 0.13	2.04 ± 0.10	475 ± 70
Brampford Speke	EXE04-02	X2173	120	1.67 ± 0.21	2.21 ± 0.11	765 ± 105
Brampford Speke	EXE04-03	X2174	98	1.49 ± 0.06	2.22 ± 0.11	685 ± 45
Brampford Speke	EXE04-04	X2175	160	1.47 ± 0.17	2.22 ± 0.11	695 ± 85
Tiverton	EXE04-05	X2176	69	2.99 ± 0.11	2.74 ± 0.13	1090 ± 70
Tiverton	EXE04-06	X2177	132	6.90 ± 0.20	3.03 ± 0.16	2290 ± 145
Bickleigh	EXE03-04	X1550	148	1.06 ± 0.06	1.97 ± 0.08	540 ± 40
Bickleigh	EXE03-09	X1555	145	0.78 ± 0.03	1.83 ± 0.07	430 ± 25
Exebridge	EXE03-10	X1556	68	9.21 ± 0.58	2.50 ± 0.11	3690 ± 290

results obtained for both these samples should be considered less reliable than the others and must be interpreted with caution, but the methodology used here is essentially the same as that used by Brown et al. (2009).

Radiocarbon Methodology

The radiocarbon dates were extracted from exposures either by the authors or, in some cases, collected through developer-led excavation over a number of years by Exeter Archaeology (now known as the Archaeological Field Unit [AFU] of Exeter City Council). For those dates derived from previous studies, the reader should refer to the original reference for further particulars. The calibrations quoted were calculated using INTER-CAL04 (Reimer et al., 2004) or those used in the original reports or papers quoted.

RESULTS

Exebridge

At Exebridge, on the southern edge of Exmoor, the Exe meets its major tributary, the Barle. The two rivers flow from relatively constricted valleys into a structural basin that has been formed by two faults related to the east-west–trending Brushford fault complex (British Geological Survey Sheets 294 and 310). Three terraces with distinct edges and several large paleochannels are visible on the valley floor (Fig. 2). There is a spring mire on the south side of the floodplain, which was cored and dated by Fyfe (2000) as part of a study of the vegetation history of the Exe Valley. A borehole record from the eastern valley edge (see Fig. 2) revealed 3.4 m of peaty clay over gravel, and Fyfe (2000) proved a depth of 4 m of peat overlying a paleochannel under the spring mire. The basal date of the paleochannel infill was 13,208–12,267 cal yr B.C. at 2σ (12,590 ± 120 uncalibrated yr B.P., UtC-8622), indicating that the channel was abandoned in the Late Glacial (marine oxygen isotope stage [MIS] 2). Historical landscape features present in the valley include the route of an abandoned railway line, embankment of the area around the main bridge, and a fish farm fed by a mill leat that follows the route of a paleochannel. Fishponds on the site of the Exe Valley Fishery are described as "post-mediaeval" (Somerset Historic Environment Record 33440), but the site of the mill itself is older and listed in the Domesday Book (A.D. 1086) as "Bugeford Mill" (Somerset Historic Environment Record 33432). Its income is quoted as from *Tempore Regis Edwardi* (TRE = from the time of Edward), and so this provides a minimum date of A.D. 1066 for the paleochannel. There is little possibility of the reference being due to another mill location given the geography of the valley floor (Fig. 2).

Several unabraded Mesolithic microliths were found by Fyfe (2000) within the riverbank silts overlying a sand bar of the Exe upstream of the confluence of the Exe and Barle (Fig. 2). Being microliths, and thus relatively easily moved, these stone tools are small (<2 cm) and typologically indicative only of a broadly Mesolithic age (12,000–6000 yr B.P.). OSL dating of the silts adjacent and below the flakes gave an age range of 3690 ± 290 yr B.P. (Table 1). These dates suggest that the flakes had been transported, probably by overbank flooding during the late Neolithic or Bronze Age. The unbroken, sharp unabraded condition of the lithics and their clustering suggest that they had not traveled far and probably only from the surface of an adjacent bar surface. At Exebridge, the pollen diagram from the spring mire provides a direct radiocarbon date for the afforestation of the floodplain by alder (*Alnus*) of 5730–5560 B.C. (Fyfe et al., 2003a). The diagram also has a pronounced peak in charcoal at the level 240 cm depth (zone EBp-4), suggesting that grass on and around the spring mire was being burnt, possibly by Mesolithic hunter-gatherers. The archaeology and the paleoecology reinforce the interpretation of the geomorphology that the stream has bifurcated in this reach, downstream of a constrained section, and that channel change in the Holocene occurred through a combination of channel abandonment (e.g., the channel under the Exebridge mire) and switching from a northerly to southerly channel by avulsion (bichannel switching) in a forested floodplain environment.

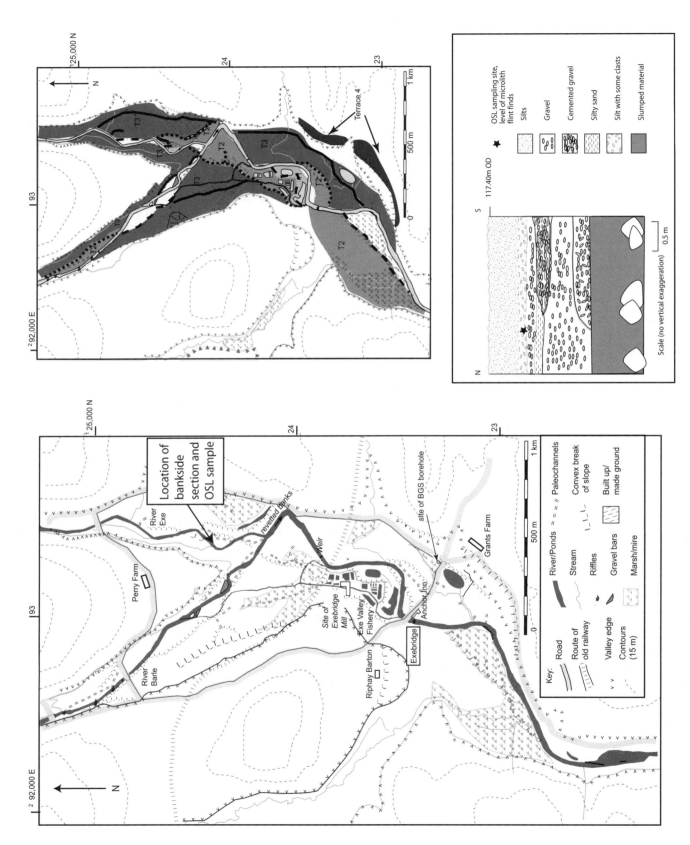

Figure 2. Geomorphological map and stratigraphic section from site of lithic finds near Exebridge. BGS—British Geological Survey; OD—ordnance datum; OSL—optically stimulated luminescence.

Washfield

At Tiverton, the floodplain widens (up to 600 m in width) close to the village of Washfield. Geomorphological mapping has revealed a dissected marginal terrace (terrace 3 sensu BGS) and floodplain paleochannels with gravels in between (Fig. 3). An OSL date of ca. 23 ka (Bennett, 2006) obtained from a sample of the matrix from the terrace 3 gravels provides some constraint on the ages of terraces. Geomorphological mapping shows channel changes, mainly in the form of channel switching. In the northern part of the Washfield reach, a wide Late Glacial paleochannel on the surface of terrace 3 follows the valley edge. Further investigation using ground-penetrating radar and augering of a cross-valley section here demonstrates braiding or anabranching on the surface of the terrace 3 gravels, which was not visible on aerial photographs due to silting up of the channels. These studies of the reach reveal a prominent paleochannel on the surface of terrace 2, along the edge of terrace 3, and another that is now used as the route of the leat from Bolham Weir. None of these channels shows any evidence of lateral migration. In the northern part of the reach, the line of the parish boundary leaves the present channel to follow an abandoned riverbank, indicating channel change that has probably occurred in historic (post-medieval) times. The weirs and bank revetting in this area are present on the first edition Ordnance Survey maps (1809) and, given their relationship to buildings, date from at least the 1700s, and possibly earlier. Evidence of channel change includes a cross section through multiple paleochannels exposed in the bank downstream of Bolham Weir, opposite another later abandoned riverbank. Some revetting and planting of poplar on a river bend has also taken place since the parish boundary was established to consolidate the present course. The stratigraphic bank-section that ends at the "head weir" of the mill leat on Figure 4 shows an oblique section of a paleochannel filled with very weakly cross-bedded sandy silts and clay. OSL samples from the paleochannel fill section give an age of 2290 ± 145 yr before 2009 (Table 1) from a channel in the lower part of the sequence and 1090 ± 70 yr from the base of the later reoccupation. An unabraded flake, of Mesolithic or possibly Neolithic/Bronze age, was found in the fill and, as at Exebridge, was probably derived from the adjacent surface of the gravel terrace.

Bickleigh

The valley floor at Bickleigh is constrained by bedrock to a width of only 250–350 m, with terrace deposits on the western side of the valley further constraining the present channel (Fig. 5). A detailed survey was undertaken here of both the surface of the floodplain and the depth to the surface of the underlying gravels (Fig. 6). The parish boundary follows the route of a major channel, suggesting that this may have been an active channel in the A.D. 1100s. This channel is cut by the modern channel, and the bank stratigraphy, which is not illustrated here but can be found in Bennett (2005), shows a wide and shallow silt-filled paleochannel fill. The two exposures of this channel section, one from each side of the present channel, were sampled for OSL dating, giving dates of 540 ± 40 yr and 430 ± 25 yr, postdating the line of the parish boundary, but predating the present channel. It appears that an avulsion occurred since the establishment of the parish boundary in the medieval period, since the route of the present Exe channel does not follow the parish boundary and so must postdate it. A further age constraint is that the main bridge in the village dates from the fourteenth century A.D. (Historic Monuments Record), indicating that since this period, the channel has not shifted at the downstream end of this reach. There is no pollen diagram from Bickleigh; however, there is one for the upper end of the Netherexe Basin at Chitterley, which provides an interpolated radiocarbon date of ca. 7200 B.C. for the afforestation of the floodplain by alder (*Alnus*) (Fyfe et al., 2003a). The interpretation is that during the Holocene, there has only been limited channel switching in three locations along the reach, in what is otherwise a bedrock- and terrace-constricted reach. The bedrock constriction and structural step (formed by a outcrop of the Crackington Formation) have provided an ideal bridging point from the aspect of a fixed and shallow channel, but at a cost, as the adjacent settlement (including two medieval mills) has always suffered from severe flooding due to the constriction of floodplain width.

Brampford Speke

Downstream of the valley constriction at Bickleigh, the less-resistant Permian bedrock (Shute and Dawlish Sandstones) forms the 1.5-km-wide valley of the Netherexe Basin. There are thick deposits of well-cemented deposits of terrace 4 on either side of the valley; those to the east form a confluence interfluve with the Culm River and indicate a much more extensive confluence zone in the Pleistocene (Brown, 2008; Howard et al., 2008). On the valley floor, terraces 1–3 are inset and show westward channel migration across the basin (uniclinal shifting sensu Bridgland, 1988). Only a few fragments of terrace 1 are present, with a terrace edge that is sinuous, and so likely to reflect a former river course. There are Neolithic–Early Bronze Age round barrows on terraces 2 and 3 that act as age constraints for terrace formation, and also suggest that either terrace 1 was emplaced later than barrow construction, or that the ground there was still low enough to flood more frequently than would have been desirable for monument construction. The positioning of an outlying or satellite barrow out in a floodplain adjacent to the river is known from several monumental complexes such as Newgrange in the Boyne Valley (O'Kelly, 1982) and Durrington Walls on the Avon River (Parker-Pearson, 2006). The presence of such barrows clearly constrains channel change to avulsion either side of the barrow and the extent to which lateral channel migration could have reworked the floodplain.

Holocene channel change was investigated at Brampford Speke, at the southern end of this basin, where there are many paleochannels and the site is listed as a geomorphological Site

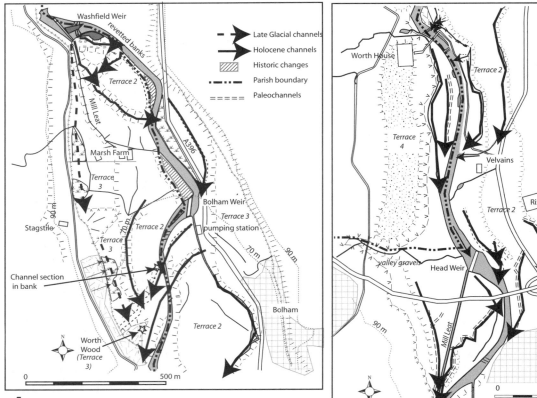

A Northern part of reach

Late Glacial channels
Holocene channels
Historic changes
Parish boundary
Paleochannels

Washfield Weir
revetted banks
Terrace 2
Mill Leat
Marsh Farm
Terrace 3
Stagstile
Terrace 2
Terrace 3
Bolham Weir
Terrace 3
pumping station
Channel section in bank
Worth Wood (Terrace 3)
Terrace 2
Bolham
N
0   500 m

B Southern part of reach

embankment: dismantled railway
Worth House
Terrace 2
Terrace 4
Velvains
Terrace 3
Terrace 2
Rix
valley gravels
Head Weir
Mill Leat
A361
90 m
N
0   500 m

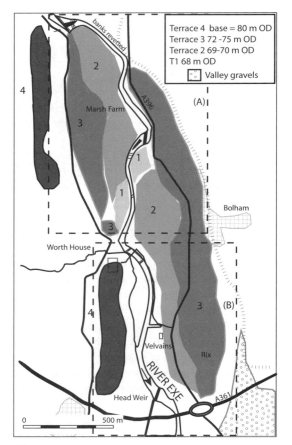

C Location of river terraces and geomorphological maps

banks revetted
Terrace 4 base = 80 m OD
Terrace 3 72 -75 m OD
Terrace 2 69-70 m OD
T1 68 m OD
Valley gravels

4
2
Marsh Farm
A396
(A)
3
1
1
2
Bolham
3
Worth House
4
Velvains
3
Rix
RIVER EXE
(B)
A361
Head Weir
0   500 m

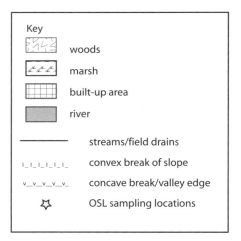

Key

woods
marsh
built-up area
river
streams/field drains
convex break of slope
concave break/valley edge
OSL sampling locations

Figure 3. Geomorphological map of the Washfield (Tiverton) reach (north and south) with inset map of terraces. OD—ordnance datum; OSL—optically stimulated luminescence.

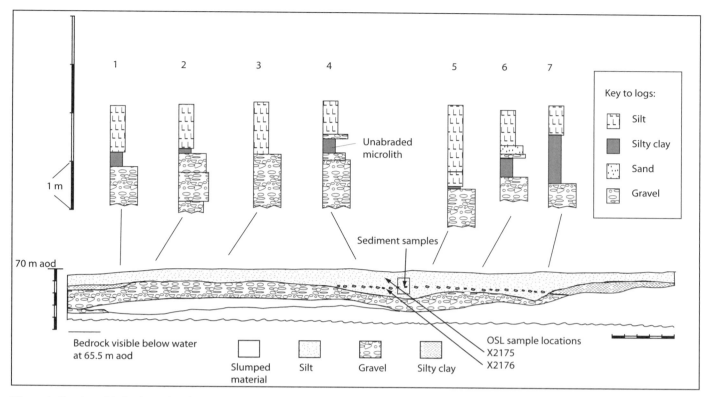

Figure 4. Stratigraphic bank section from the Washfield reach. OSL—optically stimulated luminescence; aod—above ordnance datum, equivalent to mean sea level.

of Special Scientific Interest (SSSI), and where Gregory (1997) described it as having dominant channel processes governed by return periods of between 2–5 yr. There are also several anthropogenic constructions that interfere with river flow—mainly the embankment and bridges of the old Exe Valley Railway, which was constructed in 1885. An altitudinal survey of the southern part of the reach (Fig. 7) showed that paleochannels dissect ground of a similar altitude rather than being a sequence of channels over ground that slopes toward the modern channel. Several of the paleochannels are 2–5 m deep and so are very conspicuous, but because they have been reoccupied and scoured at times of major flooding (e.g., in A.D. 2000), sediment is not preserved at their bases. Pits were dug to sample the silts immediately overlying the gravels on either side of a major paleochannel for OSL dating (Table 1). OSL age estimates obtained from each side of the channel are similar (685 ± 45 and 695 ± 85 yr before 2009 [Table 1]), suggesting that a major channel crossed the valley in the fourteenth century A.D. Part of the parish boundary follows another large paleochannel here. As Brampford Speke has an Anglo-Saxon charter, it is likely that this boundary was established before the Norman invasion of 1066 (Rose-Troup, 1938), giving a tenth-century A.D. date for channel occupation. A geomorphological study at this site in the 1970s (Hooke, 1977) using historic tithe maps and Ordnance Survey maps from between 1887 and 1962 showed that channel change over the past 200 yr

has been relatively minor and dominated by lateral shifting through bank erosion, with elements of both meander extension and oscillation. This is particularly marked just upstream of the railway bridge, where some meander extension and oscillation of the channel around an island bar can be seen on Figure 7A. The island bar itself is on the site of an earlier channel, and the sediments here appear more resistant to scouring than the overbank sediments to each side of the paleochannel. So, although there is evidence for channel change through avulsion during most of the late the Holocene, over the last 200 yr, the channel has oscillated within a restricted area and shows no signs of avulsion to a new channel location.

This work has solved what had been a paradox. Hooke (1977) had estimated from measured bank erosion rates that such channels should have reworked their floodplains in ~600 yr. However, this has always been at odds with clear evidence of Mesolithic, Neolithic, later Prehistoric, and historic in situ activity on these and other floodplains (see discussion section). This is solved by channel change being spatially restricted in the floodplain to zones or nodes of lateral migration and avulsion.

City of Exeter

The floodplain of the Exe within the City of Exeter is up to 1.2 km in width and has long been the site of human occupation

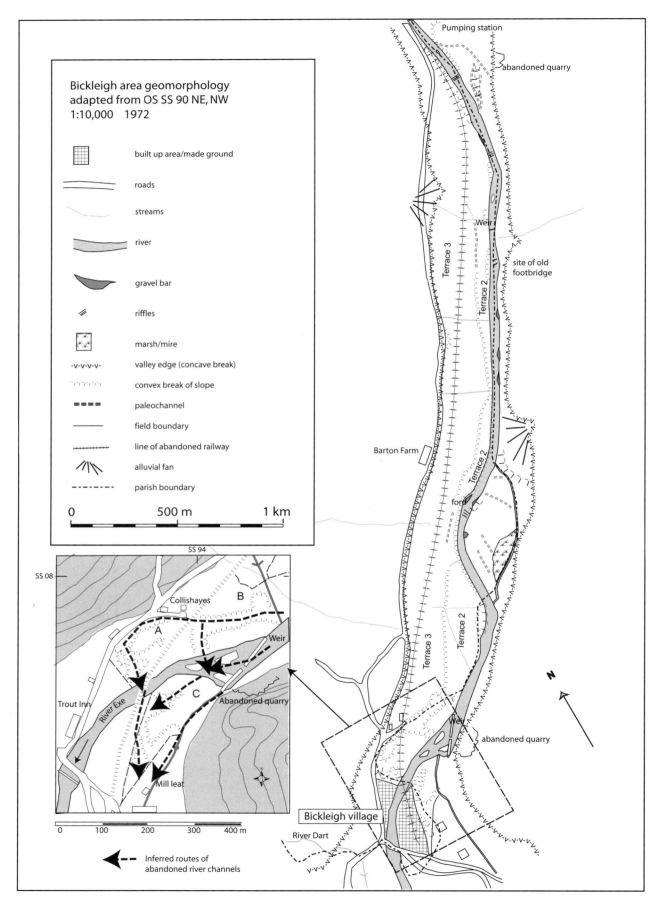

Figure 5. Geomorphological map of the reach at Bickleigh with indications of channel change.

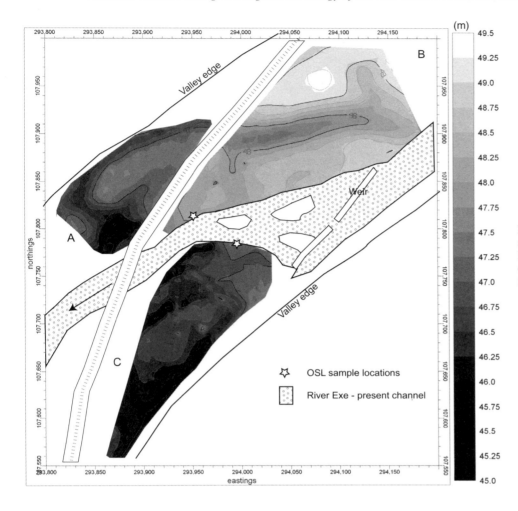

Figure 6. Digital elevation model of the surface of the floodplain gravels at Bickleigh with optically stimulated luminescence (OSL) locations (fields labeled as in Fig. 5).

and channel-related activities since the city was first established as a Roman fort in ca. A.D. 50. The city has a continuous history as a walled Roman town, Saxon settlement, and subsequently a very important medieval city and port at the tidal head of the Exe Estuary. Development-led archaeology by the Exeter Unit on the floodplain has provided the location, dimensions, stratigraphy, and radiocarbon dates from a number of paleochannels within the city limits. These have been classified by period using approximate chronological boundaries commonly used in UK archaeology (Hunter and Ralston, 1999). The Neolithic (ca. 4000–2600 B.C.) channels lie close to the present channel upstream but on the western edge of the floodplain downstream (Fig. 8). Bronze Age (2600–600 B.C.) channels lie on the southwest edge of the floodplain, with some movement to the east by the Roman period (A.D. 43–450). The Saxon-medieval (A.D. 450–1500) and post-medieval (A.D. 1500–1780) channels cluster around the existing channel. This is also where the multi-pier Exeter bridge was built ca. A.D. 1200, although a secondary channel persisted just downstream that was utilized by a mill and was preserved into historical times. In an early multiproxy paleoecological study of channel-fill sediments, Caseldine et al. (1988)

showed that at Albany Road (at the north end of the reach shown in Fig. 8), the channel was above the tidal limit at (or "from") ca. A.D. 700 to A.D. 1000. Figure 8 shows Holocene paleochannels on either side of the floodplain, and close to the present channel but very few in the middle of the floodplain, suggesting that the river had adopted a low-sinuosity anabranching style with consolidated areas of vegetation on islands between channels. This is typical of rivers at the tidal head, which in low-relief areas almost universally show a tendency to bifurcate, probably due to tidal asymmetry between the flood and ebb flows (Ahnert, 1960; Brown, 1997). The correlation between towns and cities in the British Isles and the tidal head (e.g., Gloucester, Roman-medieval London and Colchester) is not accidental because these were ideal port locations, and the common division of the channel facilitated easy crossing by fords and bridges. A major paleochannel on the western side of the valley (Reed and Sage, 1996) is still visible on the ground, and there is evidence from the radiocarbon dating for channel reoccupation at its southern end. because the area is built up, exposures are scattered, but the radiocarbon dates obtained are shown in Table 2, and the dates fall into groups, with some reoccupation of channels apparent.

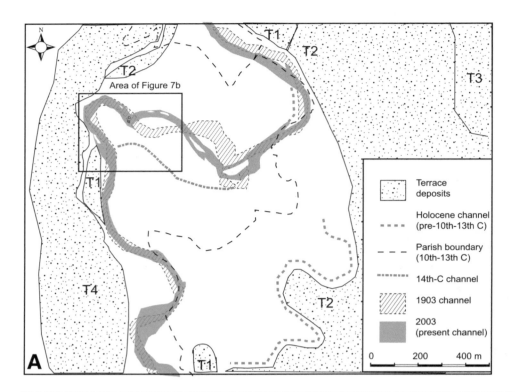

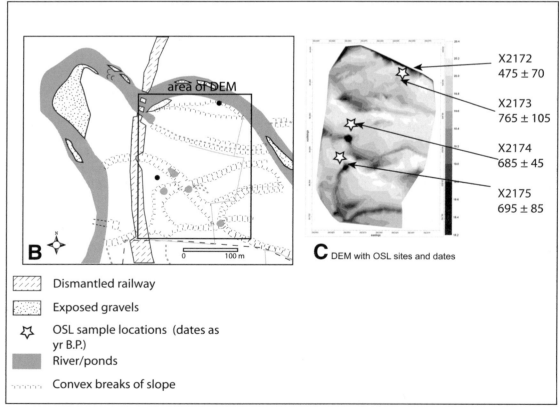

Figure 7. (A–B) Maps and (C) digital elevation model (DEM) of the floodplain at Brampford Speke with optically stimulated luminescence (OSL) dates. OSL—optically stimulated luminescence.

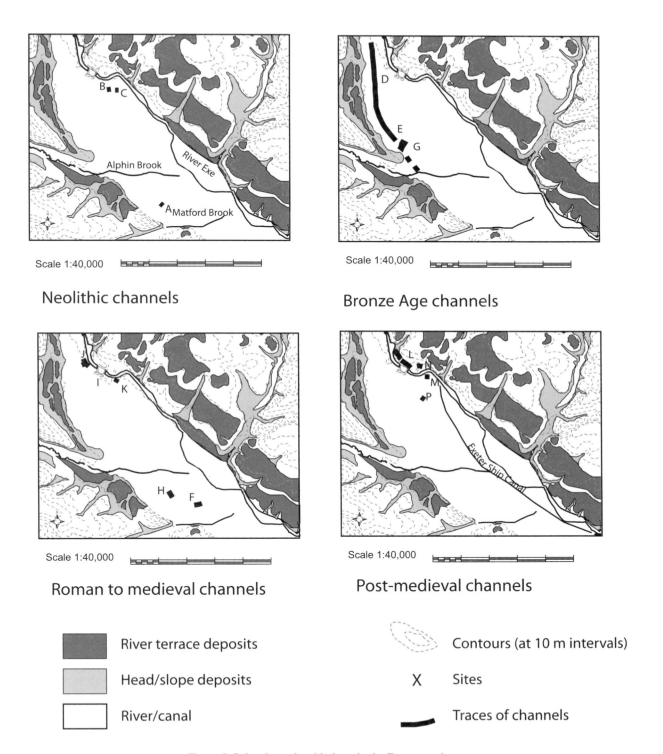

Figure 8. Paleochannels with dates in the Exeter reach.

TABLE 2. ARCHAEOLOGICAL EVIDENCE IN THE EXETER CITY AREA FOR PALEOCHANNELS OF THE EXE RIVER*

Site	Evidence/environment	Radiocarbon laboratory number	Radiocarbon date (yr B.P.)	Calibrated radiocarbon dates (at 2σ), and other evidence	Source
Neolithic					
A Matford Industrial Estate: Chrysler site (SX 92716 89651)	Paleochannel with alder fragments		5250 ± 90	4377–3811 B.C.	SMR†: R. Woodgate
B Sydney Lee Printing Works, Water Lane (SX 9185 9190)	Fragments of wood from riverbank fragment or small island overlying gravels, high organic content			3031–2590 B.C.	Stead (1997)
C Exeter Castings, Water Lane (SX 91989170)	Channel, organics from silts			3031–2590 B.C.	Dyer (1998)
Bronze Age					
D Guy's Hylton allotments, Okehampton Road (SX 9092 9242)	Organics from above gravels in channel running N-S, influencing field pattern. 'Lost bridges'			Ca. 1520 and 1090 B.C.	Reed and Sage (1996)
F Matford Industrial Estate, site P (SX 291172 92295)	E/W paleochannel, organic material from lower fill, so early silting	Waikito	2625 ± 49	1200–1360 B.C.	SMR: R. Woodgate, C. Whitton
G Sainsbury's Alphington Road (SX 9160 9080)	Three paleochannels, alder carr and wet grassland. Dates from wood fragments in fill	AA-33598 (GU 8235) Beta 133706 Beta 133707	2450 ± 50 2490 ± 50 2560 ± 50	787–399 B.C. 770–390 B.C. 795–410 B.C.	Dyer (1999)
Roman to medieval					
H Matford Industrial Estate, site K (SX 9282 8998)	Paleochannel, basal fill of channel timber *Salix*	Waikito 13260	1755 ± 41	A.D. 160–400 ± 41	SMR: R. Woodgate for Exeter Archaeology
I Albany Road (SX 915 919)	Paleochannel, clay with wood. Upper layers containing pottery	HAR-8055 HAR-8054	970 ± 80 1240	A.D. 980 ± 80 A.D. 710 (Pottery suggests twelfth-century silting of channel)	Caseldine et al. (1988)
K Pollitts Garage (SX 91819186)	Paleochannels, gray organic clay fill	A-10537	1145 ± 45	A.D. 770–990	Dyer (2000)
Post-medieval					
L Old Exe Bridge (SX 9159225)	Abandoned bridge over old channel to north of present main channel			Thirteenth century	Henderson and Jervoise (1938)

*Sources: Exeter Museums Archaeological Field Unit, Exeter City Planning, Devon County Sites and Monuments Records (SMR).
†The SMR records are from the Deveon database, which is currently unavailable electronically.

DISCUSSION

It is appears from the floodplain stratigraphy of the Exe River that relatively stable channels existed between the Late Glacial and the mid-Holocene. This is consistent with a period of geomorphic stability and a forested floodplain, as suggested by the pollen analyses at sites such as Exebridge. The relative stability is surmised from a lack of paleochannels from this period and the formation of floodplain/spring mires. The lack of early–mid Holocene paleochannels is not likely to be the result of later erosion, due in this case to the style (avulsion and restricted migration) of later floodplain evolution. The archaeological implication is that Upper Paleolithic and Mesolithic material (should it exist) could be found in situ within these floodplain sedimentary bodies, and this should be noted in development and planning considerations. The mid–late Holocene floodplain does show increased channel switching and some reoccupation of much older channels; however, change in sedimentation patterns is most marked in the late Holocene (Bronze Age to Roman period and post-medieval), when a higher frequency of channel switching occurred. For the past 200 yr, consolidation of riverbanks appears to have prevented significant channel change, except in exceptional circumstances, such as the A.D. 2000 floods. The preservation of Mesolithic artifacts on the valley floor is likely to have been due to this style of Late Glacial and Holocene floodplain development where land-surfaces on interchannel islands have been preserved by overbank deposition. The microliths found at Exebridge, Washfield, and along the Culm River are nearly all unabraded with sharp arrêtes and edges, suggesting minimal disturbance and transport. Although not discovered yet, there is no reason why hearths or the remains of structures should not be preserved in such circumstances.

Analysis of the dates of channel change summarized in Table 3 suggest agreement with the phases of fluvial change in southern Britain suggested by Lewin et al. (2005) and Johnstone et al. (2006), so the main driving force behind floodplain evolution of the Exe is likely to be climatic. It is noticeable that no dates from active channel sediments (sensu Lewin et al., 2005) were obtained in the mid-Holocene, but that there are a few dates from the Late Glacial–Holocene transition, and that there is a peak of age estimates falling into the time of the Little Ice Age. Since all of these dates came from close to channel bases, it is not unreasonable to correlate them with the timing of channel abandonment. This study suggests that channel abandonment in the Exe is most likely due to avulsion, and this is more likely in periods of aggradation and less likely in periods of relative incision, due to aggrading channel beds reducing effective bank-height. Macklin and Lewin (1993) have previously suggested eight episodes of regional and countrywide alluviation in Britain (see Table 3), and the dates from this study fall within these periods. Macklin and Lewin (1993) and Johnstone et al. (2006) also concluded that the period 8000–5200 yr B.P. was one of channel incision (and hence lack of avulsion), slow alleviation, or stability. This study revealed no direct evidence of incision during this period, suggesting that in the Exe Valley bank stability and an equilibrium between bed-material supply and alluviation are the most likely causes of channel stability. From further analysis of an archive of 506 Holocene dated ^{14}C fluvial units, Lewin et al. (2005) suggested that there is a distinct bias toward late Holocene sediments due to the higher preservation potential and late Holocene climatic instability. The dating and stratigraphy from the Exe floodplain reported in this study support this analysis, suggesting that the pattern of archaeological preservation in the Exe floodplain has been influenced by the climatic trends of the Holocene and cannot be simply extrapolated from recent estimates of channel change.

CONCLUSIONS

The Exe valley floor contains an inset late Pleistocene terrace sequence and an active floodplain with relatively high surface relief and distinct paleochannels separated by gravels that in places reach the floodplain surface. The modern channel is gravel-bedded and shows evidence of recent channel oscillation and incipient braiding. This study has resolved the floodplain paradox that arose from Hooke (1977), and other researchers' estimates of bank erosion rates on British rivers. The paradox was that when these rates (typically rates of 0.1–1 m yr^{-1})

TABLE 3. SUMMARY TABLE OF THE DATES OF CHANNEL CHANGE AT THE SITES DISCUSSED IN THE TEXT AND KEY HYDROLOGICAL PERIODS AS DEFINED BY LEWIN ET AL. (2005)

Dates (yr B.P.)	Areas of channel change	Exe catchment results
9600–8400	Lowland Britain	
4800–4200	Countrywide	
3800–3300	Mostly southern Britain	X1556 Exebridge
2800–2400	Mostly southern Britain	X2177 Tiverton? X1556 Exebridge?
2000–1600	Countrywide	
1200–800	Countrywide	X2176 Tiverton
800–400	Southern Britain	X2172, X2173, X2174, X2175 Brampford Speke X1550, X1555 Bickleigh
400–0	Upland northern and western Britain	

were extrapolated, they produced estimates of entire floodplain reworking of under 1000 yr, and yet for many floodplains, there is abundant archaeological evidence, either on the surface, or more typically buried by overbank alluviation, that parts of the floodplain surface have survived for several thousands of years (Brown, 1997, 2008). These have been referred to as "parcels" by some archaeologists (Needham, 1992) and provide some of the UK's key Prehistoric period sites due to their high preservation potential for organic remains.

From the dating of the paleochannels and avulsion in the Exe floodplain, it is proposed that the main driving force behind the floodplain evolution of the Exe appears to be climatic. In this respect, the Exe is more similar to the upland rivers of Wales, Scotland, and northern England than to southern and midland English rivers. After Late Glacial aggradation and incision, the channels appear to have been relatively stable in the early-middle Holocene, consistent with a period of fluvial stability and a vegetated/forested floodplain first dominated by birch (with pine on terraces), and from ca. 5000 B.C., alder and oak. The mid–late Holocene floodplain shows channel switching and some reoccupation of channels, the timing of which correlate with known hydroclimatic discontinuities observed elsewhere in the UK, but these may have been exacerbated by forest clearance upstream on Exmoor, and possibly by mining. There is evidence that sedimentation patterns changed in the late Holocene when periodic channel avulsion/switching occurred, until ~200 yr ago, when river banks became consolidated with only minor channel changes. It is possible that this pattern of channel avulsion/switching was active in the early and mid-Holocene, but restricted to the same limited areas as those used in the late Holocene, and the sediments were thus not preserved due to "sweeping out" of these conduits. However, where this has happened, as on the Nene River in eastern England, it has been picked up by a combination of superimposed channel beds, major hiatuses in pollen diagrams, and early Holocene basal radiocarbon dates (for an example, see Last et al., 2006).

This floodplain history has several archaeological implications, including: the reworking of some artifacts from floodplain islands into the floodplain fill; the preservation of artifacts such as barrows on the floodplain surface; the easy construction of mills and associated leats in secondary marginal-channels or paleochannels; the preservation of medieval bridges; the location of Exeter at the tidal head where there was a divided channel; and the preservation of environmental evidence in discrete paleochannels. As this list shows, the geoarchaeological potential of the valley is related to its Holocene dynamics, which both influenced and patterned human behaviors, and preserved artifactual evidence of human prehistory and history in the valley.

ACKNOWLEDGMENTS

We would like to thank the Claude F. Albritton Fund (Geological Society of America), the Ian Gass Fund (Open University), the Bill Bishop Memorial Trust, the Open University Flexible Fund, the John Daniels Memorial Fund, and the QRA-RLAHA Luminescence Award for financial support for this project. We must also thank local landowners for allowing access to sites, Exeter Museums Archaeological Field Unit for access to reports, and English Nature for permission to sample at Brampford Speke.

REFERENCES CITED

Adamiec, G., and Aitken, M.J., 1998, Dose-rate conversion factors: New data: Ancient TL, v. 16, p. 37–50.

Ahnert, F., 1960, Estuarine meanders in Chesapeake Bay area: Geological Review, v. 50, p. 390–401.

Aitken, M.J., 1998, An Introduction to Optical Dating: Oxford, Oxford University Press, 267 p.

Arnold, L.J., Bailey, R.M., and Tucker, G.E., 2007, Statistical treatment of fluvial dose distributions from southern Colorado arroyo deposits: Quaternary Geochronology, v. 2, p. 162–167, doi:10.1016/j.quageo.2006.05.003.

Atkinson, M., ed., 1997, Exmoor's Industrial Archaeology: Tiverton, UK, Exmoor Books, 160 p.

Bennett, J.A., 2005, Late Pleistocene and Holocene Fluvial Geomorphology of the River Exe, Devon, UK [Ph.D. thesis]: Exeter, University of Exeter, 258 p.

Bennett, J.A., 2006, QRA-RLAHA luminescence dating award. Optical dating of fluvial deposits from the River Exe: Devon UK: Quaternary Newsletter, v. 109, p. 53–56.

Berridge, P.J., 1985, Mesolithic sites in the Yarty Valley: Proceedings of the Devon Archaeological Society, v. 43, p. 1–24.

Bøtter-Jensen, L., 1988, The automated Riso TL dating reader system: Nuclear Tracks and Radiation Measurements, v. 14, p. 177–180, doi:10.1016/1359 -0189(88)90060-X.

Bøtter-Jensen, L., 1997, Luminescence techniques: Instrumentation and methods: Radiation Measurements, v. 27, p. 749–768, doi:10.1016/S1350-4487 (97)00206-0.

Bøtter-Jensen, L., Bulur, E., Duller, G.A.T., and Murray, A.S., 2000, Advances in luminescence instrument systems: Radiation Measurements, v. 32, p. 523–528, doi:10.1016/S1350-4487(00)00039-1.

Briant, R.M., Bates, M.R., Schwenninger, J.-L., and Wenban-Smith, F., 2006, An optically stimulated luminescence dated middle to late Pleistocene fluvial sequence from the western Solent Basin, southern England: Journal of Quaternary Science, v. 21, no. 5, p. 507–523, doi:10.1002/jqs.1035.

Briant, R.M., Wenban-Smith, F., and Schwenninger, J.-L., 2009, Solent River gravels at Barton on Sea, Hampshire (SZ 230 930) 2009, in Briant, R.M., Bates, M.R., Hosfield, R.T., and Wenban-Smith, F.F., eds., The Quaternary of the Solent Basin and West Sussex Raised Beaches: London, Quaternary Research Association, p. 161–170.

Bridgland, D.R., 1988, Uniclinal shifting: A speculative reappraisal based on terrace distribution in the London Basin: Quaternary Newsletter, v. 32, p. 15–24.

Brown, A.G., 1997, Alluvial Geoarchaeology: Floodplain Archaeology and Environmental Change: Cambridge, UK, Cambridge University Press, 377 p.

Brown, A.G., 2008, Geoarchaeology, the four dimensional (4D) fluvial matrix and climatic causality: Geomorphology, v. 101, p. 278–297.

Brown, A.G., Hosfield, R.T., Basell, L.S., Toms, P., Hounsell, S., and Young, R., 2007, The Palaeolithic Rivers of Southwest Britain: ALSF Project Number 3847: Report for English Heritage, University of Exeter and University of Reading, 194 p.; available at http://ads.ahds.ac.uk/catalogue/ archive/proswb_eh_2007/downloads.cfm (accessed 2 January 2011).

Brown, A.G., Bennett, J.A., and Rhodes, E., 2009, Roman mining on Exmoor: A geomorphological approach at Anstey's Combe: Environmental Archaeology, v. 14, p. 50–61, doi:10.1179/174963109X400673.

Brown, A.G., Basell, L.S., Toms, P.S., Bennett, J.A., Hosfield, R.T., and Scrivener, R.C., 2010, Late Pleistocene evolution of the Exe valley: A chronostratigraphic model of terrace formation and its implications for Palaeolithic archaeology: Quaternary Science Reviews, v. 29, p. 897–912.

Caseldine, C., Juggins, S., and Straker, V., 1988, Preliminary palaeoenvironmental analyses of floodplain deposits from a section near the river Exe in Exeter, Devon, in Murphy, P., and French, C., eds., The Exploitation of Wetlands: British Archaeological Reports, British Series, v. 186, p. 145–162.

Colls, A.E., Stokes, S., Blum, M.D., and Starffin, E., 2001, Age limits on the late Quaternary evolution of the upper Loire River: Quaternary Science Reviews, v. 20, p. 743–750, doi:10.1016/S0277-3791(00)00048-2.

Cullingford, R.A., 1982, The Quaternary, *in* Durrance, E.M., and Laming, D.J.C., eds., The Geology of Devon: Exeter, Exeter University Press, p. 249–290.

Duller, G.A.T., 2004, Luminescence dating of Quaternary sediments: Recent advances: Journal of Quaternary Science, v. 19, p. 183–192, doi:10.1002/jqs.809.

Duller, G.A.T., 2008, Luminescence Dating: Guidelines on Using Luminescence Dating in Archaeology: Swindon, English Heritage, 44 p.

Durrance, E.M., 1969, The buried channels of the Exe: Geological Magazine, v. 106, p. 174–189, doi:10.1017/S0016756800051980.

Durrance, E.M., 1980, A review of the geology of the Exe estuary, *in* Boalch, G.T., ed., Essays on the Exe Estuary: Exeter, The Devonshire Association for the Advancement of Science, Literature and Art, Special Volume 2, p. 41–72.

Dyer, M.J., 1998, Archaeological observations and recording at the former Exeter Castings site, Water Lane, Exeter: Exeter Museums Archaeological Field Unit Report 98.16.

Dyer, M.J., 1999, Archaeological recording during construction of a new J Sainsbury complex at Alphington Road, Exeter: Exeter Museums Archaeological Field Unit Report 99.81.

Dyer, M.J., 2000, Archaeological observations and recording at the former Pollitt's Garage site, Haven Road, Exeter: Exeter Museums Archaeological Field Unit Report 00.88.

Edwards, R.A., and Scrivener, R.C., 1999, Geology of the Country around Exeter: Memoir of the British Geological Survey Sheet 325 (England and Wales), scale 1:50,000, 183 p.

Folz, E., Bodu, P., Bonte, P., Joron, J.L., Mercier, N., and Reyss, J.L., 2001, OSL dating of fluvial quartz from Le Closeau, a late Palaeolithic site near Paris—Comparison with ^{14}C chronology: Quaternary Science Reviews, v. 20, p. 927–933, doi:10.1016/S0277-3791(00)00062-7.

Fox, A., 1969, The Upton Pyne cemetery: Proceedings of the Devon Archaeological Society, v. 27, p. 75–78.

Fuchs, M., Straub, J., and Zöller, L., 2005, Residual luminescence signals of recent river flood sediments: A comparison between quartz and feldspar of fine- and coarse-grain sediments: Ancient TL, v. 23, p. 1.

Fyfe, R.M., 2000, Palaeochannels of the Exe Catchment: Their Age and an Assessment of Their Archaeological and Palaeoenvironmental Potential [Ph.D. thesis]: Exeter, Department of Archaeology, University of Exeter, 310 p.

Fyfe, R.M., Brown, A.G., and Coles, B.J., 2003a, Mesolithic to Bronze Age vegetation change and human activity in the Exe Valley, Devon, UK: Proceedings of the Prehistoric Society, v. 69, p. 161–181.

Fyfe, R.M., Brown, A.G., and Rippon, S.J., 2003b, Mid- to late-Holocene vegetation history of Greater Exmoor, UK: Estimating the spatial extent of human-induced vegetation change: Vegetation History and Archaeobotany, v. 12, p. 215–232, doi:10.1007/s00334-003-0018-3.

Gregory, K.J., 1997, River Exe at Brampford Speke, Devon, *in* Gregory, K.J., ed., Fluvial Geomorphology of Great Britain: London, Chapman and Hall, p. 252–255.

Henderson, C., and Jervoise, E., 1938, Old Devon Bridges: Exeter, A. Wheaton and Co. Ltd., 96 p.

Hooke, J.M., 1977, The distribution of changes in river channel patterns: The example of Devon River channel changes, *in* Gregory, K.J., ed., River Channel Changes: Chichester, John Wiley, p. 265–280.

Hosfield, R.T., Brown, A.G., Basell, L.S., and Hounsell, S., 2006, Beyond the caves: The Palaeolithic rivers of south-west Britain: Geoscience in South-West England, v. 11, p. 183–190.

Howard, A.J., Brown, A.G., Carey, C.J., Challis, K., Cooper, L.P., Kincey, M., and Toms, P., 2008, Archaeological resources and prospection within Temperate river valleys: Elucidating floodplain evolution, confluence zone dynamics and archaeological preservation: A case study from the River's Trent and Soar, UK: Antiquity, v. 82, no. 318, p. 1040–1054.

Hunter, J., and Ralston, I., 1999, The Archaeology of Britain: An Introduction from the Upper Palaeolithic to the Industrial Revolution: Abingdon, Routledge, 450 p.

Huntley, D.J., Godfrey-Smith, D.I., and Thewalt, M.L.W., 1985, Optical dating of sediments: Nature, v. 313, p. 105–107, doi:10.1038/313105a0.

Johnstone, E., Macklin, M.G., and Lewin, J., 2006, The development and application of a database of radiocarbon-dated Holocene fluvial deposits in Great Britain: Catena, v. 66, p. 14–23, doi:10.1016/j.catena.2005.07.006.

Last, J., Baxter, I., Brown, A.G., Crummy, N., Dodwell, N., Fryer, V., Gale, R., Gardner, R., Hatton, J., Henry, K., McDonald, T., and McSloy, E., 2006, Tales from the river bank: A prehistoric landscape at Grendon, Northamptonshire: Proceedings of the Prehistoric Society, v. 71, p. 333–360.

Lewin, J., Macklin, M.G., and Johnstone, E., 2005, Interpreting alluvial archives: Sedimentological factors in the British Holocene fluvial record: Quaternary Science Reviews, v. 24, p. 1873–1889, doi:10.1016/j.quascirev.2005.01.009.

Lian, O., and Roberts, R.G., 2006, Dating the Quaternary: Progress in luminescence dating of sediments: Quaternary Science Reviews, v. 25, p. 2449–2468, doi:10.1016/j.quascirev.2005.11.013.

Macklin, M.G., and Lewin, J., 1993, Holocene river alluviation in Britain: Zeitschrift für Geomorphologie, N F suppl-Bd, v. 88, p. 109–122.

Mejdahl, V., 1979, Thermoluminescence dating: Beta-dose attenuation in quartz grains: Archaeometry, v. 21, p. 61–72, doi:10.1111/j.1475-4754.1979.tb00241.x.

Murray, A.S., and Wintle, A.G., 2000, Luminescence dating of quartz using an improved single-aliquot regenerative-dose protocol: Radiation Measurements, v. 32, p. 57–73, doi:10.1016/S1350-4487(99)00253-X.

Murray, A.S., Olley, J.M., and Caitcheon, G.G., 1995, Measurement of equivalent doses in quartz from contemporary water-lain sediments using optically stimulated luminescence: Quaternary Geochronology, v. 14, p. 365–371.

Needham, S., 1992, Holocene alluviation and interstratified settlement evidence in the Thames Valley at Runnymede Bridge, *in* Needham, S., and Macklin, M.G., eds., Alluvial Archaeology in Britain: Oxbow Monographs 27: Oxford, Oxbow Books, p. 249–260.

O'Kelly, M.J., 1982, Newgrange: Archaeology, Art and Legend: London, Thames and Hudson, 240 p.

Olley, J.M., Caitcheon, G.G., and Murray, A.S., 1998, The distribution of apparent dose as determined by optically stimulated luminescence in small aliquots of fluvial quartz: Implications for dating young sediments: Quaternary Geochronology, v. 17, p. 1033–1040.

Parker-Pearson, M., 2006, The Stonehenge Riverside Project, Summary Interim Report on the 2006 Season: http://www.shef.ac.uk/content/1/c6/02/21/27/summary-interim-report-2006.pdf (accessed 1 January 2011).

Pickard, R., 1933, A Palaeolithic implement from Exeter and a note on the Exeter gravels: Proceedings of the Devon Archaeological Exploration Society, v. 2, p. 206–212.

Prescott, J.R., and Hutton, J.T., 1994, Cosmic ray contributions to dose rates for luminescence and ESR dating: Large depths and long-term time variations: Radiation Measurements, v. 23, p. 497–500, doi:10.1016/1350-4487(94)90086-8.

Reed, S.J., and Sage, S.A., 1996, Archaeological Evaluation at Guy's Hylton Allotments, Okehampton Road, Exeter: Exeter Museums Archaeological Field Unit Report 96.46.

Reimer, P.J., Baillie, M.G.L., Bard, E., Bayliss, A., Beck, J.W., Bertrand, C., Blackwell, P.G., Buck, C.E., Burr, G., Cutler, K.B., Damon, P.E., Edwards, R.L., Fairbanks, R.G., Friedrich, M., Guilderson, T.P., Hughen, K.A., Kromer, B., McCormac, F.G., Manning, S., Bronk Ramsey, C., Reimer, R.W., Remmele, S., Southon, J.R., Stuiver, M., Talamo, S., Taylor, F.W., van der Plicht, J., and Weyhenmeyer, C.E., 2004, INTCAL04 terrestrial radiocarbon age calibration, 0–26 cal kyr BP: Radiocarbon, v. 46, p. 1029–1058.

Rhodes, E.J., 2007, Quartz single grain OSL sensitivity distributions: Implications for multiple grain single aliquot dating: Geochronometria, v. 26, p. 19–29, doi:10.2478/v10003-007-0002-5.

Rhodes, E.J., and Schwenninger, J.-L., 2007, Dose rates and radioisotope concentrations in the concrete calibration blocks at Oxford: Ancient TL, v. 25, p. 5–8.

Riley, H., and Wilson-North, R., 2001, The Field Archaeology of Exmoor: Swindon, English Heritage, 192 p.

Roberts, A., 2000, Late Upper Palaeolithic and Mesolithic hunting-gathering communities 13,000–5,500 BP, *in* Kain, R., and Ravenhill, W., eds., The Historical Atlas of South West England: Exeter, University of Exeter Press, p. 47–50.

Rodnight, H., Duller, G.A.T., Wintle, A.G., and Tooth, S., 2006, Assessing the reproducibility and accuracy of optical dating of fluvial deposits: Quaternary Geochronology, v. 1, p. 109–120, doi:10.1016/j.quageo.2006.05.017.

Rose-Troup, F., 1938, The Anglo-Saxon Charter of Brentford (Brampford), Devon: Transactions of the Devonshire Association, v. 70, p. 253–275.

Rowland, J.C., Lepper, K., Dietrich, W.E., Wilson, C.J., and Sheldon, R., 2005, Tie channel sedimentation rates, oxbow formation age and channel migration rate from optically stimulated luminescence (OSL) analysis of floodplain deposits: Earth Surface Processes and Landforms, v. 30, p. 1161–1179, doi:10.1002/esp.1268.

Silvester, R.J., Berridge, P.J., and Uglow, J., 1987, A fieldwalking exercise on Mesolithic and Neolithic sites at Nether Exe: Devon Archaeological Society Proceedings, v. 45, p. 1–21.

Stead, P.M., 1997, Archaeological evaluation and recording at the former Sydney Lee Printing Works Site, Water Lane, Exeter: Exeter Museums Archaeological Field Unit Report 97.64.

Toms, P.S., Brown, A.G., Basell, L.S., and Hosfield, R.T., 2008, Palaeolithic Rivers of South-West Britain Optically Stimulated Luminescence Dating of Residual Deposits of the Proto Axe, Exe, Otter and Doniford: English Heritage Research Department Scientific Dating Report Series No. 2-2008, 52 p.

Walling, D.E., and Moorhead, P.W., 1987, Spatial and temporal variation of the particle-size characteristics of fluvial suspended sediment: Geografiska Annaler, ser. A, Physical Geography, v. 69, p. 47–59, doi:10.2307/521366.

Wintle, A.G., and Murray, A.S., 2006, A review of quartz optically stimulated luminescence characteristics and their relevance in single-aliquot regeneration dating protocols: Radiation Measurements, v. 41, p. 369–391, doi:10.1016/j.radmeas.2005.11.001.

Wymer, J., 1999, The Lower Palaeolithic Occupation of Britain: Salisbury, Wessex Archaeology and English Heritage, 2 vols.

Zimmerman, D.W., 1971, Thermoluminescent dating using fine grains from pottery: Archaeometry, v. 13, p. 29–52, doi:10.1111/j.1475-4754.1971.tb00028.x.

MANUSCRIPT ACCEPTED BY THE SOCIETY 3 AUGUST 2010

The Geological Society of America
Special Paper 476
2011

Urban geoarchaeology and sustainability: A case study from Manhattan Island, New York City, USA

Joseph Schuldenrein
Michael Aiuvalasit
Geoarcheology Research Associates, 92 Main Street, Yonkers, New York 10701, USA

ABSTRACT

Sustainable archaeological practice involves the efficient performance of archaeological work in areas affected by development interests. In urban settings, planning agencies have recognized that geoarchaeological strategies are time and cost efficient. Deep testing methods minimize footprints to generate stratigraphic models that inform on past native environments, subsequent landscape change, absolute chronology, and site formation. When coupled with background historic and environmental data, geoarchaeological probing supplements or even precludes the need for costly excavation. In this study, the Metropolitan Transportation Authority Capital Construction Company (MTACC) sponsored the drilling and detailed stratigraphic analysis of four deep borings in preparation for a new subway tunnel in New York City. A more expansive set of boring samples was taken by the MTACC for geotechnical purposes. Our stratigraphic construct facilitated "retrofitting" of the MTACC observations to develop a laterally extensive baseline sequence. An allostratigraphic model was developed for a ten-block length of the Upper East Side of Lower Manhattan on the strength of radiocarbon dates and ethnobotanic and malacological analyses. Finally, geographic information system (GIS) modeling generated a series of time slices chronicling the transformation of the project area from Late Glacial times through the area's prehistoric and historic past.

INTRODUCTION

"Sustainability" is a relatively recent and multidimensional concept that asserts the need for balancing development concerns with dwindling environmental and cultural resources. Insofar as archaeology offers insights into the human ecology of previous cultures—even chronicling the prehistory and history of sustainability—it opens a window to patterns of cultural impact on the finite natural environment across a broad range of past civilizations and landscapes. In the developed world, the practice of archaeology has been annexed to the environmental movement. The preservation ethic currently drives the overwhelming bulk of archaeological exploration (King, 2004;

McManamon et al., 2008). Such exploration is directed by cultural resource and heritage planners, with funding from public and private sources.

The increasing importance of the preservation ethic accounts for paradigm shifts in archaeological practice as well. Traditional academic research designs are centered on problems in the human condition selected by time and place. Selection is based on the intellectual questions of interest to the researcher and the place in which it is optimally addressed. The reverse is true under the paradigm of sustainability, where regulations mandate that archaeology be implemented in areas likely to be impacted by development. In other words, the time and place of research and even archaeological protocols are dictated by the needs of

Schuldenrein, J., and Aiuvalasit, M., 2011, Urban geoarchaeology and sustainability: A case study from Manhattan Island, New York City, USA, *in* Brown, A.G., Basell, L.S., and Butzer, K.W., eds., Geoarchaeology, Climate Change, and Sustainability: Geological Society of America Special Paper 476, p. 153–172, doi:10.1130/2011.2476(12). For permission to copy, contact editing@geosociety.org. © 2011 The Geological Society of America. All rights reserved.

preservation and mitigation of impacts to the environment (i.e., sustainability).

Geoarchaeology has found a place in compliance-driven archaeology along parallel routes. Under the interdisciplinary umbrella, geoarchaeology emphasizes the symbiotic relationship between ancient cultures and their landscapes. As human ecological paradigms find increasing favor in research archaeology, the pragmatic aspects of earth science–based methodologies emerge as logical and tenable strategies for prediction, field exploration, and analysis. Geoarchaeological approaches are central in assessing such preservation-related objectives as: documenting contexts for buried sites; reconstructing landscapes of occupation and abandonment; and, perhaps most importantly, projecting preservation expectation and context on the basis of present and past geographic settings. A critical new trend, and one that is central to the evolving sustainability environment, is the maximization of data yield in locations that have been and continue to be targeted for reclamation and development. These targeted settings can contain archaeological records that are both fragmented (due to past destruction) and threatened (because of planned development).

The most intricate settings for unraveling the threatened and fragmented archaeological record are contemporary cities and urban networks. Paradoxically, these contexts may afford the strongest potential for meaningful archaeological interpretation because they preserve the densest loci of cultural materials. On the other hand, they offer great interpretive challenges because of the range of disturbance processes that compromise traditional archaeological integrity. Adding to the complexity, there is a broad array of safety and economic concerns in urban areas, which create logistical and observational restrictions. Still, the mandates of regulatory compliance afford twenty-first-century archaeologists opportunities to hone their skills because of the repeated threats to the same or subjacent pieces of property. The challenge is to formulate research strategies that integrate advanced technologies with traditional approaches to maximize information yield in settings where integrity is increasingly compromised.

In this paper, we present the results of investigations that applied deep-core drilling techniques to recover a series of late Quaternary sediments buried beneath thick caps of historic fill in the heart of New York City. Given the reasonably secure regional stratigraphic framework, a broad sampling of prehistoric site types along the Lower Hudson shoreline, and the prohibitive limitations to deep excavation, the strategy afforded the only window to the identification of potentially rich prehistoric sediment complexes. The approach has rarely been utilized in New York City and only sporadically in similar metropolitan areas in North America. Investigations of this nature are more common in Europe, as demonstrated by Ammerman et al. (1999) in their study of the relationship between sea level and human habitation at Venice; investigations of buried coastal environments at the ancient city of Pompeii (Pescatore et al., 2001); and in a recent assessment of prehistory and alluvial geoarchaeology beneath contemporary London (Morley, 2010). The objective of our study was not so much to recover in situ archaeological deposits, a serendipitous

likelihood at best, but rather to isolate buried landform-sediment assemblages with the potential for archaeological deposits. The resolution of the archaeo-stratigraphic context provides urban planners and reviewing agencies with scientifically sound sensitivity models to guide future planning projects.

THE SECOND AVENUE SUBWAY PROJECT

In 2007, we directed a project for which the objective was to identify buried prehistoric and historic surfaces in advance of construction of a subway line in Upper Manhattan, one of the densest urban landscapes in North America (Fig. 1). Strong prospects for archaeological preservation were signaled by the presence of a former estuary along the margin of the East River, which was built over and infilled during the late nineteenth century. Further suggestions of the extent and depth of the marsh were provided by geotechnical borings furnished by engineering geologists that disclosed thick accumulations of "organic sediment" overlying a silty sand complex beneath 3+-m-thick urban fills (Fig. 2). The origins of the organics were presumably Holocene estuarine landforms unconformably sealing late Pleistocene lacustrine basins (Schuldenrein et al., 2007; Newman et al., 1969) across New York harbor. Such depositional contexts have been linked to Archaic and Woodland period occupations (ca. 6000–1000 yr B.P.) in the Lower Hudson River basin and along limited expanses of the undisturbed shorelines in the New York City area (Cantwell and di Zerega Wall, 2001). Estuarine landscapes have been broadly linked to ecotonal subsistence regimes on the brackish-water margins across the U.S. Northeast during the middle to late Holocene transition (Bernstein, 1993; Schuldenrein et al., 2007; Thorbahn and Cox, 1988). Accordingly, the likelihood of exposing buried archaeologically intact surfaces warranted testing under U.S. federal and New York State cultural resource guidelines (i.e., National Historic Preservation Act of 1966; New York State Preservation Act of 1980).

Practically, a broad range of logistical difficulties impeded the implementation of a comprehensive subsurface testing program. These included the maze of underground utilities that span the project impact area; safety procedures mandated for even small-scale urban excavations; disruptions to traffic and commerce; and, ultimately, the enormous costs attendant to any and all of these procedures.

The overarching objective was to obtain a preliminary window on subsurface stratigraphy in advance of assessing archaeological integrity. The research design initially targeted the footprint of the project impact area, but its reach was more ambitious. A methodological focus emerged that will be helpful to planners confronting compliance issues in analogous settings both in Manhattan and other urban areas. A staged research plan was designed as follows:

1. Create an overview of regional and local late Quaternary geology to provide a chronostratigraphic framework for the depositional successions recorded in the geotechnical profiles.

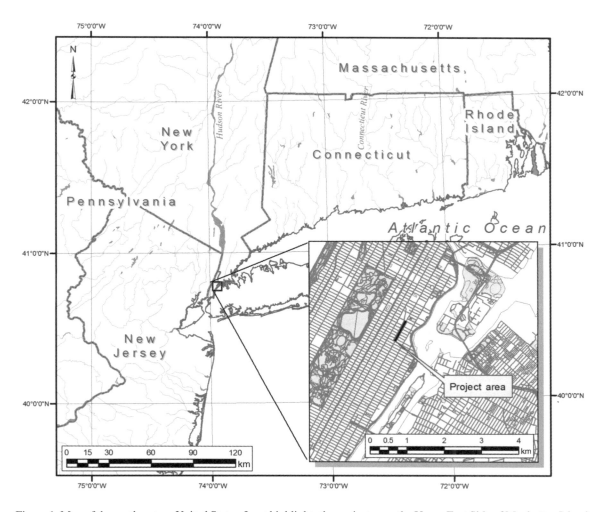

Figure 1. Map of the northeastern United States. Inset highlights the project area, the Upper East Side of Manhattan Island.

2. Review historic maps to isolate the locations of preindustrial, late Holocene subtidal stream and marsh complexes.
3. Design a limited subsurface coring program based on the results of stages 1 and 2.
4. Construct a baseline landscape history based on the core sequences and bolstered by examination of select sediment specimens preserved during the geotechnical work.
5. Analyze sediments from both phases of the work for sedimentological, geochemical, biotic, and microfossil data.
6. Radiometrically date organic materials preserved within key units.
7. Assemble a site-specific stratigraphy and paleoenvironmental succession.
8. Formulate a regional model of archaeological expectation that would be applicable for analogous urban contexts.
9. Develop a geographic information system (GIS)–based model of landform and site expectation that could guide planners for future development projects.

METHODS

Geoarchaeological coring locations were laid out with respect to alignments of former (tidal) channel margins with the assumption that these would conform to locations of early historic sites, if not settings flanking older marsh basins (Fig. 3). In some cases, locations had to be moved because of logistic concerns (chiefly, utility pathways and hazardous materials concerns). Mapping was finalized using coordinates from a global positioning system (GPS) field unit, and U.S. Geological Survey (USGS) topographic maps.

As noted, coring was deemed the most efficient method for previewing depositional contexts and recovering paleoenvironmental specimens (pollen, macrobotanical remains, mollusks) and radiometric samples. In total, five borings were selected. Subsurface testing was initiated using a truck-mounted split spoon auger that extracted 1.5-in.-diameter (3.8 cm) cylindrical samples of up to 0.6 m (2 ft) near-continuous lengths. Cores were

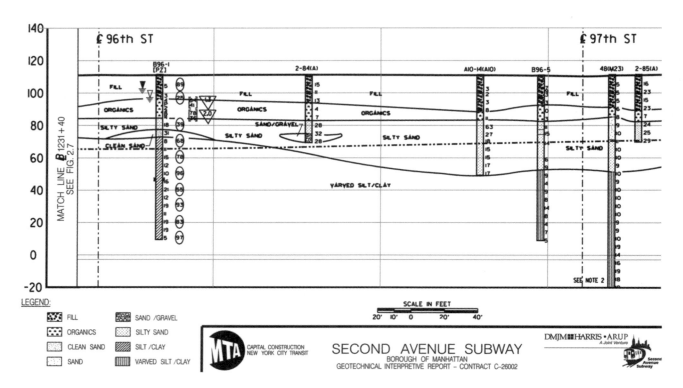

Figure 2. Geotechnical boring cross section of central portion of the project impact area. Layer labeled "organics" calls attention to possible presence of estuarine sediments of Holocene age, while "varved silt-clay" indicates late Pleistocene lacustrine beds.

excavated to a depth of 18 m (60 ft) unless bedrock or otherwise consolidated matrix was encountered. Upon extraction, samples from the split spoon were photographed, collected in plastic bags, and stored in (top-down) oriented sample boxes. Basic stratigraphic descriptions were made in the field (Fig. 4).

A second phase of field activity included examination of sediment specimens from 39 locations during the geotechnical phase of the planning study (see Fig. 3). Where possible, stratigraphy from these locations was reconstructed to include the sequences observed in the cores. In many cases, these helped fill stratigraphic gaps by refining facies relationships at locations or settings that could not be accessed during the coring phase of our work.

The entire collection of borings was described using standardized lithostratigraphic terminology (USDA, 1994; ISSC, 1990). A basic lithostratigraphic taxonomy was deemed optimal for this study to register dynamic changes in depositional environments (Holliday, 2004). Follow-up subsampling included recovery of organic, bulk, and shell radiometric specimens; particle size analysis and total organic matter by loss on ignition (LOI); palynological and macrofloral analysis; and mollusk shell identification.

ENVIRONMENTAL AND HISTORIC BACKGROUND

The first comprehensive late Quaternary landscape history for the New York City region was developed in a seminal paper by Newman et al. (1969). The model was structured around an overarching sequence beginning with bedrock (typically gneiss and schist), overlain by late Wisconsinan lake beds and or till, then by various estuarine facies, and capped by urban fill. These sequences were projected to extend up to several hundred meters in depth across most of the New York metropolitan area, conditional on local topographies, erosional processes, and the accelerated pace of urban development. The outlines of this stratigraphic framework have largely been confirmed by limited but increasingly sophisticated geological and geomorphological investigations. Over the past few decades, methodological advances, specifically in paleoenvironmental research, radiometric calibration, and now GIS, have refined the baseline sequences and incorporated more localized reconstructions (see Schuldenrein et al., 2007, and references therein).

Deep archaeological stratigraphies remain poorly known, especially beyond Lower Manhattan. Few prehistoric sites have been registered in a primary context anywhere on the island. While there is a significantly larger number of early historic sites, evidence documenting the natural landscapes encountered by the seventeenth-century Dutch settlers is sparse, in part because of the limited attention paid to environmental archaeology until relatively recently. It had long been assumed that the "made land" of New York City—dominated by deep and extensive accumulations of poorly sorted fill—precludes the probability of uncovering pre-urban landform relations. However, a recent synthesis of

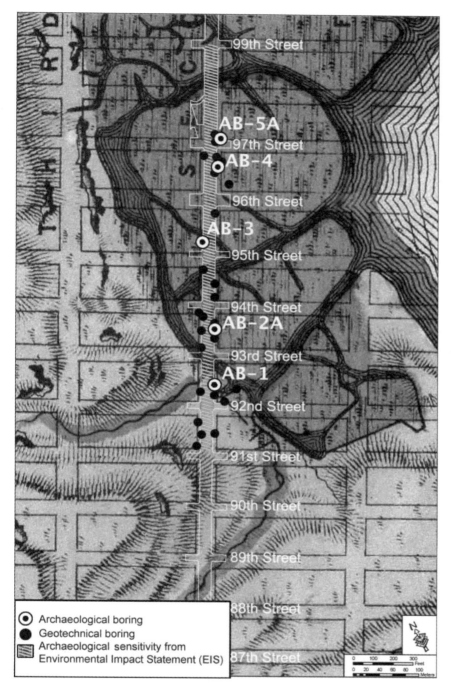

Figure 3. Viele map (1874) of project area with coring locations. The tidal drainage net was reconfigured and rechanneled in the historic period. Project impact area along Second Avenue is hachured.

the city's archaeology has documented variably thick historic fill mantles across much of Lower Manhattan; these are extensive but discontinuous (Cantwell and di Zerega Wall, 2001). Current excavations have exposed nearshore and glacial sediments linked to the early historic and prehistoric shorelines of Lower Manhattan (see Yamin and Schuldenrein, 2007), and regulatory agencies are now paying closer attention to these relationships. North of Midtown, the streets are underlain by thin urban fills capping regolith and bedrock (variously removed by development). Finally, the city's shorelines contain extensive and complex interdigitations of historic nearshore deposits (with considerable anthropogenic components) and older reworked Holocene estuarine facies.

The following section summarizes the baseline geological and related landscape sequences insofar as they pertain to the Second Avenue Subway impact area (Fig. 5).

Figure 4. Split spoon coring in Manhattan at Second Avenue Subway Project: (A) drill locality AB-4; (B) drilling operation; (C) sample in core tube; and (D) split sample in laboratory.

Bedrock Geology

The orogenic and structural components of northeastern North America's bedrock complexes account for the preglacial topography and terrain. Rifts in the continental crust trend from north to south. The Newark Basin is the primary geologic region to the west, and the Atlantic Basin lies to the east. Manhattan Island contains the core of resistant rock material between the basins and is named the Manhattan Prong (Isachsen et al., 1991). The bedrock of the Manhattan Prong consists of the New York Group of Lower Paleozoic and/or Precambrian schist, gneiss, and marbles. The project area straddles a northwest-southeast fault across Manhattan, offsetting the relatively soft Inwood Marble of the Harlem Lowlands to the north from the more resistant mica schist of the Manhattan Formation to the south. A ridge of older resistant Fordham Gneiss forms the uplands immediately to the west of the project area. The gneiss is not typically exposed in Manhattan, but it underlies the entire New York City region (Fischer et al., 1970; Schuberth, 1968).

Late Pleistocene Glacial Events

The Laurentide ice sheet advanced over the area at least twice during the Pleistocene Epoch, though the chronologies of

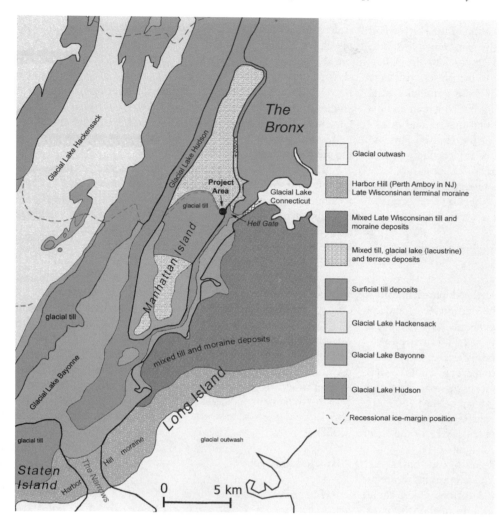

Figure 5. Surface geology and Pleistocene glacial lakes (modified from Cadwell, 1991; Stone et al., 2002). Note project location at margins of proglacial lake and till complexes. NJ—New Jersey.

the advances remain uncertain (Stanford, 2010; Ridge, 2003; Sanders and Merguerian, 1994). The Hudson-Mohawk Lobe of the latest or Wisconsinan ice sheet advanced to its southern terminus, the Harbor Hill moraine, by around 20,000 yr B.P. (Sirkin, 1986; Sirkin and Stuckenrath, 1980). As the glaciers retreated, two processes drastically reworked the landscape. Initially, recessional moraines formed at the margin of the glacier while it retreated. To the south and southeast of Manhattan, the Harbor Hill moraine features glacial detritus that extended in an arcuate form across most of Long Island and much of Staten Island (Fig. 5). Deposits of till behind the moraines blanketed the landscape in irregular fashion. The tills formed the parent material for later Holocene landforms (Cadwell, 1991).

The second process was the formation of proglacial lakes, which filled deep preexisting depressions, the outlines of which were partially predetermined by the bedrock geology, but also by glacial incision and the cyclic retreats of the ice sheets. The Harbor Hill moraine dammed the glacial meltwater and inhibited drainage into the Atlantic. Evidence for the lakes that formed at the melting glacial front takes the form of laminar to more massive silts and clays in the valleys of what are now the Hudson, Hackensack, and Passaic Rivers. A complex succession of glacial lakes including Lake Hackensack and Hudson, as well as Bayonne, occupied what is now the East River (at the edge of Hell Gate); their distributions have been recently remapped (Stone et al., 2002; Stanford, 2010). The levels of the proglacial lakes were controlled by the contemporaneous altitudes of spillways through adjacent lowlands or across channels cut into the terminal moraines. In the New York City area, the proglacial lake complexes were variously dammed behind the Harbor Hill moraine. The earliest of these lakes, Lake Bayonne, spread across the New York harbor area and East River, while its broader basin spilled into the lowlands to the west (of Staten Island; Fig. 5). Further ice retreat from western Long Island allowed additional lowering of lake level to the glacial Lake Hudson level, which was flushed eastward through the East River at Hell Gate. This final lake was contained within the glacially scoured and deepened Hudson River channel that progressively expanded northward with ice retreat until the Mohawk valley lowland was deglaciated ca. 12,000 yr B.P. (13,875 cal yr B.P.) (Stone et al., 2002).

These lakes were sustained until a portion of the Harbor Hill moraine was breached at what is now the Verazanno Narrows. This allowed the impounded waters to empty into the Atlantic. Lake Hudson emptied and gave rise to the present drainage lines of the Hudson River. The timing of these terminal glacial events remains uncertain (Stanford, 2010), but Newman and his coauthors (Newman et al., 1969) noted that marine and brackish water filled the 27-m-deep channel of the Hudson River at 12,500 ± 600 yr B.P. (14,830 cal yr B.P.), as evidenced by marine and brackish-marine microfossils at upstream locations along the present Hudson. There have been various interpretations as to the rate of drainage, and recent investigations suggest that it occurred rapidly (Donnelly et al., 2005; Thieler et al., 2007).

Holocene Sea-Level Rise and Estuarine Formation

The breaching of the Verrazano Narrows and sea-level rise commensurate with the Holocene led to the development of estuarine environments in New York Harbor, the Hudson River, and the East River. The earliest phases are poorly understood, and models of early Holocene landforms are largely based on inferred sea-level rise. Factors accounting for the history of the regional Holocene transgressions—punctuated by minor regressive pulses—are complex and beyond the scope of present discussion. They are, however, related to rates and patterns of subsidence, isostatic rebound, and sedimentation. For present purposes, we draw on a revision to Newman's model (Newman et al., 1969) for the New York Bight (Schuldenrein et al., 2007, their figure 6.1).

The revised model, illustrated in Figure 6, uses basal peat ages as the only dependable measure for determining correlations for shifting sea-level elevations at locations where there is chronostratigraphic information. Integration of the results of local and regional sequences with the New York Bight data set shows that the relative rise of sea level for the New York Bight is a smooth curve extending 9000 yr in the past (Schuldenrein et al., 2007). The data suggest a rising trend over the past 5000 yr at a net rate of between 1.4 and 1.5 mm/yr. Prior to 5000 cal yr B.P., the trend is more difficult to discern, largely due to the scarcity of earlier radiocarbon-dated stratigraphy. However, there is a convergence of data sets for the earlier Holocene, indicating a pre–7000 cal yr B.P. transgression rate of 9 mm/yr. The rapid rise following deglaciation is in agreement with the Atlantic Coast regional model, positing a rise on the order of 10 mm/yr (0.4 in./yr) rate for this period (Fleming et al., 1998). In sum, the rate of sea-level rise for the first 5000 yr is ~8 times higher than that of the past 5000 yr.

For geoarchaeological purposes, it should be noted that the recent study of submerged oyster reefs in Tappan Zee (Carbotte et al., 2004), ~20 miles (32 km) upstream of the project area has provided corroborating evidence for the revised Holocene model. Shell dates produced the absolute chronology for this study and resulted in a calculated rate of relative sea-level rise of 1.6 mm/yr; the trend calculated for dated oyster reefs is 1.8 mm/yr. These data demonstrate that living oyster communities adjusted to water depth and salinity and were able to keep pace with the rate of sea-level rise for at least 5000 yr. Carbotte et al. (2004) also noted that oyster growth was not continuous through time but showed distinct breaks in colonization. These observations have been confirmed in other oyster-based prehistoric subsistence studies along the Hudson (Salwen, 1964; Newman et al., 1969; Claassen, 1995; Schuldenrein, 1995), which show that there were prehistoric periods when shellfish were not an important part of the diet of humans living in the area.

The records for the past 3000 yr underscore a refined chronology for transgressing and regressing sea level. The data argue for shorter-term pulses that are related to both climatic and geomorphic changes. Extraregional evidence from the Mid-Atlantic and New England coasts comes from salt-marsh studies in Delaware Bay (Fletcher et al., 1993); foraminifer studies on Long Island Sound in Connecticut (Varekamp et al., 1992); and in salt-marsh stratigraphic studies near the mouth of the Raritan River, New Jersey (Kenen, 1999). The updated New York Harbor model (Fig. 6) includes relevant late Holocene dates from the present study. Prehistoric periods are linked to chronological scale and document the linkage between oyster availability—based on salinity in the estuary—and the archaeological record. The data are compelling for the past 5000 yr, where archaeological information is accessible at depths up to 5 m. For the earlier (Early-Middle Archaic) periods, sea-level rise was steep and accelerated. Any surviving evidence would be overridden by many meters of sediment.

Historic Landscape

The primary sources for the landscape configurations presented here are *The Historical Guide to New York City*, published in 1906 (Bolton and Hall), and historic maps, specifically the Viele projection (1874) (Fig. 3). The project setting is in an area that was known as Hell Gate Bay. Hell Gate Bay is south of the Harlem Plains, where the village of what is now Harlem was founded in 1637 by Dutch immigrants. The terrain is described as "meadow lands" and "salt flats," and the historic maps depict the area as marshlands with a discrete channel net. As shown, a dominant back-channel offsets the estuary from the higher terrain, and the lower basin is dissected by a series of subtidal, probably channelized drainages that connect the bay to the East River. The marsh was part of a larger basin that once extended to the north. It was subsequently separated by a slight rise that had the indigenous name transcribed as "*Rechawanes*," which is interpreted to mean Great Sands (Riker, 1904, p. 122). This interfluve separated Hell Gate Bay from one of the larger creeks in the area, variously known through time as Montagne's Creek, Mill Creek, and Harlem Creek (Bolton and Hall, 1906).

A place name that has stood the test of time is Horns Hook, which is the promontory to the south of the marsh that in part protects the area from the irregular currents at Hell Gate. The uplands immediately to the southwest of the project area have also been known as Rhinelander's or Observation Point (Bolton

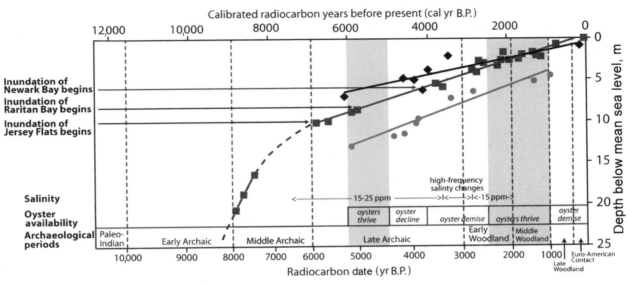

Figure 6. Sea-level curve (squares) for New York Bight since the end of the Pleistocene (from Schuldenrein et al., 2007). Trend line through circles is from shell dates taken from submerged oyster reefs (Carbotte et al., 2004). Trend line through diamonds depicts dates procured from this investigation. Key prehistoric periods in North American chronology are shown.

and Hall, 1906). The area no longer retains the name of Hell Gate Bay, because it was infilled before the twentieth century. A large powerhouse of the Metropolitan Railroad Company was built at the location (Bolton and Hall 1906), which has since been replaced by mixed urban development of hospitals, schools, businesses, and residences.

ESTUARINE ARCHAEOLOGY OF THE LOWER HUDSON

The archaeological record of the Lower Hudson includes a broad array of estuarine sites that have been examined from the human ecological perspective (ca. Butzer, 1982). Recent examples with major prehistoric and stratified components include the sites of Dogan Point on the Hudson (Claassen, 1995), and Old Place (Geoarcheology Research Associates, 1996, 1997; Ritchie and Funk, 1971) on Staten Island. The cultural sequences begin with the Middle Archaic, and vertical stratification shows intervals of local site abandonment, presumably related to pulsations in the sea-level record and frequent changes in subsistence resources affected by the migrating estuarine margins (Schuldenrein, 1995). On the basis of foram and geophysical studies, it has been determined that peak mesohaline conditions in the Hudson Estuary were reached around 6500 yr B.P. (Weiss, 1974; Carbotte et al., 2004), thus affording populations access to oysters and plant resources clustered along the brackish waters.

The aforementioned accounts of the late Quaternary of the Lower Hudson suggest that the changing geography of oyster beds is a measure of both variability in prehistoric site land use

and environmental change. At 8000 cal yr B.P., the Hudson had a connection to the Long Island Sound via the East River at Hell Gate, at an elevation −16 m below current sea level (mbsl). Sea level continued to rise rapidly until ca. 6000–5000 cal yr B.P., whereupon coeval distributions of oyster beds and basal marsh deposits signal stabilization of estuarine conditions and the onset of near-contemporary brackish landscapes. A relative abundance of oyster-rich Late Archaic and Woodland sites is noted during the middle–late Holocene. These site types continued into later prehistoric periods but are less conspicuous due to subsequent historical occupations and destruction (Cantwell and di Zerega Wall, 2001). Locally, the East River began functioning as a tidal strait between Long Island Sound and the New York Harbor, with continued input of freshwater from the Hudson River and minor tributaries.

The archaeological database for New York City generally identifies a significant number of prehistoric sites on the edges and margins of slackwater, marsh, and nearshore locations in Lower Manhattan. The setting of the Second Avenue project represents such a locale. Most of these prehistoric sites are linked to resource-rich estuarine landscapes with distal freshwater (i.e., wetlands) components. Artifact assemblages nearly always include shell (oyster) elements as well as diagnostic points and lithics. Some sites preserve evidence of complex resource procurement strategies, again centered on oyster- and shell-based economies. Perhaps most significantly, these are multicomponent sites in which occupations reflect changing resource bases conditioned by environmental dynamism and succession (Claassen, 1995; Schuldenrein, 1995). The regional evidence is consistent with the timing of Archaic and/or subsequent habitats along these shoreline settings. There is a more limited possibility for preservation of historic sites.

INVESTIGATIONS

Lithostratigraphy and Chronology

The sediment boring logs illustrated in Figure 7 depict the composite sequence and its lateral variability over a north-south span of seven city blocks (92nd to 97th Streets). The dimensions of the impact zone were 400 m (south-north; along Second Avenue) by 23 m (east-west), with a depth of 20 m. The sequence stratigraphy is structured by analytical units (AUs), numbered sequentially from older to younger units (bottom to top) and utilizing a lithostratigraphic taxonomy (ISSC, 1994). The lithostrata represent changes in the depositional environment through time. The textural and structural properties of a particular deposit differentiate the lithostrata from one another. The regional bedrock geology (Fischer et al., 1970; Schuberth, 1968) and, to a lesser degree, the late Quaternary mapping (Stone et al., 2002; Fullerton, 1992) offered guidelines for facies recognition and chronostratigraphic expectation. Microstrata within the Holocene sequences were recognized both in the field and more comprehensively by follow-up sedimentological, pollen, and malacological analysis. Thus, AU-IV was subdivided into three stratigraphic zones (des-

ignated a, b, and c; bottom to top), based on sedimentology and fossil content, specifically, shell populations that varied in type and frequency within the parent marsh matrix.

Absolute chronologies were constructed on the basis of radiocarbon dates (n = 10) procured from all units and cores, although AB-5A was sampled most intensively, since it presented the most complete and varied stratigraphy (Table 1).

Table 2 integrates the key descriptive features of the six lithostrata by dominant sedimentological properties. Chronostratigraphic assignments are based on the radiocarbon determinations and correlations with regional bedrock and late Quaternary mapping units. Depositional environments are similarly inferred, although we stress that the chronology of the proglacial lakes is poorly documented regionally (the present dates are among the most recent and reliable obtained for the New York Bight), and the postglacial nearshore and late Holocene estuarine successions are inferred from field stratigraphies exclusively.

The vertical sequence extends from differentiated historic fill caps immediately beneath sidewalk pavements (AU-VI and AU-V), through variable late Holocene estuarine facies (AU-IV), middle Holocene fluviomarine sands (AU-III), terminal Pleistocene glaciolacustrine varves and rhythmites (AU-II), and upper till and bedrock-regolith complexes (AU-VI) (Fig. 7). The estuarine deposits rest unconformably atop the eroded lacustrine varves at an elevation of −10 m and are overlain by historic fills at present sea-level elevations.

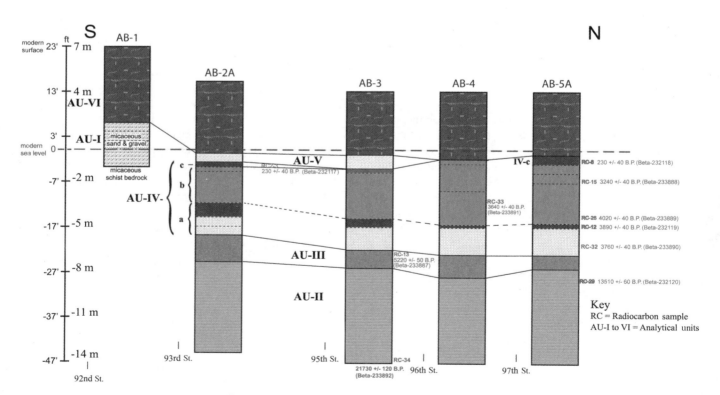

Figure 7. Cross section of cores with radiocarbon dates.

TABLE 1. RADIOCARBON DATES

Beta laboratory number	Core no.	Analytical unit	Depth below surface (m)	Elevation above (+) and below (−) sea level (m)	Material	Method*	$^{13}C/^{12}C$ ratio	Age range (cal 2σ range, ^{14}C yr B.P.)	Age (conventional ^{14}C yr B.P.)	Calibrated (OxCal 4.0) age (yr B.P.)†
232117	AB-2A	IV-c	5.5–6.1	−0.6 to −1.2	Peat	AMS	−12.9	420–400 and 320–270 AND 210–140 and 20–0	230 ± 40	212.5
232118	AB-5A	IV-c	4.3–4.9	−0.3 to −0.9	Wood	AMS	−26.2	420–400 and 320–270 AND 210–140 and 20–0	230 ± 40	212.5
233888	AB-5A	IV-b	5.5–6.1	−1.5 to −2.1	Organic sediment	AMS	−22	3560–3380	3240 ± 40	3471.5
233891	AB-4	IV-b	7.3–7.9	−3.4 to −4.0	Organic sediment	AMS	−22.2	4080–3850	3640 ± 40	3970
233889	AB-5A	IV-b	8.2–8.5	−4.6 to −4.9	Organic sediment	AMS	−20.4	4580–4420	4020 ± 40	4598.5
232119	AB-5A	IV-a	8.5–9.1	−4.6 to −5.2	Organic sediment	AMS	−25.4	4420–4230 and 4200–4160	3890 ± 40	4291
233890	AB-5A	IV-a	9.8–10.4	−5.8 to −6.4	Organic sediment	AMS	−22.2	4240–4060 and 4050–3990	3760 ± 40	4113.5
233887	AB-3	III	10.4–11.0	−6.4 to −7.0	Organic sediment	AMS	−21.6	6180–6150 and 6120–5900	5220 ± 50	6041.5
232120	AB-5A	II	12.8–13.4	−8.8 to −9.4	Organic sediment	AMS	−21.4	16,500–15,820	13,570 ± 60	16,166 §
233892	AB-3	II	15.2–15.8	−11.2 to −11.9	Organic sediment	AMS	−24.9	§	21,730 ± 120	§

*AMS—accelerated mass spectrometry.
†Calibrated date consists of midpoint of 2σ OxCal 4.0 calibration (Bronk Ramsey, 1995, 2001).
§Sample could not be calibrated because it is outside the calibration curve.

Sedimentology

Particle-size analysis and organic matter assays were undertaken to track variability in the developmental history of the estuary over the last 3500–4000 yr. The 7-m-thick sediment column from AB-5A provided the most complete and best-dated vertical sequence between the Pleistocene glaciolacustrine unconformity (top of AU-II) and the historic fill (base of AU-VI). Age ranges are from ca. 3800 to 200 yr B.P.; the upper determination marks the basal Euroamerican surface (Fig. 7). The core preserved the nearshore deposit (AU-III) as well as each of the three facies of the evolving estuarine microenvironments (AU-IV) (Fig. 8).

The sedimentological break between the glacial lake sediments and Holocene nearshore deposits is signaled by the abrupt change in the particle-size signature. Uniformly well-sorted and symmetrically skewed silt distributions give way to the strongly finely skewed coarse sands of the fluviomarine complex (AU-III). The onset of estuarine conditions (AU IV-a) is expressed in a fining-upward sequence; mean grain sizes grade from medium sand to silts. The uppermost marsh facies of AU-IV-a contains the highest concentrations of organics (2.47%). Progressively coarser skewness and poorer sorting characterize the upward-fining succession to AU-IV-a.

The mud-flat facies of unit IV-b demonstrates remarkable uniformity. Organic matter is consistent at around 1%, while mean grain sizes are medium silts that are better sorted than nearshore sands, while trending from coarse to finely skewed, and back to coarse skewed at the top of the unit. According to Flemming's (2000) textural classification of intertidal deposits (based on tripartite sand-silt-clay proportions), unit IV-b can be classified as a silt mud flat, broadly analogous to modern macrotidal flats.

The stable historical marsh of unit IV-c caps the mud flat, and particle sizes point to a complex depositional environment, probably attributable to historic impacts to the marsh surface. The silts are very poorly sorted, and organic matter increases to 2.26%. It is likely that human activity disrupted the hydrology of the embayment, as reflected in the sediment record. The marsh itself may have been artificially regulated and stabilized.

Macrofloral and Palynological Analysis

Macrofossil and palynological sampling at AB-5A was solely from AU-IV-b, the saltwater mud-flat facies (subsurface depths of ~−3.3 to −6.7 m; Fig. 7). Loss-on-ignition assays (LOI) were undertaken in conjunction with the pollen processing, and we found organic matter concentrations on the order of 1%–2%, i.e., very low in comparison with other Hudson marshes, which contain 20%–40% organics.

Macrofloral samples were dominated by seeds of *Ruppia maritimia* (widgeon grass) throughout AU-IV-b. These are typically characteristic of submerged, brackish estuarine microenvironments. The *R. maritimia* habitat is a shallow (subtidal) seabed or tidal channel that tolerates a wide range of salinities from 0 to

TABLE 2. SUMMARY OF ANALYTICAL UNITS (AUs)

Description	Depositional environment	Radiometric dates
AU-I: Manhattan Formation bedrock and glacial tills (late Pleistocene)		
Very dark-gray (10YR3/1) gravelly silty sand to regolith, weathered micaceous sands and angular schist rock fragments, coarsening to contact with schist bedrock.	Underlying bedrock of Manhattan Formation schists grading to regolith and capped by till of sands and gravels.	n/a
Cores: AB-1, and numerous MTACC cores below AU-II		
AU-II: Glaciolacustrine deposits (late Pleistocene)		
Reddish brown (5YR4/3) medium to coarse silt with occasional varves of 2–5-cm-thick silty fine sand and fine sandy clayey silt, micaceous. Deposits overlie AU-I and extend to 27 to 49 m below the surface.	Lacustrine sediments register terminal Pleistocene glacial lake Bayonne/Hudson. Slightly coarser than typical lacustrine sediments implicate delta/fan progradation at lake margins.	13,570 ± 60 ^{14}C yr B.P. (Beta-232120); and 21,730 ± 120 ^{14}C yr B.P. (Beta-233892).
Cores: AB-2A, 3, 4, and 5A		
AU-III: Fluviomarine sands (middle Holocene)		
Light olive brown (2.5YR5/4) to dark-gray (10YR4/1) sand. Sand is a heterolithic quartzitic (60%) and micaceous (40%) medium to coarse sand, with granule schist, white limestone, quartzite, and red siltstone rock fragments.	Complex agglomeration of postlacustrine, high-energy fluvial and beach sands marking interface of glacial lake recession and onset of Holocene estuary	5220 ± 50 ^{14}C yr B.P. (Beta-233887).
Cores: AB-2A, 3, 4, and 5A		
AU-IV-a: Basal marsh sands and silts capped by weak soil (late Holocene)		
Upward-fining complex of micaceous gray to very dark-gray (10YR4/1, 3/1) silty sand; very dark-gray (10YR3/1) to (GLEY 3/N) organic slightly silty sand to silt. Organics are partially to entirely decayed. Locally intact vegetation mats are preserved. Dark greenish gray (GLEY 4/1) mottling in silts beneath organic mats underscores hydromorphism in weak soil (Bg horizon).	Transition from a higher-energy (perhaps a beach or nearshore) environment to tidal marsh. Elevated organics mark onset of marsh genesis. Freshwater fern pollen points to marsh microhabitat. Radiocarbon dates converge around marsh initiation after 4 ka.	Dates are inverted, with a date of 3890 ± 40 ^{14}C yr B.P. (Beta-232119) from the organic horizon capping this deposit and 3760 ± 40 ^{14}C yr B.P. (Beta-233890) from the lower fining-upward sand sequence in core AB-5A.
Cores: Upper organic portion found in AB-2A, 4, and 5A; lower transitional sands found in AB-2A, 3, 4, and 5A		
AU-IV-b: Aggrading saltwater tidal marsh and mud-flat fines (late Holocene)		
Very dark-gray to dark-gray (GLEY 3/N, 4/N) organic silt sediment matrix with micaceous component; partially disaggregated sedge/grasses and few (1%) partially decayed roots at base with *Ruppia maritimia* seeds. Shell fragments increase up-profile (to 5% of matrix).	Tidal saltwater mud flat in equilibrium with sea-level rise. Incipient histic (peat enriched) soil formation between ca. 4 ka and 3 ka.	3240 ± ^{14}C yr B.P. (Beta-233888) in the upper portion of this unit; 3640 ± 40 ^{14}C yr B.P. (Beta-233891) in the middle; and 4020 ± 40 ^{14}C yr B.P. (Beta-233889) at the base.
Cores: AB-2A, 3, 4, and 5A		
AU-IV-c: Terminal marsh fringe silts, sands, and clays (historic)		
Very dark grayish brown (10YR3/2) organic slightly silty sand to slightly silty clay with abundant (30%) partially to fully decayed plant fragments of wood, grass, and roots. Inclusions of upper historic fill.	Historic subaqueous surface of the metastable mud flat. Development of a histic (Oe) horizon, variably truncated by historic disturbances.	230 ± 40 ^{14}C yr B.P. (Beta-232117); 230 ± 40 ^{14}C yr B.P. (Beta-232118).
Cores: AB-2A and 5A		
AU-V: Basal fill (historic)		
Grayish brown (10YR5/2) medium to coarse sand with minor (2%) component of possible rip-up clasts and transported clays.	Stratification, bedding, and sorting of matrix suggest episodic historic erosional events or a high-energy storm.	n/a
Cores: AB-2 and 3		
AU-VI: Upper fill cap (historic–recent)		
Heterogeneous mixture of road construction material (concrete, asphalt, cinders, gravels), fill (clean sands, silts, and cinders), buried construction materials (brick and wood fragments), and occasional domestic debris (ceramics, cinders, metal).	Differing fill bodies are mixed and stacked (i.e., road construction material with variable clast content and introduced domestic debris).	n/a
Cores: All cores found between 0 and 16′ (0 and ~5 m) below ground surface		

70 ppt (La Peyre and Rowe, 2003). High concentrations of charcoal and *Carya* (hickory) were also present. The general absence of seeds and relatively low pollen counts from salt-marsh species (such as *Cyperaceae* and *Poaceae*) suggests that the depositional environment was initially not that of a vegetated salt marsh, but

rather an estuarine mud flat. Variability within the column is reflected in the lowest levels. The pollen spectrum at the base of AU-IV-b featured *Pteridium* (brackenfern) and *Osmunda* (fern) pollen, both of which are not salt-tolerant species. These species signify the presence of a nearby freshwater wetland and likely

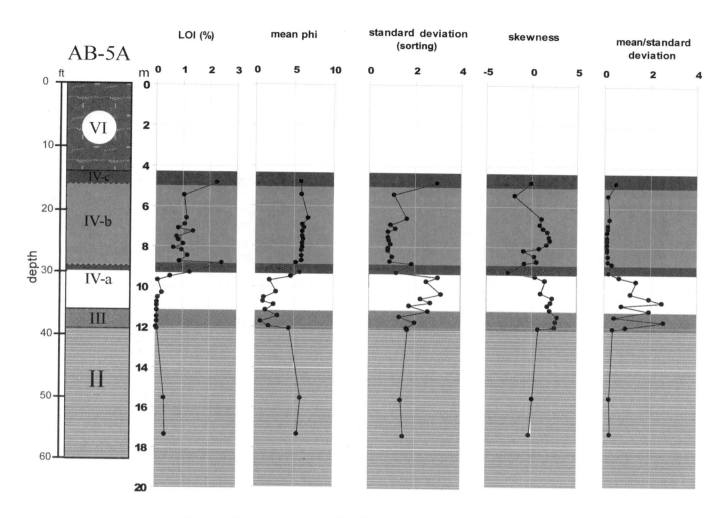

Figure 8. Sedimentological profile of core AB-5A. LOI—loss on ignition.

demonstrate the transition from nearshore and freshwater marsh environments registered in AU-IV-a to the onset of brackish conditions.

Locally, the macrofloral and pollen signatures converge around a trend to more saline conditions over the course of peak marsh margin sedimentation. On a larger scale, the prominence of *Carya* (hickory) is indicative of an overall trend to warmer and drier climates during this interval. Higher salinity is consistent with disruptive drought pulses during this time frame.

Malacology

Three molluscan genera were identified from units AU-IV-a and AU-IV-b (in AB-4 and AB-5A). *Macoma* and *Nassarius* are the most prominent. Identification on the species level was limited by fragmentary preservation contexts in some cases. Provisional indications are that the *Macoma* species is either *Macoma balthica* or *Macoma calcarea*, while the *Nassarius* species were

likely *Nassarius trivittatus*, *Nassarius vibex*, or *Nassarius obsoleta*. The *Nassarius* and *Macoma* species are endemic to cold-water and shallow estuarine environments, most probably a mud flat. *Macoma* species inhabit intertidal to deeper water, while *Nassarius* resides in shallow-water mud flats. The *Nassarius* species tolerate salinities ranging from midestuarine to marine at 15–25 ppt. The only other taxon was a sample of *Argopecten* that could not be identified to the species level. *Argopecten* is generally found in deeper, clearer water, and it was probably mobilized and transported during a tidal inundation, as it is not indigenous to estuaries.

Summary

Taken together, the sedimentology, paleobiotic, and malacology data suggest that the cores penetrated a subaqueous mud flat (AU-IV-b). It does not appear to have been a tidal microenvironment that sustained a salt grass marsh. Sedimentological and environmental data from AU-IV-a demonstrate a complex environment transitioning from a freshwater to marine landscape. The simultaneous presence of freshwater plant species and marine mollusk shells indicates a complex cycle of nearshore geomorphic processes during the transgression.

SYNTHESIS: MODELING LANDSCAPE CHANGE IN NEW YORK CITY

Stratigraphy and the Landscape Succession

This section integrates the limited exposures at the Second Avenue project area with broader paleolandscape models for late Quaternary Hudson Valley evolution. We begin with a summary of subsurface relations as illustrated in Figure 9.

Six lithostrata preserve the local landform history, beginning with the late Pleistocene lake and upland tills; the subsequent disappearance of the lake and attendant erosion of the till margins; the emergence and sustained evolution of an estuary regulated by marine shoreline cycles during the middle to late Holocene; and finally the Euroamerican settlement and rapid overhaul of the natural shoreline during the industrial and commercial phases of neighborhood development. While the sequence is chronicled by unconsolidated sediments, and the radiometric materials that date them, there are temporal gaps of equal or longer duration, attesting to extensive intervals of nondeposition (Fig. 10). Sustained erosion coupled with long-term edaphic adjustments prob-

ably account for the absence of early postglacial sediments. The missing record of the pre-Euroamerican estuary is probably a function of the estuary's attaining an equilibrium state as rates of sea-level rise slowed during the late Holocene. Other factors contributing to shoreline stabilization include intrusive and large-scale reclamation projects and relandscaping during the historic to recent periods.

The most detailed chronostratigraphies and reconstructions were developed for estuarine environments that evolved over the interval 4600–3200 yr B.P. Figure 6 illustrates the regression line for sea-level rise and documents the succession of middle to late Holocene development along the Hell Gate estuary. The curve was generated on the basis of the radiocarbon dates; the fit with the recently revised sea-level model for the New York Bight is compelling (Schuldenrein et al., 2007).

GIS Modeling and the Prehistoric Environment

The incorporation of project stratigraphies with regional landform histories allows us to generate a diachronic model for the evolution of Hell Gate Bay. This is depicted in a time-transgressive, graphic representation of landscape form and process (Fig. 11). Time slices were created using a combination of modern elevation data, historical bathymetry, historical landform maps, and projected sea-level information. A digital elevation model (DEM) for the Central Park Quadrangle (USGS 7.5 min series topographic maps) was used as the base, which was

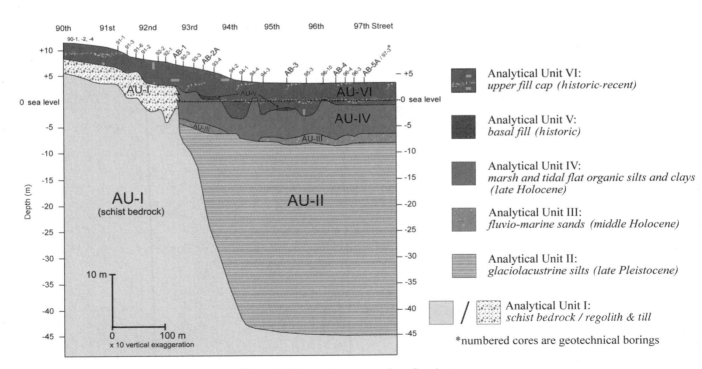

Figure 9. Schematic cross section of project area.

modified within a GIS to reflect the prelandfill topography of parts of the Harlem plain. Bathymetry was digitized from a georeferenced digital image of the "Navigation Chart of Hell Gate and its Approaches" (1875), retrieved from the image archives of the Historical Map and Chart Collection, Office of Coast Survey/National Ocean Service/National Oceanic and Atmospheric Administration (NOAA). This chart was considered more accurate than modern bathymetric data because it predates most of the late nineteenth– and early twentieth–century dredging activities. The location and outline of the historic period's low-lying wetlands were digitized from a georeferenced image of the map "Sanitary & Topographical Map of the City and Island of New York" (Viele, 1874). The elevation of this wetland was lowered for older time periods in accordance with information generated in the course of this study's subsurface investigations. The shoreline for each period reflects the sea-level curve depicted in Figure 6.

This model generated eight temporal projections for landform evolution (Figs. 11A–11H). The temporal projections correspond to key occupation periods in the northeastern prehistoric chronology and afford a glimpse at the subsistence environments utilized during these time frames. The footprint of the Second Avenue project impact area is shown for reference.

ARCHAEOLOGICAL ASSESSMENT

Cantwell and di Zerega Wall (2001, p. 13) noted that "…[larger sites] located at the confluences of rivers, along sheltered shorelines, on well-drained soils, or near fresh water… were often destroyed in the early years of the city's modern history." While renewed interest in prehistory has been brought about by compliance legislation, the massive scope and extent of subsurface disturbance across Manhattan Island are such that the probability of encountering buried prehistoric sites is relatively small. Prospects for identifying historic occupations are somewhat greater, given the broad range of documentary sources available. The geoarchaeological approach offers additional and unique site-prospecting guidelines. First, by delimiting and isolating the composition of historic fills, it calls attention to the types and ages of human activities that modified the historic landscape. Second, for prehistoric archaeology, it discloses the ages and landform complexes that could have sustained human populations for known periods and adaptive stages in the regional aboriginal succession.

The foregoing archaeological assessment is based on a series of inter-related variables, such as the footprint (three-dimensional) of the project impact area; the methods of subsurface testing; the

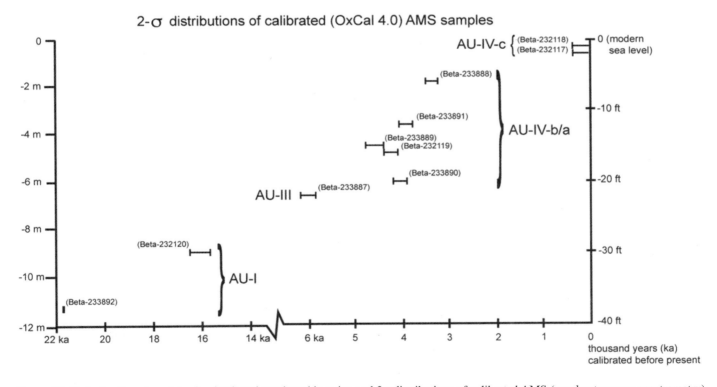

Figure 10. Plot of radiocarbon dates by depth and stratigraphic units, and 2σ distributions of calibrated AMS (accelerator mass spectrometry) samples. Calibration for the ^{14}C determinations was provided by the Oxford University (OXCAL) system (c14.arch.ox.ac.uk/oxcal.html). The midpoint of the calibration range (2σ calibration) serves as the calibrated date, which is used in our interpretations and reported as cal yr B.P. Note major depositional gaps at 15 ka–6 ka, 6 ka–4.7 ka, and 3 ka–1 ka.

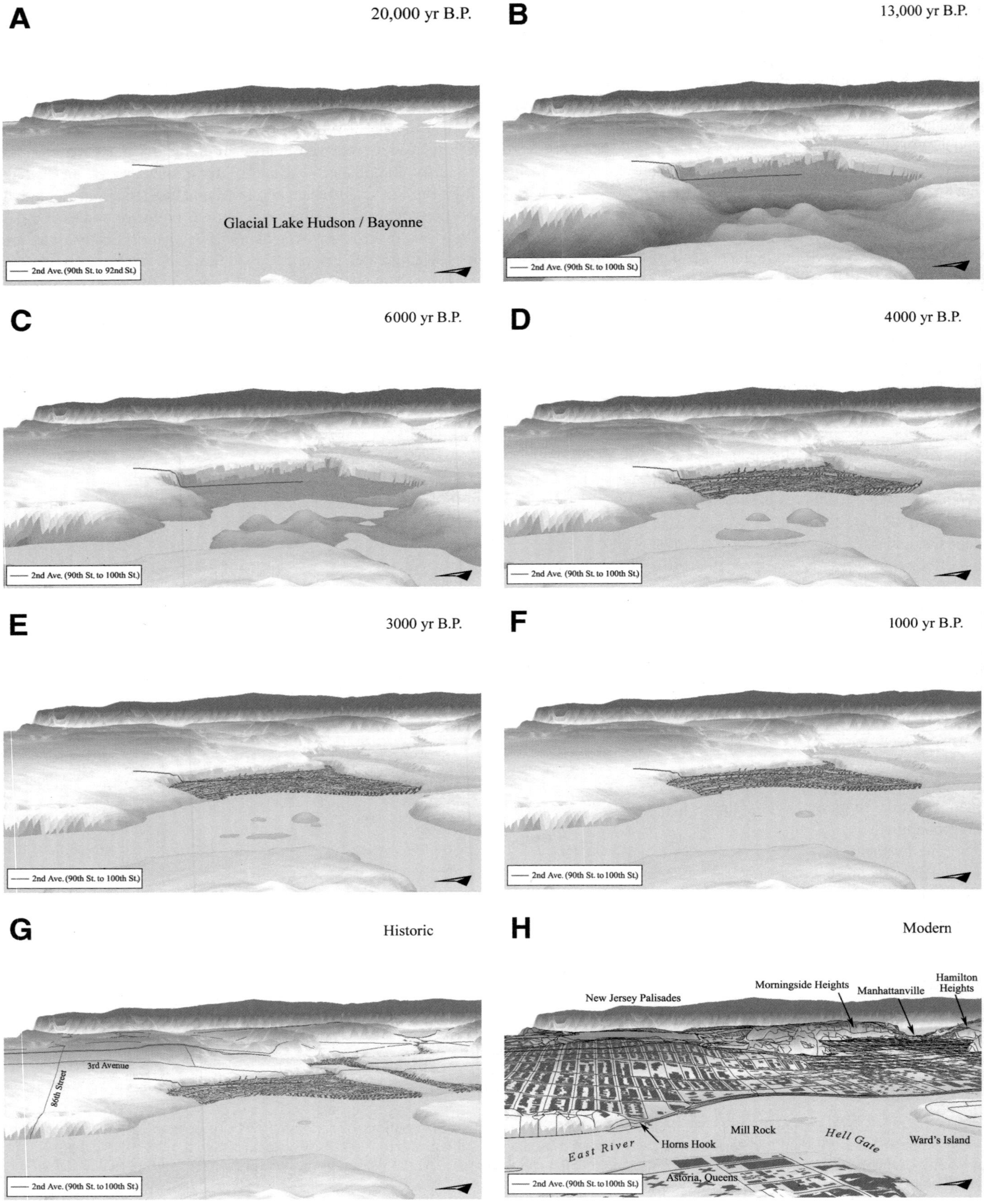

A 20,000 yr B.P.

Glacial Lake Hudson / Bayonne

2nd Ave. (90th St. to 92nd St.)

B 13,000 yr B.P.

2nd Ave. (90th St. to 100th St.)

C 6000 yr B.P.

2nd Ave. (90th St. to 100th St.)

D 4000 yr B.P.

2nd Ave. (90th St. to 100th St.)

E 3000 yr B.P.

2nd Ave. (90th St. to 100th St.)

F 1000 yr B.P.

2nd Ave. (90th St. to 100th St.)

G Historic

86th Street

3rd Avenue

2nd Ave. (90th St. to 100th St.)

H Modern

New Jersey Palisades

Morningside Heights

Manhattanville

Hamilton Heights

East River

Horns Hook

Mill Rock

Hell Gate

Ward's Island

Astoria, Queens

2nd Ave. (90th St. to 100th St.)

Figure 11. (A) Pleistocene glacial Lake Hudson–Bayonne complex inundates most of the project area. Lake elevations are ~30 ft (9 m) higher than modern sea level. The terrain above 92nd street was submerged; the segment between 90th and 92nd streets was not. This is consistent with field results, because lacustrine sediments were not identified between 90th and 92nd streets but were prominent in all cores to the north. (B) Drainage of glacial lakes and incision of lacustrine deposits. By 13,000 yr B.P., the proglacial lakes had drained, and sea level was 22 m below modern levels. Exposed, steep-sided terraces flanked the ancestral trenches of the Harlem and East Rivers. The project area was perched above the floodplain. It is probable that small tributaries from Manhattan drained across the project area, although no evidence for these was observed in the cores. (C) Emerging nearshore environment. By 6000 yr B.P., sea level had risen to a level (–11 m) where marine waters encroached onto the proximal edges of the lake terrace. During this very dynamic time period, a complex of freshwater fluvial sands and transgressing marine deposits began aggrading atop the lacustrine terrace surface. (D) Estuarine formation. At 4000 yr B.P., the entire terrace surface was subject to tidal cycles, as sea level had risen to between –6 and –7 m. Organic muck and silts suggest the formation of marshes, which would have transgressed across the project area commensurate with rising sea level. The presence of freshwater pollen species indicates that at these early stages of estuarine formation, the marsh still had a significant freshwater component. This would have been a habitat optimally suited for prehistoric (Late Archaic) activity, with convenient access to marine and terrestrial resources. (E) Zoned salt flats. Landward advance of mesohaline marshes (proximal) and subaqueous saline mud flats (distal). By 3000 yr B.P., fringing marsh biomes continued to develop, and the majority of the project terrain consisted of subaqueous mud flats. From 4000–3000 yr B.P., estuarine sedimentation is registered by mineral and organic sediment, reflecting pulses in sea-level rise. Shortly after 3000 yr B.P., the mud flats had stopped aggrading in response to general deceleration of sea-level rise. The environment would have remained attractive to later prehistoric groups (transitional Archaic to Woodland). (F) Stabilized subaqueous saline mud flat. At 1000 yr B.P., the landscapes reached a homeostatic state. This is signaled by the minimal accumulations of organic material on the mud flat bottoms. (G) Historic saline, thinly vegetated mud flat. The landform is referred to historically as a "meadowlands." During the early Euroamerican period, surfaces were level, subject only to tidal cycles. Thin and diffuse organic lenses and minor peats implicate changing (humanly influenced) edaphic conditions as subaqueous vegetation communities expanded across the landform. (H) Modern land surface built up by domestic debris, construction material, and fill. The infilling during the late nineteenth century reclaimed the major land segments of Hell Gate Bay. The landform was capped with ~3–6 m of fill material to raise shore elevations 4–4.5 m above sea level.

---

previously documented archaeological record; the age of buried deposits; and the composition, thickness, and preservation potential of buried deposits.

Table 3 reconstructs the buried landform history in an archaeological preservation model for the eastern shoreline of Manhattan Island and then projects these observations into a more regional paradigm. Source documents for the broader human ecological constructs of the greater New York City area include extensive late Quaternary mapping efforts for the Lower Hudson and northern New Jersey (Stone et al., 2002) and a recent synthesis for New York Harbor and Lower Manhattan (Schuldenrein et al., 2007). Sea-level projections are also integrated within the paleogeographic model. The archaeological probability assessment is proposed on a ranked scale for high, moderate, low, and no probability.

The lowermost (lake) sediments (AU-II) preclude archaeological preservation because they correspond to the terminal Pleistocene glacial lake basin. They predate the generally accepted time frame for human presence in North America and could not otherwise have sustained human activity. Negligible to low probabilities are assigned to Paleoindian time periods, since the underlying dated landforms (Lake Hudson) predate human arrival, and the radiocarbon-dated sequence indicates a depositional hiatus between AU-II and AU-III during the Paleoindian period. There is a low probability for Early and Middle Archaic sites because the landforms are residual features of high-energy loci (i.e., channel floors, braided floodplains) of AU-III, which would have eroded sites away; moreover, early to middle Holocene sites would have been small, consisting of minor assemblages susceptible to even localized reworking and displacement. A moderate preservation ranking is given to the two late Holocene estuarine and organic

sediment complexes AU-IV-a and AU-IV-b (4200–3200 yr B.P.), which correlate to the Late Archaic period. The basal estuarine matrices (up to 3 m thick) represent quiescent settings—marshes and mud flats flanked by aquatic (wetlands) biomes—when prehistoric peoples were known to have utilized resource-rich estuaries in the Lower Hudson. The estuarine microenvironment—sustaining saltwater and freshwater resources—is both an optimal preservation and settlement locus. Sites are likely to have been dominated by oyster middens and food-processing stations. Nevertheless, the likelihood for encountering sites is tempered by an expectedly diffuse site distribution and restricted site signature (i.e., small shell mounds, food-processing stations) and significant disturbances along the interfaces between uplands and littoral settings ringing Hell Gate Bay. The upper estuarine complex (AU-IV-c) defines a discontinuous (<0.3 m), vegetation- and sediment-choked marsh. Its expression is not sufficiently deep or extensive enough to form an assessment of preservation potential, but disturbances and a compressed sequence suggest that the potential for prehistoric Woodland occupations is low. The uppermost (fill) complexes (AU-V and AU-VI) are not intact and likely represent disturbed marsh meadows capped and filled historically, with a moderate potential for intact historical sites associated with eighteenth- and nineteenth-century utilization of Hell Gate Bay.

CONCLUSIONS

The investigations for the Second Avenue Subway offered a unique opportunity for geoarchaeological inquiry of a buried Manhattan landscape, one that had never been previously examined for such purposes. The study represents the first integrated

TABLE 3. CHRONOSTRATIGRAPHIC SUMMARY

Age (yr B.P., uncalibrated)	Archaeological period	Regional sea-level model (m) (Schuldenrein et al., 2007)	Analytical unit	Landform	Archaeological probability
0–500	Historic	0	V–VI	Marsh meadows infilled in nineteenth century	Moderate
1000	Late Woodland	–1.5	IV-c	Stable brackish mud flat	Low
2000	Middle Woodland	–3			
3000	Early Woodland	–4.5	IV-b	Brackish marsh transitions to a subaqueous mud flat	
4000	Late Archaic	–6.5			Low to moderate
5000		–8	IV-a	Freshwater marsh and shoreline transitioning to brackish marsh	Moderate
6000		–9	III	Fluvial-shoreline environment	Low
7000	Middle Archaic	–11		Initially an eroded surface of lacustrine terrace deposits (postbreaching of Narrows) that eventually sees a complex of high-energy beach and fluvial channel deposits as rising sea level reaches surface of terrace	Low
8000		–16			
9000	Early Archaic	–23			
10,000					
11,000 to 12,000	Paleoindian				None to low
12,000 to 15,000	Pre-Cultural/ Pre-Clovis?		II	Pleistocene glacial lake, breaching of the Narrows and Long Island Sound	None
15,000+	Pre-Cultural			Pleistocene glacial lake (freshwater)	None

human paleoecological study of an estuary in Manhattan and demonstrates the utility of employing earth science methods to solve archaeological problems in cultural resource investigations.

An integrated research design was structured around an extensive database that included: baseline surface geology maps, geotechnical and engineering maps, and historical maps and records. Collectively, these data sets allowed us to streamline the field effort. Specifically, they guided the placement of cores at those locales that would provide the deepest and richest paleoenvironmental data sets. In this case, a more than reasonable expectation for recovery of thick Holocene organic matrices—confirming the presence of the estuary—was a target of the subsurface exploration. The procurement of the expected sediment type and its diagnostic potential for buried landscape reconstruction was the first step in the development of a paleoecological model, which was indexed by radiocarbon dates, bolstered by retrieval of microfloral and faunal remains, and fine-tuned by a sedimentologically based history of estuarine zonation.

The paleoenvironmental model was next transformed into a three-dimensional projection of human subsistence environments with the use of an integrated digital elevation model (DEM) and GIS platform. Archaeological components were fed into the landscape reconstructions at key temporal breaks in the prehistoric succession. It was possible, therefore, to project the changing human and physical geography of the Second Avenue terrain through time.

Finally, a model for archaeological expectation was generated based largely on the aforementioned data sets and reconstructions. The data confirm that the only sealed and preserved sediments with archaeological potential are those of the estuarine depositional complex dated to ca. 4200–3000 yr B.P. No direct or artifactual evidence of archaeological remains was identified.

While it was clear that the prospects of encountering a prehistoric or even historic site along the Second Avenue footprint was inherently low, the stronger possibility of synthesizing both the depositional sequence and the chronology facilitated construction of a regionally applicable model of archaeological probability. The estuarine environment, sealed beneath a protective covering of several centuries of urban fill, was documented as a potential subsistence environment during the middle to late Holocene when aboriginal Americans took advantage of a lush biome. The buried landform model serves as a scientific basis for assessing preservation potential, not only for the location itself, but as a baseline, regional protocol for future development and planning concerns.

Perhaps most significantly, the field work began and ended with excavation of five discontinuous core segments through the rubble of Upper Manhattan. The data yield underscores the enormous potential of geoarchaeological methodologies in increasingly challenging landscape settings. As converging planning and preservation interests continue to underwrite most archaeological exploration worldwide, the application of innovative and sustainable approaches is the key to expanding archaeological inquiry.

ACKNOWLEDGMENTS

We are indebted to Chris Bennett and his staff at the Second Avenue Project, Metropolitan Transportation Authority Capital Construction Company (MTACC), for the opportunity to work on this project. Zack Davis (Louis Berger Associates) coordinated initial phases of the archaeological effort. Pollen and macrobotanical analyses were carried out by Dorothy Peteet (Lamont-Doherty Laboratories, Columbia University, New York). Lynn Wingard (U.S. Geological Survey) performed the malacological studies, and Randa Harris (University of West Georgia) undertook the sedimentological and geochemical studies. Mark Smith conducted the GIS analyses with his usual impeccable standards of professionalism. We appreciate the constructive comments of three anonymous reviewers and the invitation by volume editor Tony Brown to contribute this paper.

REFERENCES CITED

Ammerman, A.J., McClennen, C.E., De Min, M., and Housley, R., 1999, Sea-level change and the archaeology of early Venice: Antiquity, v. 73, p. 303–312.

Bernstein, D.J., 1993, Prehistoric Subsistence on the Southern New England Coast: The Record from Narragansett Bay: New York, Academic Press, 188 p.

Bolton, R.P., and Hall, E.H., 1906, Historical Guide to the City of New York: New York, City History Club of New York, 472 p.

Bronk Ramsey, C., 1995, Radiocarbon calibration and analysis of stratigraphy: The OxCal program: Radiocarbon, v. 37, no. 2, p. 425–430.

Bronk Ramsey, C., 2001, Development of the radiocarbon calibration program OxCal: Radiocarbon, v. 43, no. 2A, p. 355–363.

Butzer, K.W., 1982, Archaeology as Human Ecology: Cambridge, UK, Cambridge University Press, 380 p.

Cadwell, D.H., 1991, Surficial Geologic Map of New York, Lower Hudson Sheet: New York State Museum Map and Chart Series 40, scale 1:250,000.

Cantwell, A.M., and di Zerega Wall, D., 2001, Unearthing Gotham: The Archaeology of New York City: New Haven, Connecticut, Yale University Press, 374 p.

Carbotte, S.M., Bell, R.E., Ryan, W.B.F., McHugh, C., Slagle, A., Nitsche, F., and Rubenstone, J., 2004, Environmental change and oyster colonization within the Hudson River estuary linked to Holocene climate: Geo-Marine Letters, v. 24, p. 212–224, doi:10.1007/s00367-004-0179-9.

Claassen, C., 1995, Dogan Point: A Shell Matrix Site in the Hudson Valley: Franklin Pierce College Occasional Publications in Northeastern Anthropology 14: Bethlehem, Connecticut, Franklin Pierce College, 182 p.

Donnelly, J.P., Driscoll, N.W., Uchupi, E., Keigwin, L.D., Schwab, W.C., Thieler, E.R., and Swift, S.A., 2005, Catastrophic meltwater discharge down the Hudson Valley: A potential trigger for the Intra-Allerød cold period: Geology, v. 33, p. 89–92, doi:10.1130/G21043.1.

Fischer, D.W., Isachsen, Y.W., and Rickard, L.V., 1970, Geologic Map of New York State, Lower Hudson Sheet: New York State Museum Map and Chart Series 15, scale 1:250,000.

Fleming, K., Johnston, P., Zwartz, D., Yokoyama, Y., Lambeck, K., and Chappell, J., 1998, Refining the eustatic sea-level curve since the Last Glacial Maximum using far- and intermediate-field sites: Earth and Planetary Science Letters, v. 163, p. 327–342, doi:10.1016/S0012-821X(98)00198-8.

Flemming, B.W., 2000, A revised textural classification of gravel-free muddy sediments on the basis of ternary diagrams: Continental Shelf Research, v. 20, p. 1125–1137, doi:10.1016/S0278-4343(00)00015-7.

Fletcher, C.H., Pizzuto, J.E., Suku, J., and Van Pelt, J.E., 1993, Sea-level rise acceleration and the drowning of the Delaware Bay coast at 1.8 ka: Geology, v. 21, p. 121–124, doi:10.1130/0091-7613(1993)021<0121:SLRAAT>2.3.CO;2.

Fullerton, D.S., 1992, Quaternary Map of the Hudson River 4°× 6° Quadrangle, United States and Canada (NK-18): U.S. Geological Survey Miscellaneous Investigations Series Map I-1420, scale 1:1,000,000.

Geoarcheology Research Associates (GRA), 1996, Staten Island Bridges Program: Modernization and Capacity Enhancement Project; Phase IB: Geomorphological Analysis, Final Report of Field Investigation: New York, report prepared for Parsons, Brinckerhoff, Quade, and Douglas, Inc., 21 p.

Geoarcheology Research Associates (GRA), 1997, Enhancement Project; Phase IB/3: Geomorphological Analysis, Final Report of Field Investigations: Report on Coring and Additional Radiocarbon Dating: New York, report prepared for Parsons, Brinckerhoff, Quade, and Douglas, Inc.

Holliday, V.T., 2004, Soils and Archaeological Research: Oxford, UK, Oxford University Press, 448 p.

International Subcommission on Stratigraphic Classification (ISSC), 1994, International Stratigraphic Guide (2nd edition; edited by Amos Salvador): Boulder, Colorado, Geological Society of America, 214 p.

Isachsen, Y.W., Landing, E., Lauber, J.M., Rickard, L.V., and Rogers, W.B., 1991, Geology of New York: A Simplified Account: Albany, New York State Museum, 284 p.

Kenen, O.K., 1999, Brackish Estuarine Marsh Sediments in the Raritan River Estuary and Their Relationship to Sea Level during the Late Holocene [M.S. thesis]: Rutgers, State University of New Jersey, 140 p.

King, T.F., 2004, Cultural Resource Laws and Practice: Walnut Creek, California, AltaMira Press, 408 p.

La Peyre, M.K., and Rowe, S., 2003, Effects of salinity changes on growth of *Ruppia maritimia* L: Aquatic Botany, v. 77, no. 3, p. 235–241, doi:10.1016/S0304-3770(03)00109-8.

McManamon, F.P., Stout, A., and Barnes, J.A., 2008, Managing Archaeological Resources: Global Context, National Programs, Local Actions: Walnut Creek, California, Left Coast Press, 299 p.

Morley, M.W., 2010, The Battersea Channel: A former course of the River Thames?: The London Archaeologist, v. 12, p. 188–194.

National Historic Preservation Act (NHPA), 1966 (as amended in 2006), 16 U.S.C. 470. Advisory Council on Historic Preservation, electronic document: http://www.achp.gov/nhpa.html (accessed December 2008).

Newman, W., Thurber, D., Zeiss, H., Rokach, A., and Musich, L., 1969, Late Quaternary geology of the Hudson River estuary: A preliminary report: Transactions of the New York Academy of Sciences, v. 31, p. 548–570.

New York State Preservation Act (NYSPA), 1980, Section 14.09. New York State Preservation Office, available at http://nysparks.state.ny.us/shpo/environ/preservation.htm (accessed December 2008).

Pescatore, T., Rosaria Senatore, M., Capretto, G., and Lerro, G., 2001, Holocene coastal environments near Pompeii before the A.D. 79 eruption of Mount Vesuvius, Italy: Quaternary Research, v. 55, no. 1, p. 77–85, doi:10.1006/qres.2000.2186.

Ridge, J.C., 2003, The last deglaciation of the northeastern United States: A combined varve, paleomagnetic, and calibrated ^{14}C chronology, *in* Hart, J., and Cremeens, D., eds., Geoarchaeology in the Glaciated Northeast: Albany, New York State Museum, p. 15–48.

Riker, J., 1904, Revised History of Harlem: New York, New Harlem Publishing, 946 p.

Ritchie, W.A., and Funk, R.E., 1971, Evidence for Early Archaic occupations on Staten Island: Pennsylvania Archaeologist, v. 41, no. 3, p. 45–49.

Salwen, B., 1964, Current research, Northeast: American Antiquity, v. 29, p. 541.

Sanders, J.E., and Merguerian, C., 1994, The glacial geology of New York City and vicinity, *in* Benimoff, A.I., ed., The Geology of Staten Island, New York; XI Annual Meeting Field Guide and Proceedings: Trenton, Geological Association of New Jersey, p. 93–200.

Schuberth, C.J., 1968, The Geology of New York City and Environs: Garden City, New York, The Natural History Press, 304 p.

Schuldenrein, J., 1995, Prehistory and the changing Holocene geography of Dogan Point, *in* Claassen, C., ed., Dogan Point: A Shell Matrix Site in the Lower Hudson Valley: Franklin Pierce College Occasional Publications in Northeastern Anthropology 14: Bethlehem, Connecticut, Franklin Pierce College, p. 39–64.

Schuldenrein, J., Larsen, C.E., Aiuvalasit, M.A., Smith M.A., and Malin-Boyce, S., 2007, Geomorphological/Archaeological Borings and GIS Model of the Submerged Paleoenvironment in the New York/New Jersey Harbor and Bight in Connection with the New York and New Jersey Harbor Navigation Project, Port of New York and New Jersey: Portland, Maine, report prepared for NEA Inc., 172 p.

Sirkin, L., 1986, Pleistocene stratigraphy of Long Island, New York, *in* Cadwell, D.H., ed., The Wisconsinan Stage of the First Geological District, Eastern New York: Albany, New York State Museum, p. 6–21.

Sirkin, L., and Stuckenrath, R., 1980, The post-Washingtonian warm interval in the northern Atlantic coastal plain: Geological Society of America Bulletin, v. 91, p. 332–336, doi:10.1130/0016-7606(1980)91<332:TPWIIT>2.0.CO;2.

Stanford, S.D., 2010, Onshore record of Hudson River drainage to the continental shelf from the late Miocene through the late Wisconsinan deglaciation, USA: Synthesis and revision: Boreas, v. 39, no. 1, p. 1–17, doi:10.1111/j.1502-3885.2009.00106.x.

Stone, B.D., Stanford, S.D., and White, R.W., 2002, Surficial Geological Map of Northern New Jersey: U.S. Geological Survey Miscellaneous Investigations Map I-2540: Trenton, New Jersey, scale 1:100,000.

Thieler, E.R., Butman, B., Schwab, W.C., Allison, M.A., Driscoll, N.W., Donnelly, J.P., and Uchupi, E., 2007, A catastrophic meltwater flood event and the formation of the Hudson Shelf Valley: Palaeogeography, Palaeoclimatology, Palaeoecology, v. 246, p. 120–136, doi:10.1016/j.palaeo.2006.10.030.

Thorbahn, P., and Cox, D., 1988, The effect of estuary formation on prehistoric settlement in southern Rhode Island, *in* Nicholas, G., ed., Holocene Human Ecology in Northeastern North America: New York, Plenum Press, p. 167–184.

U.S. Department of Agriculture (USDA), 1994, Soil Survey Manual: Washington, D.C., Soil Conservation Service, U.S. Department of Agriculture Handbook 18, 503 p.

Varekamp, J.C., Thomas, E., and van de Plassche, O., 1992, Relative sea level rise and climate change over the last 1500 years: Terra Nova, v. 4, p. 293–304, doi:10.1111/j.1365-3121.1992.tb00818.x.

Viele, E.L., 1874, Topographical Atlas of the City of New York Including the Annexed Territory. Showing Their Original Water Courses and Made Land: Prepared under the Director of Egbert L. Viele, Civil and Topographical Engineer: New York, Map Division, New York Public Library, scale 1:12,000.

Weiss, D., 1974, Late Pleistocene stratigraphy and paleoecology of the Lower Hudson River estuary: Geological Society of America Bulletin, v. 85, p. 1561–1580, doi:10.1130/0016-7606(1974)85<1561:LPSAPO>2.0.CO;2.

Yamin, R., and Schuldenrein, J., 2007, Landscape archaeology in Lower Manhattan: The Collect Pond as an evolving cultural landmark in early New York City, *in* Hicks, D., McAtackney, L., and Fairclough, G., eds., Envisioning Landscape: Situations and Standpoints in Archaeology and Heritage: Walnut Creek, California, Left Coast Press, p. 75–100.

MANUSCRIPT ACCEPTED BY THE SOCIETY 3 AUGUST 2010

The Geological Society of America
Special Paper 476
2011

The contribution of English Heritage Aggregates Levy Sustainability Fund research to geoarchaeology and sustainability

Ingrid Ward

17 Brickfield Cottages, Somerleyton, Suffolk NR325QW, UK

ABSTRACT

Cultural resources are an important nonrenewable national asset that, like the mineral resources in which they can occur, are finite and need protection. In the six years since 2002, geoarchaeological research funded by English Heritage (EH) through the Aggregates Levy Sustainability Fund (ALSF) has significantly enhanced our understanding and ability to safeguard the historic environment in areas impacted by aggregate extraction. Most of the funding has been allocated toward strategic research and survey aimed at characterization of both the mineral and archaeological resources, and also toward monitoring and management of the archaeological resources. A smaller but significant contribution has been directed at development and application of new survey and specialist archaeological dating techniques, as well as unexpected discoveries. Such research is aimed at reducing irreversible damage of the archaeological resource as the result of aggregate extraction and ultimately provides the fundamental evidence on which minerals planning policies can be based, thus protecting the finite resources for future generations.

THE ENGLISH HERITAGE AGGREGATES LEVY SUSTAINABILITY FUND

English Heritage (EH) is the official advisory body to the UK government on the historic environment. The government set out its view on the desirability of sustainable development via its Planning Policy Guidance (PPG) and Mineral Policy Guidance (MPG) notes. PPG16 (1990) "Archaeology and Planning" delineates the government's policy on archaeological remains on land and how they should be preserved or recorded, both in an urban setting and in the countryside (see also Humble, 2008). In April 2002, the Aggregates Levy Sustainability Fund (ALSF) was introduced by the UK government for a 2 yr introductory period in order to address a range of environmental problems in areas affected by extraction of primary land-won and marine-dredged aggregates resources. As a major distributor of the fund, English Heritage supports projects that seek to reduce the impact of aggregate extraction on the historic environment, both terrestrial and marine. The distribution of funding to terrestrial (£19.7) and marine (£4.3) research is approximately proportional to the amount of aggregate resources that are obtained from terrestrial (79%) and marine (21%) sources. The scheme has since been extended to March 2008, with a further extension pending (full details of the ALSF can be obtained from Defra, 2003).[1]

Since the inception of the scheme, English Heritage has funded over 250 research projects to the total of almost £24m, a full list of which can be found on the English Heritage Web site (www.english-heritage.org.uk/ALSF) or through Defra (http://alsf.defra.gov.uk). The ALSF is used by English Heritage to fund research that lies beyond the scope of PPG16, in particular, where archaeological discoveries are made after planning permission has been granted, which are unexpected and could not reasonably

---

[1]The ALSF scheme will now cease as of 31 March 2011.

Ward, I., 2011, The contribution of English Heritage Aggregates Levy Sustainability Fund research to geoarchaeology and sustainability, *in* Brown, A.G., Basell, L.S., and Butzer, K.W., eds., Geoarchaeology, Climate Change, and Sustainability: Geological Society of America Special Paper 476, p. 173–182, doi:10.1130/2011.2476(13). For permission to copy, contact editing@geosociety.org. © 2011 The Geological Society of America. All rights reserved.

have been predicted. The launch of the ALSF also coincided with the transfer of responsibilities for England's maritime archaeology to English Heritage, providing a timely boost to funding of essential research into the marine historic environment affected by aggregate extraction. The majority of English Heritage's research funding has, however, been allocated to strategic research and surveys aimed at defining the potential impacts on known archaeological resources within areas currently impacted by aggregates extraction, and defining potential archaeological resources within areas likely to be at risk from future aggregates extraction. Geoarchaeological methods and concepts have been central in much of this research, including site survey, resource mapping, predictive modeling, scientific dating, and conservation. Such work has justifiably been given the highest priority because it is this type of research that can potentially deliver the greatest benefits in terms of understanding and safeguarding the historic environment (Thompson, 2006).

This chapter outlines some of the contributions that ALSF research funded through English Heritage has made to geoarchaeology and the sustainability of our cultural heritage. Further, it illustrates how geoarchaeological approaches offer a means of synthesizing the mutual developments of particular environments and their archaeological records, thereby informing frameworks that aid the prospection, understanding, and management of the archaeological resource. Information on English Heritage's position on mineral extraction and the historic environment and the contribution made by the ALSF to this is given by Humble (2008).

GEOARCHAEOLOGICAL RESOURCES

The extraction of primary aggregates represents 82% by tonnage of all non–fossil fuel minerals extracted from the land and sea in the UK. It is the characteristics of the geological deposits (age and origin) from which hard (crushed rock) and soft (sand and gravel) aggregate deposits are obtained that primarily determine the nature of archaeological impact that may occur from extraction. Moreover, there remains, particularly in glaciofluvial landscapes, a close genetic relation among landscape relief, surface geology, soils and drainage patterns, and the nature of human activity, such as archaeological sites, cultural patterns, and settlements (Knight et al., 1999). Understanding the geological characteristics of the deposit therefore provides the essential foundation for any large-scale evaluation of archaeological or paleoenvironmental potential. Importantly, the most complete and informative sedimentary and paleoenvironmental sequences are not necessarily associated with archaeological sites themselves (Bell et al., 2006).

Depending on the mode and age of formation, sand and gravel deposits may seal, contain, and/or underlie single- or multiple-episode archaeological deposits. Hard aggregates are almost exclusively of pre-Pleistocene and generally pre-Tertiary origin, and quarrying will only affect archaeology overlying or very occasionally concealed in caves and fissures within the exploited

rock (Brown, 2009). Sand and gravel resources are largely derived from a range of Pleistocene and Holocene sources, the majority of which are fluvially derived, resulting in a concentration of quarries along a drainage network, especially corridors of high-order rivers or fossil valleys (Fig. 1). Pleistocene-age gravel deposits of glacial, glaciofluvial, fluvial, and beach origin form much of the Lower or Middle Paleolithic record, while late Devensian and Holocene sand and gravel deposits host much of the buried archaeology of valley landscapes (Brown, 2009). Thus, evidence of early hominid activity may be sealed by significant thicknesses of gravel units, such as the 700,000-yr-old remains at Happisburgh and Pakefield (Rose, 2006; Wymer and Robins, 2006), or it may be contained within them, such as the 500,000-yr-old remains at Eartham quarry, otherwise known as Boxgrove (Roberts and Parfitt, 1999). However, the alluvium that serves to protect many archaeological sites also presents challenges in terms of remote detection and extraction and remains an ongoing research focus for ALSF funding.

Marine dredging also presents complexities for prospection of archaeological sites. Marine sand and gravel deposits (i.e., those below 18 m at low tide) are of the same geological origins as those found on land, but they are now submerged as a result of fluctuating sea levels over the past 2 m.y. (Gubbay, 2005). Sands and gravels dredged off southern and eastern England simply represent the downstream, submerged equivalents of deposits quarried in river valleys onshore. Deposits in the Irish Sea and central North Sea originate from the same ice masses that covered northern Britain during the last glaciation. Consequently, in many areas, aggregate deposits form a continuum from land to sea. The most recent drowning of the UK continental shelf occurred around 8500 yr ago; hence, any prehistoric archaeological material will occur as primary deposits in older deposits or as secondary (reworked) deposits in Holocene-age material. Wrecks will occur in the most recent deposits or on the seabed. The international importance of marine sand and gravel is therefore evident both in economic terms (see also European Marine Sand and Gravel Group, http://www.ciria.org/emsagg/introduction .htm) and in historic terms.

GEOARCHAEOLOGICAL RESEARCH IN THE TERRESTRIAL ENVIRONMENT

Characterizing the Landscape

In order to manage aggregate landscapes and secure sustainability of the archaeological resource, it is necessary to at least gain some knowledge of the character and formation of that resource. Therefore, several ALSF projects have been aimed at characterizing the historic environment of aggregate landscapes, including river valleys such as Lower Lea Valley (see http://www.molas.org.uk/pages/projectsLeaValley.asp), the Swale-Ure Washlands (The Landscape Agency, 2005; Bridgland et al., 2010), the Ribble Valley (Chiverrell et al., 2008; Quartermaine and Chiverrell, 2007), the Trent Valley (Knight and Howard,

Figure 1. Map showing distribution of sand and gravel resources and quarries in the UK, and location of areas mentioned in text (modified from Hannis, 2007). River valleys are not only rich sources of sand and gravel, but they have also been focal areas for human activity for at least the last 10,000 yr.

2004; Howard, 2005), and the Till-Tweed catchment (Passmore et al., 2006). Other nonriver landscapes include coastal areas such as the Sussex/Hampshire coastal corridor (Bates et al., 2007), areas of cover sands such as in Vale of Pickering (Powlesland et al., 2006), and uplands producing crushed rock aggregates, such as the Magnesian Limestone belt of South and West Yorkshire (Roberts et al., 2007). A common theme amongst these projects is predictive mapping of the paleolandscape and archaeological resource using geographical information systems (GIS) in order to provide information that will assist future mitigation and management of the landscape and provide a framework for future research. Such landscape character assessments are fundamental to ensuring sustainable development.

Geophysical Survey

Geophysical techniques remain the main noninvasive tool for archaeological evaluation (for a full review of these, see Lin-

ford, 2006). Research through the ALSF has shown geophysical methods to be useful both for large-scale surveys of aggregates landscapes, such as the Vale of Pickering in Yorkshire (Powlesland et al., 2006), as well as for localized exploration, such as the Catholme ceremonial complex in Staffordshire (Watters, 2006). The Vale of Pickering project, one the largest archaeological research projects in Europe, has demonstrated that even with traditional methods of aerial photography and magnetometry, a great deal can still be discovered between areas where site-specific surveys have already been undertaken (Powlesland et al., 2006). At Catholme, visual and quantitative analyses of the geophysical signatures from a combination of resistivity, magnetic gradient, and ground-penetrating radar (GPR) surveys are now being used to provide a three-dimensional output of the ceremonial complex structure and remaining archaeological features (Fig. 2; Watters, 2006), ultimately conserving the historic environment through reconstruction of the archaeological deposits and their contextual landscape.

Figure 2. Crop marks and (inset) geovisualization of the Sunburst monument from the Catholme ceremonial complex, Staffordshire, UK. Modeling and visualization from ground-penetrating radar, electrical tomography, and archaeological data allow for greater interpretation of the archaeological feature (image courtesy of Meg Watters, University of Birmingham).

Other archaeogeophysical techniques being progressed through ALSF research are remote sensing using ground-penetrating radar (GPR) and airborne light detection and ranging (LiDAR). Realizing the potential of LiDAR to provide direct visual records of very slight earthwork remains, English Heritage undertook a survey of the Stonehenge landscape, where new sites were discovered and known ones extended (Bewley et al., 2005). An even more difficult undertaking is the remote sensing of heritage features beneath dense tree canopy, but successful surveys have been achieved in the Forest of Dean (Crutchley, 2006; Devereux et al., 2005; Crow et al., 2007) using last pulse data from LiDAR (Fig. 3). In another study, backscatter laser intensity measurements from LiDAR were used to remotely determine soil properties, such as organic content and soil moisture (Challis et al., 2007). This allows identification of areas of preferential organic preservation in areas affected by aggregate extraction, thereby demarcating zones of archaeological potential. Such research helps develop knowledge and appreciation of the historic environment that is, or may be, affected by aggregate extraction.

When used in combination with GIS, these archaeogeophysical techniques can be used to develop predictive modeling of paleoenvironmental and archaeological resources in areas rich in aggregates (e.g., Carey et al., 2006), benefiting planning authorities and improving future decision making. Research in the Ribble Valley has also shown that the combined use of LiDAR, digital elevation modeling data, and GIS can provide a rapid assessment of the limits and volume of near-surface terrace deposits, as well as the location of possibly unproductive paleochannels, thereby improving the accuracy and cost-effectiveness of geomorphologically based aggregate assessments and archaeological risk assessments (Chiverrell et al., 2008).

Chronostratigraphy

Chronostratigraphy is important to dating of primary aggregate deposits and to archaeological remains found within them and provides essential ground-truthing of all landscape models. Optically stimulated luminescence (OSL) of sands and amino acid racemization (AAR) of molluscs form the principal methods for direct dating of aggregate, and in particular Paleolithic, deposits and together comprise over a third of the dating undertaken for ALSF projects (Fig. 4). Examples of the successful use of OSL dating of Paleolithic deposits include Lynford Quarry, Norfolk (Schwenninger and Rhodes, 2005), and the Sussex/Hampshire corridor (Schwenninger et al., 2006). Useful but unsuccessful attempts were also made to use AAR dating on molluscs from both these sites. More successful application of AAR dating has been undertaken in the Swale-Ure Washlands (Penkman and Collins, 2007), the proto–Medway valley (Penkman et al., 2007), and the Trent valley (e.g., Penkman and McGrory, 2007). These

Figure 3. Computer modeled image of the last-pulse return of the light detection and ranging data for the Forest of Dean survey, showing the forest floor after the process of removing vegetation (Crow et al., 2007; their figure 2; image courtesy of Peter Crow, Forest Research). These surveys have revealed evidence for an extensive history of mining and quarrying, including bell pits, quarry faces, rail and track-ways, spoil heaps, and scowles.

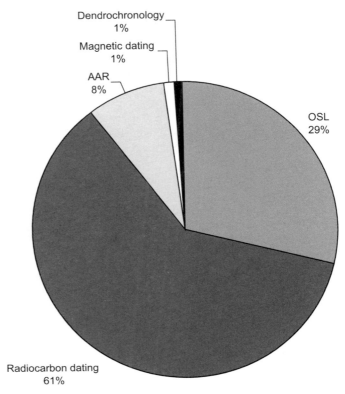

Scientific dating undertaken for ALSF projects (2002-8)

Figure 4. Pie chart showing relative distribution of dating methods applied to Aggregates Levy Sustainability Fund (ALSF) projects from 2002 to 2008. Although optically stimulated luminescence (OSL) and amino acid racemization (AAR) are principal direct dating methods for aggregate deposits, radiocarbon dating is still the most popular method used.

and other recent AAR results (e.g., Parfitt et al., 2005) are significantly improving our understanding of British Quaternary stratigraphy and its links to continental Europe and the marine record.

Despite the suitability of OSL and AAR dating for sand and gravel deposits, radiocarbon dating remains the standard technique for dating archaeological sites on aggregate deposits (Fig. 2) (see also Bayliss et al., 2007, 2008). Radiocarbon dating of waterlogged plant and macrofossil material can provide a reliable chronology of floodplain sequences (e.g., Nene Valley, Suffolk Rivers), while radiocarbon dating of articulated bones can provide an indirect chronology of sediments and gravel terraces in which they occur (e.g., Boismier, 2003). Unfortunately, the poor survival and quality of macrofossil, bone, and antler material from sand and gravel deposits can severely limit the construction of reliable chronologies (see Brock et al., 2007). Carbonized organic matter, including carbonized plant macrofossil (e.g., Ladle and Woodward, 2009), cremated bone (e.g., Carver et al., 2009), and carbonized residue from the internal surfaces of

ceramics (e.g., Beamish, 2009) may survive better. In all cases, it is necessary to consider the taphonomy of the sample and the geomorphological and stratigraphic context in which it is found (Bayliss et al., 2007, 2008).

Although utilized less (Fig. 2), other methods used to date aggregate sites include magnetic dating and dendrochronology. An example of the latter is the dating of bog-oaks preserved in paleochannels of the Trent valley, which provided the chronology of geomorphic change at the Trent-Soar confluence and valuable reference data for prehistoric dendrochronology in England (Bayliss et al., 2008).

Monitoring and Management

In addition to resource characterization, it is impossible to sustain a resource without some degree of monitoring and management. Quite a few ALSF projects have integrated geoarchaeological techniques and approaches into guidance documents that deal with the archaeological planning approach to aggregate extraction both at a regional and national scale (e.g., Waddington and Passmore, 2006). These guidance documents recognize the generic associations among landform, sediment, and archaeological and/or paleoenvironmental features.

Throughout much of the UK, the underlying geology has provided a rich archaeological heritage, good agricultural productivity, a variety of wetland and terrestrial habitats, and a wealth of sand and gravel resources. As outlined by Knight et al. (1999), the economic need for continued aggregate production and the conservation need to maintain landscape cultural, ecological, and geomorphic resources should not be seen as end members for landscape management. Rather, they form part of a continuum of approaches toward sustainable landscape development on different spatial and temporal scales. The mineral industry has the potential to provide a range of after-use schemes with associated environmental, social, and economic benefits on a scale not possible with other land uses. To this end, the Swale-Ure project has developed strategic guidance to deal with the consequences of mineral planning approvals and workings (The Landscape Agency, 2005).

GEOARCHAEOLOGICAL RESEARCH IN THE MARINE ENVIRONMENT

Characterizing the Landscape

Pressures on the minerals industry, including the need to reduce demand for land-based quarrying, are forcing further consideration of international trading in aggregates and use of alternative supply options, such as marine dredged materials. Approximately 21% of sand and gravel used in England and Wales is from marine sources, which is second only to Japan in the production of marine aggregates (Fox, 1993). Current marine aggregate supplies normally come from licenses situated ~10 km offshore, but future supplies will come from even further offshore, from water depths in excess of 20 m (BMAPA, 1997). In recognition of this, and with the support of the marine industry, the ALSF has funded a number of projects aimed at enhancing our archaeological understanding of the UK continental shelf (Westley et al., 2004) and our ability to predict potential areas of archaeological preservation (Fitch et al., 2005, 2007; Gaffney et al., 2007). The landscape models of the southern North Sea in particular (Gaffney et al., 2007) provide very tangible visualizations of the seafloor (e.g., Fig. 5) and significantly enhance our understanding of this submerged paleolandscape. Similar mapping and visualization have been provided from multibeam bathymetric data of the submerged paleovalley of the Arun River in the northern English Channel (Gupta et al., 2004).

The archaeological significance of surveying the broader deposits of paleoriver systems offshore (at least in southern and southeastern England) was recently made evident with the recovery of 28 Paleolithic hand axes off the coast of East Anglia (see http://www.wessexarch.co.uk/projects/marine/bmapa/north-sea-handaxes/). The northeast coast of East Anglia is an important area for human history, with Britain's oldest archaeological remains (ca. 700,000 yr B.P.) located in former river deposits of the Cromer Forest-bed at Happisburgh and Pakefield (Rose,

Figure 5. Seismic data cube illustrating chronostratigraphic relationship between Holocene and earlier features of an area near Dogger Bank in the southern North Sea (Gaffney et al., 2007, their figure 9.3; image courtesy of Vince Gaffney, University of Birmingham). The figure illustrates the significant potential of high-resolution geophysical survey to reveal Holocene and late Pleistocene features with which archaeological remains may be associated.

2006; Wymer and Robins, 2006). At the same time, the submerged river systems in this area have considerable potential as aggregate resources and are increasingly being favored for extraction licenses over the long-standing Outer Thames Estuary. The support given by the marine aggregates industry to ALSF research is a recognition of the potential for both discovery and destruction of this submerged archaeological resource.

Geophysical Survey

The better the baseline information, the better chance there is of identifying sustainable aggregate supply patterns for the future, with minimal impact on the most important archaeological and historic sites. Developments in marine geophysical techniques in particular have done much to improve the prospection of seabed deposits, but they have also helped in the characterization of archaeological remains exposed on and buried within marine aggregate deposits (see also Dunkley and Buxton, 2005; Dix, 2007). High-resolution sonar and enhanced geophysical processing techniques provide rapid means of archaeological site survey and evaluation, helping to discriminate wood- and metal-dominated archaeological sites, and ultimately aiming to improve management of the marine historic environment (Dix, 2007). Geophysical techniques can also be used to help define and quantify the physical impacts, such as dredge plume impacts (Dix and Lambkin, 2005), of aggregate extraction on marine deposits and associated archaeology. This information can be used to better estimate the shape and size of exclusion zones that might be applied around historic marine assets close to dredge sites. Thus, methodological studies such as these not only afford increased protection to the archaeological resource, but also aid in refinement of the mitigation strategies, which will reduce time and costs for the industry.

Geophysical exploration, and, in particular, use of high-resolution three-dimensional (3-D) seismic data, has also been a core part of mapping and modeling the drowned landscape of the English Channel (Gupta et al., 2004) and the southern North Sea (Fitch et al., 2005, 2007; Gaffney et al., 2007). Such maps are particularly useful in helping to define ancient riverine and coastal features, such as buried paleochannels, river terraces, coastal barriers and beach-dune systems, with potential implications for explaining the distribution of known archaeological sites (e.g., Rømer et al., 2006) and for predicting new archaeological sites (Neal and Roberts, 2000). Both from the industry and heritage perspective, projects that result in the acquisition and interpretation of data for increasing understanding of the presently poorly understood marine historic environment are considered particularly useful (see Stone and Satchell, 2007).

Chronostratigraphy

While improving the spatial characterization of the marine aggregate resource, there remains a complementary need for temporal characterization and ground-truthing of such infor-

mation. Radiocarbon dating has been used to date littoral and freshwater deposits off Great Yarmouth and to date peat deposits from the paleo-Arun as part of the Seabed Prehistory Project (Bayliss et al., 2008). Radiocarbon and paleoenvironmental analysis of peat recovered from the paleo-Arun confirms that terrestrial environments, and hence the potential for human activity, existed in this area from the last glaciation until the early Mesolithic (Leather et al., 2007). Increasing numbers of marine ALSF projects, such as the Paleo-Arun River project (e.g., Gupta et al., 2004), are incorporating some program of OSL dating, and future ALSF research may also explore the use of AAR dating in marine environments. Such information will provide an important link between conformable terrestrial and marine deposits (cf. Bates et al., 1997, 2007), and some continuity between disparate working elements of the aggregate industry.

Monitoring and Management

There are always going to be unexpected discoveries in extraction sites (e.g., Johnson and Waddington, 2008), but the aim for both heritage managers and industry is to reduce this unpredictability. In the marine environment, it is clear that high-resolution geophysical surveys are providing increasing detail of submerged surfaces with which to improve archaeological prospection. The next step is to use some of these outputs to improve our understanding of the association between certain landform elements and known types of archaeological and paleoenvironmental remains (e.g., Waddington and Passmore, 2006) and hence develop a first-order geomorphological estimation of the unknown archaeological and paleoenvironmental potential (see Ward and Larcombe, 2008). This will also provide a better context for interpreting new discoveries, such as the hand axes off East Anglia, and also those reported as part of the Protocol for Reporting Finds (BMAPA and EH, 2005).

ALSF AND SUSTAINABILITY

There has been a long-standing association between archaeology and aggregate extraction (see also Humble, 2008), and the quarry industry itself recognizes the importance of our national heritage as part of social progress and sustainability (see http://www.qpa.org/sus_social_heritage01.htm). Many interesting archaeological remains have been discovered as a result of quarrying, including some of the earliest evidence for colonization of Britain and most significant remains from our Ice Age past (Buteux, 2006). Indeed, the very origins of Paleolithic archaeology stem from mineral extraction (Wymer, 1968). The ALSF provides the opportunity to continue and extend this association to aggregate and related commercial groups, heritage planners and policy makers, archaeologists, Quaternary scientists, and the general public. The development of a sounder understanding of heritage resources increases the confidence of all stakeholders (Flatman et al., 2008).

The aggregate community also recognizes that mineral resources are important nonrenewable national assets that, like the cultural resources contained within them, are finite and need protection. To this effect, guidance for delineating Minerals Safeguarding Areas (MSAs) is being developed through the British Geological Survey, much of it based on findings from other ALSF-funded research (Hannis, 2007). As the aggregate industry invests in prospecting and environmental studies to assess new resource options, there is a concomitant need to invest in prospecting and management of cultural resources in these same areas. Such research underpins good-practice mechanisms aimed at securing longer-term environmental benefits relating to aggregate resources and ultimately provides the fundamental evidence on which minerals planning policies can be based.

The range of ALSF projects funded by English Heritage has generated a better foundation of knowledge for the management of heritage resources associated with aggregate reserves. A review of the impact that ALSF projects aimed at developing new guidance, standards, and best practice have had on the aggregates industry, archaeological curators, and practitioners is provided by Flatman et al. (2008). This report is one of three commissioned through the English Heritage's ALSF as part of a wider overview on sustainable aggregate management (see www.sustainableaggregates.com).

CONCLUSIONS

This review illustrates the usefulness of ALSF in promoting strategic research on archaeological practice, management, and understanding of areas impacted by aggregate extraction. Geoarchaeological methods, in particular, provide new knowledge and new ways of exploring the aggregate resource and a means of characterizing the landscapes in which archaeological sites are located, as well as predicting and identifying the nature and potential for archaeologically and paleoenvironmentally sensitive deposits, often in areas that have hitherto been little understood. This in turn allows the aggregates industry to revise their own exploration strategies in the light of this knowledge base, and ultimately enables the long-term sustainable management of the historical landscape, thus safeguarding it for future generations.

Several reviews have provided recommendations for future ALSF research (Thompson, 2006; Newell, 2006; Flatman et al., 2008), highlighting the need to test and refine methods developed for modeling fluvial systems and apply the successes of local pilot projects more widely. A central factor to this is the continued development and application of integrative methodologies and techniques, particularly geophysical techniques, for accurate prediction and evaluation of marine and terrestrial cultural resources in all aggregate landscapes. Technical research and development also ensure that the money invested by aggregates companies and other funding bodies is used as effectively as it can be (Thompson, 2006). Finally, there is a particular need to build on successful collaborations with industry to ensure long-term sustainability of this relationship (Flatman et al., 2008).

ACKNOWLEDGMENTS

The author wishes to thank the dating team for the statistics on Aggregates Levy Sustainability Fund dating, Kath Buxton for her helpful comments on the draft manuscript, and the two anonymous reviewers for their helpful comments. It should be noted that the views expressed by the author do not necessarily represent those of English Heritage.

REFERENCES CITED

Bates, M.R., Parfitt, S.A., and Roberts, M.B., 1997, The chronology, palaeogeography and archaeological significance of the marine Quaternary record of the west Sussex coastal plain, southern England, U.K.: Quaternary Science Reviews, v. 16, p. 1227–1252, doi:10.1016/S0277-3791(96)00119-9.

Bates, M.R., Bates, R.C., and Briant, R., 2007, Bridging the gap: A terrestrial view of shallow marine sequences and the importance of the transition zone: Journal of Archaeological Science, v. 34, p. 1537–1551, doi:10.1016/j.jas.2007.02.027.

Bayliss, A., Bronk Ramsey, C., Cook, G., and van der Plicht, J., 2007, Radiocarbon Dates—From Samples Funded by English Heritage under the Aggregates Levy Sustainability Fund 2002–4: London, English Heritage, 175 p.

Bayliss, A., Cook, G., Bronk Ramsey, C., van der Plicht, J., and McCormac, G., 2008, Radiocarbon Dates—From Samples Funded by English Heritage under the Aggregates Levy Sustainability Fund 2004–7: London, English Heritage, 204 p.

Beamish, M., 2009, Neolithic and Bronze age activity on the Trent valley floor: Excavations at Egginton and Willington, Derbyshire, 1998–1999: Derbyshire Archaeological Journal, v. 129, p. 17–172.

Bell, M., Chisham, C., Dark, P., and Allen, S., 2006, Mesolithic sites in coastal and riverine contexts in southern Britain: Current research and the management of the archaeological resource, in Rensink, E., and Peeters, H., eds., Preserving the Early Past: Investigation, Selection and Preserving of Palaeolithic and Mesolithic Sites and Landscapes: Amersfoort, Nederlandse Archeologische Rapporten, v. 31, p. 25–39.

Bewley, R.H., Crutchley, S.P., and Shell, C.A., 2005, New light on an ancient landscape: Lidar survey in the Stonehenge World Heritage Site: Antiquity, v. 79, no. 305, p. 636–647.

Boismier, W.A., 2003, A Middle Palaeolithic site at Lynford Quarry, Mundford, Norfolk: Interim statement: Proceedings of the Prehistoric Society, v. 69, p. 315.

Bridgland, D.R., Innes, J.B., Long, A.J., and Mitchell, W.A., 2010, Late Quaternary Landscape Evolution of the Swale-Ure Washlands, North Yorkshire: Oxford, Oxbow Books.

British Marine Aggregate Producers Association (BMAPA), 1997, The Marine Option: Quarry Management, February 1997, p. 17–22.

British Marine Aggregate Producers Association (BMAPA) and English Heritage (EH), 2005, Protocol for Reporting Finds of Archaeological Interest: London, British Marine Aggregate Producers Association and English Heritage, 25 p.

Brock, F., Higham, T., and Bronk Ramsey, C., 2007, Radiocarbon Dating Bone Samples Recovered from Gravel Sites: London, English Heritage Research Department Report 30/2007, 26 p.

Brown, A.G., 2009, Aggregate-Related Archaeology: Past, Present and Future: Kings Lynn, English Heritage/Heritage Marketing and Publications, 26 p.

Buteux, S., 2006, Quarrying and the Ice Age: The hidden benefits of extraction: Quarry Management, November 2006, p. 11–16.

Butzer, K.W., 1978, Toward an integrated, contextual approach in archaeology: A personal view: Journal of Archaeological Science, v. 5, p. 191–193, doi:10.1016/0305-4403(78)90039-0.

Carey, C., Brown, T.G., Challis, K.C., Howard, A.J., and Cooper, L., 2006, Predictive modelling of multiperiod geoarchaeological resources at a river confluence: A case study from the Trent-Soar, UK: Archaeological Prospection, v. 13, p. 241–250, doi:10.1002/arp.295.

Carver, M.O.H., Hills, C., and Scheschkewitz, J., 2009, Wasperton: A Roman, British and Anglo-Saxon Community in Central England: Suffolk, Boydell Press, 384 p.

Challis, K., Howard, A.J., Kincey, M., Moscrop, D., Carey, C.J., Hill, T., Smith, D.N., Gearey, B.R., and Thompson, A., 2007, Analysis of the Effectiveness of Airborne Lidar Backscattered Laser Intensity for Predicting Organic Preservation Potential of Waterlogged Deposits: HP Vista Report to English Heritage, 176 p.

Chiverrell, R.C., Thomas, G.S.P., and Foster, G.C., 2008, Sediment–landform assemblages and digital elevation data: Testing an improved methodology for the assessment of sand and gravel aggregate resources in north-western Britain: Engineering Geology, v. 99, no. 1–2, p. 40–50, doi:10.1016/j.enggeo.2008.02.005.

Crow, P., Benham, S., Devereux, B.J., and Amable, G.S., 2007, Woodland vegetation and its implications for archaeological survey using LiDAR: Forestry, v. 80, no. 3, p. 241–252, doi:10.1093/forestry/cpm018.

Crutchley, S., 2006, Case Study: Forest of Dean: www.ceg.ncl.ac.uk/heritage3d/downloads/case%study%2015.pdf (accessed 11 December 2006).

Defra, 2003, Recycling and Waste: Aggregates Levy Sustainability Fund in England: www.defra.gov.uk/ENVIRONMENT/WASTE/aggregates/index.htm (accessed 5 December 2006).

Devereux, B.J., Amable, G.S., Crow, P., and Cliff, A.D., 2005, The potential of airborne Lidar for detection of archaeological features under woodland canopies: Antiquity, v. 79, no. 305, p. 648–660.

Dix, J.K., 2007, Acoustic characterisation of archaeological materials in the marine environment: Developments and challenges, *in* Satchell, J., and Palma, P., eds., Managing the Marine Cultural Heritage: Defining, Accessing and Managing the Resource: York, Council for British Archaeology, p. 17–24.

Dix, J.K., and Lambkin, D., 2005, Modelling Exclusion Zones for Marine Aggregate Dredging: http://www.noc.soton.ac.uk/soes/research/groups/geophysics/aggregates/Index.htm (accessed 26 January 2010).

Dunkley, M., and Buxton, K., 2005, Maritime and coastal heritage: The Aggregates Levy Sustainability Fund: Conservation Bulletin, v. 48, p. 13–15.

Fitch, S., Thompson, K., and Gaffney, V., 2005, Late Pleistocene and Holocene depositional systems and the palaeogeography of the Dogger Bank, North Sea: Quaternary Research, v. 64, p. 185–196, doi:10.1016/j.yqres.2005.03.007.

Fitch, S., Gaffney, V., and Thomson, K., 2007, In sight of Doggerland: From speculative survey to landscape exploration: Internet Archaeology, v. 22 (Mesolithic Archaeology): http://intarch.ac.uk/journal/issue22/fitch_index.html (accessed 26 January 2010).

Flatman, J., Short, J., Soeser, J., and Lee, E., 2008, ALSF Dissemination Project 2002–2007 Benchmark Report: Sustainable Heritage—Aggregates Extraction and the Historic Environment: London, University College London Centre for Applied Archaeology on Behalf of English Heritage, 48 p.

Fox, R.A., 1993, The offshore aggregate industry in the UK: Underwater Technology, v. 19, no. 2, p. 17–23.

Gaffney, V., Thomson, K., and Fitch, S., 2007, Mapping Doggerland: The Mesolithic Landscapes of the Southern North Sea: Oxford, Archaeopress, 143 p.

Gubbay, S., 2005, A Review of Marine Aggregate Extraction in England and Wales, 1970–2005: London, Report for Crown Estate, 37 p.

Gupta, S., Collier, J., Palmer-Felgate, A., Dickinson, J., Bushe, K., and Humber, S., 2004, Submerged Palaeo-Arun River: Reconstruction of Prehistoric Landscapes and Evaluation of Archaeological Resource Potential. Integrated Projects 1 and 2: London, Final Report Project for English Heritage, Version 1.1, 372 p.

Hannis, S., 2007, Mineral safeguarding for sustainable communities: Mineral Planning, v. 110, p. 3–4.

Howard, A.J., 2005, The contribution of geoarchaeology to understanding the environmental history and archaeological resources of the Trent Valley, UK: Geoarchaeology, v. 20, no. 2, p. 93–107, doi:10.1002/gea.20038.

Humble, J., 2008, Mineral Extraction and the Historic Environment: London, English Heritage, 20 p.

Johnson, B., and Waddington, C., 2008, Prehistoric and Dark Age settlement remains from Cheviot Quarry, Millfield Basin, Northumberland: The Archaeological Journal. v. 165, no. 1, p. 107–264.

Knight, J., and Howard, A.J., 2004, Trent Valley Landscapes: The Archaeology of 50,000 Years of Change: King's Lynn, Heritage Marketing and Publications, 200 p.

Knight, J., McCarron, S.G., McCabe, A.M., and Sutton, B., 1999, Sand and gravel aggregate resource management and conservation in northern Ireland: Journal of Environmental Management, v. 56, p. 195–207, doi:10.1006/jema.1999.0280.

Ladle, L., and Woodward, A., 2009, Excavations at Bestwall Quarry Wareham 1992–2005. Volume 1: The Prehistoric Landscape: Dorset National History and Archaeological Society Monograph 19, 402 p.

The Landscape Agency, 2005, Swale and Ure Washlands Mineral Site After-Use Strategy: Consultation Document: http://www.northyorks.gov.uk/CHttpHandler.ashx?id=1875&p=0 (accessed 26 January 2010).

Leather, S., Russell, J.W., Tizzard, L., Paddenberg, D. and Callan, N., 2007, The Seabed Prehistory project, *in* Newell, R., and Garner, D., eds., Marine Aggregate Extraction: Helping to Determine Good Practice: London, Marine Aggregates Levy Sustainability Fund, p. 86–89.

Linford, N., 2006, The application of geophysical methods to archaeological prospection: Institute of Physics Publishing, v. 69, p. 2205–2257.

Neal, A., and Roberts, C.L., 2000, Applications of ground-penetrating radar (GPR) to sedimentological, geomorphological and geoarchaeological studies in coastal environments, *in* Pye, K., and Allen, J.R.L., ed., Coastal and Estuarine Environments: Sedimentology, Geomorphology and Geoarchaeology: Geological Society of London Special Publication 175, p. 139–171.

Newell, R., 2006, Marine ALSF Science Review: Aggregate Research in UK Waters: www.seasurvey.co.uk (accessed 28 May 2008).

Parfitt, S.A., Barendregt, R.W., Breda, M., Candy, I., Collins, M.J., Russell Coope, G., Durbidge, P., Field, M.H., Lee, J.R., Lister, A.M., Mutch, R., Penkman, K.E.H., Preece, R.C., Rose, J., Stringer, C.B., Symmons, R., Whittaker, J.E., Wymer, J.J., and Stuart, A.J., 2005, The earliest record of human activity in northern Europe: Nature, v. 438, p. 1008–1012, doi:10.1038/nature04227.

Passmore, D.G., Waddington, C., and Van der Schriek, T., 2006, Enhancing the evaluation and management of river valley archaeology: Geoarchaeology in the Till-Tweed catchment: Northern England: Archaeological Prospection, v. 13, p. 269–281, doi:10.1002/arp.293.

Penkman, K.E.H., and Collins, M., 2007, Swale-Ure Washlands: A late Quaternary landscape history, amino acid racemization report: English Heritage Research Department Report Series, 74/2007, 37 p.

Penkham, K.E.H, and McGrory, S., 2007, The Lower and Middle Palaeolithic occupation of the middle and lower Trent catchment and adjacent areas, as recorded in the river gravels used as aggregate resources: Amino acid racemization analysis: English Heritage Research Department Report Series, 75/2007, 38 p.

Penkman, K.E.H., Preece, R.C., Keen, D.H., Maddy, D., Schreve, D.C., and Collins, M., 2007, Amino acids from the intra-crystalline fraction of mollusc shells: Applications to geochronology: Quaternary Science Reviews, v. 26, p. 2958–2969, doi:10.1016/j.quascirev.2007.06.034.

Powlesland, D., Lyall, J., Hopkinson, G., Donoghue, D., Beck, M., Harte, A., and Stott, D., 2006, Beneath the sand—Remote sensing, archaeology, aggregates and sustainability: A case study from Heslerton, the Vale of Pickering, North Yorkshire, UK: Archaeological Prospection, v. 13, p. 291–299, doi:10.1002/arp.297.

Quartermaine, J., and Chiverrell, R.C., 2007, Aggregate Extraction in the Lower Ribble Valley: Report for English Heritage: http://www.liv.ac.uk/geography/research/ribble/Project_Report.htm (accessed 26 January 2010).

Roberts, I., Deegan, A., Berg, D., and Ford, L., 2007, Archaeological Cropmark Landscapes of the Magnesian Limestone: A Study of the Cropmark Regimes of the Magnesian Limestone Belt and Its Margins in South Yorkshire, West Yorkshire and Parts of North Yorkshire and North Nottinghamshire: London, Aggregates Levy Sustainability Fund report for English Heritage, 114 p.

Roberts, M.B., and Parfitt, S.A., 1999, Boxgrove: A Middle Pleistocene Hominid Site at Eartham Quarry, Boxgrove, West Sussex: London, English Heritage, English Heritage Monograph Series Archaeological Report 17, 456 p.

Rømer, S., Breuning-Madsen, H., Balstrøm, T., and Jensen, A-E., 2006, Short Contribution: Mapping Quaternary deposits as a method for explaining the distribution of Mesolithic sites in reclaimed landscapes: An example from Vålse Vig, southeast Denmark: Geoarchaeology, v. 21, no. 1, p. 113–124.

Rose, J., 2006, Bytham River aggregates: Quarry Management, November, p. 21–22.

Schwenninger, J.L., and Rhodes, E., 2005, Optically stimulated luminescence (OSL) dating of sediments from a Palaeolithic site at Lynford Quarry, Norfolk: London, English Heritage Centre for Archaeology Report 25/2005, 25 p.

Schwenninger, J., Rhodes, E.J., Bates, M.R., Briant, R.M., and Wenban-Smith, F., 2006, Optically stimulated luminescence (OSL) dating of Quaternary deposits from the Sussex/Hampshire coastal corridor: London, English Heritage Centre for Archaeology Report 20/2006, 50 p.

Stone, G., and Satchell, J., 2007, Archaeology within Marine Aggregate Environmental Statements: London, Final Report as submitted to English Heritage, 83 p.

Thompson, A., 2006, Review of Land-Based ALSF Research in England, 2002–2005: http://www.defra.gov.uk/environment/waste/aggregates/pdf/alsf-research06.pdf (accessed 27 May 2008).

Waddington, C., and Passmore, D., 2006, Planning for the Future: Guidance for Managing the Archaeological and Palaeoenvironmental Resource in the Till-Tweed Valleys, Northumberland: London, UK, Archaeological Research Services Ltd. and English Heritage, 22 p.

Ward, I., and Larcombe, P., 2008, Determining the preservation rating of submerged archaeology in the post-glacial southern North Sea: A first-order geomorphological approach: Environmental Archaeology, v. 13, no. 1, p. 59–83, doi:10.1179/174963108x279229.

Watters, M.S., 2006, Geovisualization: An example from the Catholme ceremonial complex: Archaeological Prospection, v. 13, p. 282–290, doi:10.1002/arp.290.

Westley, K., Dix, J.K., and Quinn, R., 2004, A Re-Assessment of the Archaeological Potential of Continental Shelves, Aggregates Levy Sustainability Fund Project 3362: London, Final Report prepared for English Heritage, 236 p.

Wymer, J.J., 1968, Lower Palaeolithic Archaeology in Britain; as Represented by the Thames Valley: London, John Baker, 234 p.

Wymer, J., and Robins, P., 2006, Happisburgh and Pakefield: Current Archaeology, v. 201, p. 458–467.

Manuscript Accepted by the Society 3 August 2010

The Geological Society of America
Special Paper 476
2011

Aggregate-related archaeology in England in a changing environment

Antony G. Brown

Palaeoenvironmental Laboratory University of Southampton (PLUS), School of Geography, Highfields Campus, University of Southampton, Southampton, SO17 1BJ, UK

ABSTRACT

The Aggregates Levy Sustainability Fund (ALSF) tax on aggregate (sand and gravel) producers in England has provided the funding for a large number of aggregate-related archaeological projects by English Heritage since 2002. One of these projects was a review, presented herein, of aggregate-related archaeology both prior and subsequent to the introduction by the UK government of new Planning Guidance Note 16 (PPG16) in 1990. This guidance advised local authorities to impose archaeological conditions upon aggregate producers seeking new permissions and extensions for aggregate working. The review commissioned by English Heritage also examined the temporal and spatial variation in interventions using data collected by the Archaeological Investigations Project (AIP) based at Bournemouth University. This paper reveals trends over time largely related to the state of the economy and aggregate demand, and more significantly, large regional variations in both the number of archaeological interventions and the number of interventions encountering archaeology. While some of this variation is geologically related (hard aggregate– vs. soft aggregate–dominated regions), some variation is not, and may relate to variations in the archaeological planning process. Observations are also made as to the problems faced by archaeological interventions in aggregate quarries in accordance with planning procedures. This paper also draws attention to the probable direct and indirect effects of the changing hydrological and legislative climate on the aggregate industry and the implications this could have for aggregate-related archaeology in England, and by implication other developed countries.

BACKGROUND

Approximately half the aggregates (sand and gravel) used in the UK are still derived from primary sources, predominantly land-derived primary aggregates, and 40% of this material is derived from soft-rock sources (Office of National Statistics, 2005; British Geological Survey, 2005). These are sand and gravels largely of Pleistocene and occasionally Holocene age. This continued exploitation drives aggregate-related archaeology

through assessments, evaluations, watching briefs, and occasionally excavations. It is therefore inevitable that the potential of this branch of, what is in effect "rescue archaeology," is dependent upon the economic and legislative environment of aggregate production. Partly in order to offset impacts on the archaeological and heritage resource, some of the proceeds from a tax on the industry in the form of the Aggregates Levy Sustainability Fund (ALSF) have been used to support aggregate-related archaeology through a series of projects administered by English Heritage (Ward, this

Brown, A.G., 2011, Aggregate-related archaeology in England in a changing environment, *in* Brown, A.G., Basell, L.S., and Butzer, K.W., eds., Geoarchaeology, Climate Change, and Sustainability: Geological Society of America Special Paper 476, p. 183–194, doi:10.1130/2011.2476(14). For permission to copy, contact editing@geosociety.org.

volume). One of the projects supported by the tax was a review of aggregate-related archaeology before and after the application of Planning Guidance Note 16 (PPG16), which effectively required planning authorities in England and Wales to assess and evaluate the archaeological resource prior to any granting of new permissions to extract aggregate. The review, which remained unsummarized until presented here, also considered the regional and temporal variation in the number of aggregate-related interventions (assessments, evaluations, and excavations) since 1991 for a 10 yr period using data collected by the Archaeological Interventions Project (AIP). Additionally, using published sources, research experience, and interviews with some of the stakeholders in the aggregates industry, an analysis was conducted of the ways in which environmental change may affect aggregate extraction and therefore aggregate-related archaeology. These elements of the review form the basis of this research paper.

For such a small island, English primary aggregates come from a very wide range of geological contexts. These include hard rocks, largely Carboniferous limestone but also Mesozoic conglomerates (e.g., Triassic pebble beds), Tertiary gravels, Pleistocene terrace gravels (by far the most important source of soft aggregate), glacial sand and gravels, blown sand, and in a few cases Holocene gravels. These sources all have different archaeological potential, as illustrated by Figure 1. This is not the place to discuss the resulting biases on archaeology (see Howard and Macklin, 1999; Brown, 2008, 2009), but it is important to note that factors that alter the relative cost of these sources can cause source-substitution, and this would eventually impact archaeology. This point is developed in relation to environmental change later herein.

METHODS

The pre-1991 data are based upon literature searches and earlier reviews, particularly Fulford and Nichols (1992) and Benson and Miles (1974). An attempt was made to try and even out coverage geographically by concentrating searches, particularly of the gray literature, in areas with less published data. However, a full review of all the gray literature was not possible, and so variation in the degree of coverage still exists. The post-1991 review was based upon both the aforementioned methodology and the AIP gazette data. These data were compiled by AIP, who provided a list of all mineral extraction–related interventions. This list was then manually sorted to extract only those related to aggregates. In a few cases, the mineral type was not recorded, and so those sites were not included in the final listing, and regional analysis was based upon a statistical analysis of these AIP-derived data. The review of the potential effect of environmental change on aggregate-related archaeology is based upon a seminar held at the Museum of London in 2002, published data and official government information, and an interview conducted with D. Pollock of the Quarry Products Association (QPA), which is the largest trade association representing the aggregates industry in the UK.

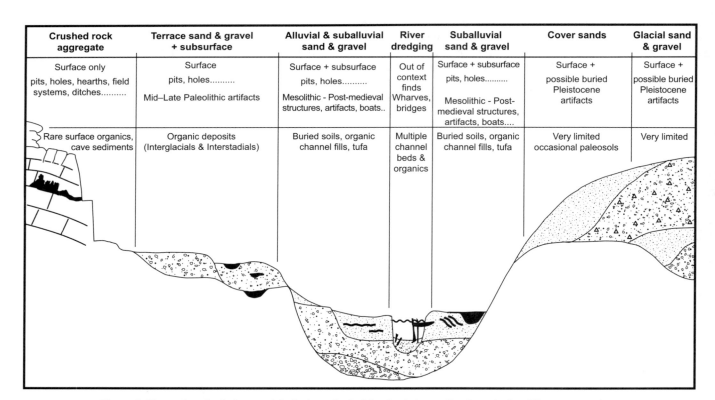

Figure 1. The archaeological potential of a hypothetical lowland river valley in a glaciated limestone region.

TEMPORAL VARIATION

There are no quantitative data available that could allow objective analysis of temporal variation in aggregate-related archaeology prior to 1990 and the development of AIP. The overall trend of interventions has, unsurprisingly, been rising over the decade 1990–2000. As can be seen in Figure 2A, interventions rose until 1996 and then declined before rising again in 2000 and 2001. The rise in the early 1990s was undoubtedly due to the proportion of interventions such as field evaluations being prompted by PPG16 as it became more widely known and understood (Darvill and Russell, 2002). This in part reflects a national trend in planning applications (Darvill and Russell, 2002), but may also result from the desire of companies to submit planning applications prior to a review of consents and any change in local authority policy after the 1994 Minerals Guidance and following the 2002 guidelines (Fig. 3). It is also possible to look at the trends over the 10 yr span by region, as graphed in Figure 2B. While most regions have increased over the decade (except Greater London), the trends are different. Some UK Local Government regions show a steady rise (South East and East England), others show a less clear trend (West Midlands, northwest England, and Yorkshire), and several are characterized by a large increase in the year 2001. The decline in the interventions in Greater London is undoubtedly due to a reduction in aggregate production and lack of new sites due to the effective sterilization of resource by urban development, infrastructure, and public opinion. Indeed, the Greater London Authority does not produce a minerals local area plan, and the only borough that does is Havering.

REGIONAL VARIATION

Although no relevant statistical data exist pre-1991, an attempt was made to assess regional variation from the published literature. This highlighted another problem with assessing aggregate-related archaeology, which is definitional, because many excavation reports do not include details of the proposed, or active, quarrying that prompted intervention. The definition used here for the pre-PPG16 period included all interventions into soft aggregates, but only working quarries in the case of hard aggregates (relatively few in number). A second problem was the definition of what constitutes a site, as in reality, gravel quarries are highly clustered, and several excavations have typically occurred in the same quarry. The most useful convention is to use the quarry name because it is used in planning consent, has locational specificity, and is the general convention followed by Quaternary scientists and geologists. Approximately 250 sites were excavated between the late 1960s and 1991 that have been published and can be argued to have had regional importance, and it is these sites that were used to produce a regional breakdown for pre-PPG16 (Fig. 2C). This definition does not include all the "sites" that appear in gazetteers (e.g., Wymer, 1999), because, in many cases, the site is a single find or a small number of finds, no excavation was necessarily conducted, and it may only have

importance in relation to an analysis of distributions. As can be seen from Figure 2C, the pre-PPG16 regional picture was highly skewed. This is an exaggeration of the combined effect of the distribution of easily accessible terrace gravel deposits with the historical demand for aggregate. Within the major regions, it is also clear that the work in the Upper Thames has had a major impact, since Oxfordshire is the county with the highest number of sites falling into this category (23).

The number of interventions is clearly an inadequate method of assessing archaeology; however, neither financial data nor, at present, the locations of all contracts are available on a national basis. As a measure of worth, however, it has been possible to compile statistics on the number of interventions not revealing archaeology. This has been defined as conservatively as possible and so only includes those sites that revealed no archaeological features (even undated) or artifacts (no pottery, flint, or artifacts at all). The results are graphed by area in Figure 2D, where they are expressed as a percentage of all the interventions over the decade. Greater London has been excluded due to the low number of AIP-recorded interventions.

Overall, the numbers are comparable with the national average (10%–20%; Darvill and Russell, 2002), but the variance is greater, and while this may be due to the smaller sample size, it most likely reflects the regional variation. As can be seen from Figure 2D, the counties with the highest number of interventions not recording archaeology are the North West, South West, and North East Regions. This pattern and individual county records strongly suggest that this corresponds with higher percentages of aggregates from hard rock sources. There are probably two main nonarchaeological reasons for this:

1. The areas evaluated or assessed are generally smaller due to a smaller land-take to production ratio.
2. Sites on hard rock such as limestone are more likely to have undergone erosion or irreparable plow damage than those on soft aggregates.

In addition, there are, of course, archaeological explanations, which include:

1. The hard rock sites tend to be at the very steep edges or slopes of upstanding upland blocks and so may be less attractive locations for settlement and human activity.
2. The hard rock quarries are predominantly located in upland areas far from major population centers (the Lake District, the Pennines, and the Mendip Hills).
3. The hard rock, with often shallow soils, is not suitable for the digging of ditches or arable cultivation and is more likely to have been under continuous rough grazing, thus leaving a minimal archaeological signature, even in between visible and scheduled ancient monuments.
4. This pattern may reflect a poorer state of archaeological knowledge and variability in the techniques and methods of evaluation and assessment employed across the county.

There are several ways in which the future of aggregate archaeology can be viewed. The first method is through demand forecasting, which is effectively closely related to the demand

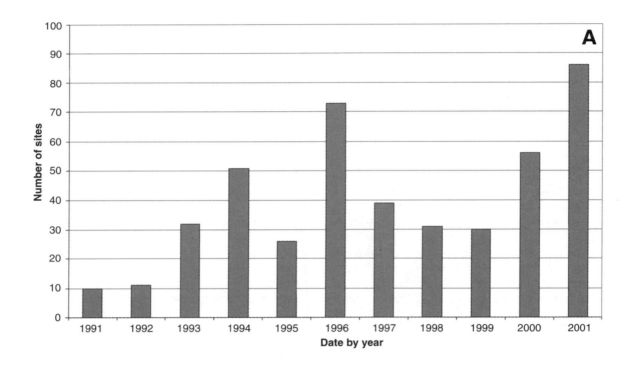

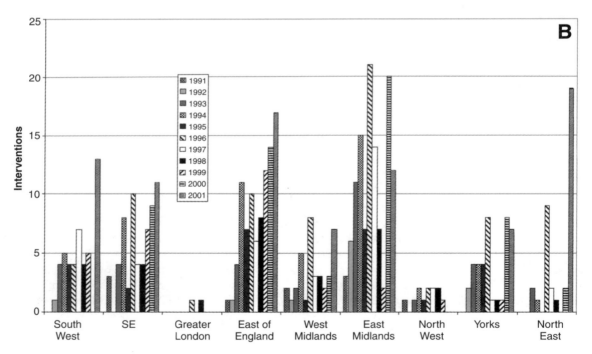

Figure 2. Trends in aggregate-related archaeological interventions in England. (A) The trend of interventions 1991–2001 (data from Archaeological Investigations Project [AIP]). (B) The number of interventions 1991–2001 by region (data from AIP). (C) The number of well-documented pre–Planning Guidance Note 16 (PPG16) aggregate-related sites by region (see text for definition). (D) The number of interventions recording no pre- or post-medieval archaeology or "no archaeology." SW—South West; SE—South East; WM—West Midlands; EM—East Midlands; E of E—East of England; NW—North West; Yorks—Yorkshire; NE—North East.

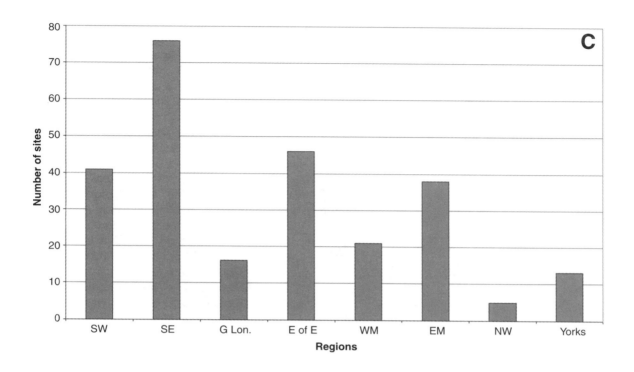

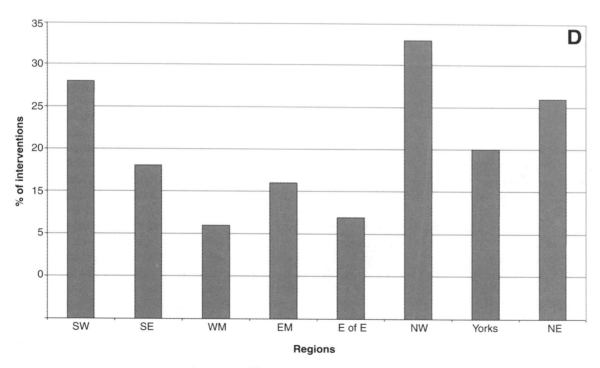

Figure 2. (*Continued*).

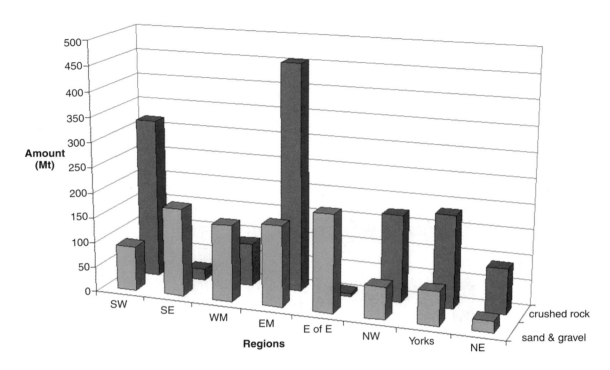

Figure 3. Revised (2002) guidelines for primary aggregate needs in England. See the Figure 2 caption for an explanation of abbreviations.

for new infrastructure and is the responsibility of central government. Central government in England makes regional estimates for aggregate provision in conjunction with the National Coordinating Group (NCG) and Regional Aggregate Working Parties (RAWPs). Resulting from the 2002 revised guidance established by the government (ODPM, 2002) and RAWPs, there has been a revision of the mineral local plans (MLPs) by county councils and unitary authorities, and this should theoretically affect aggregate extraction through the planning process. The guidance revised the estimate of total demand for all aggregates in England between 2001 and 2016 to around 3.4 billion tonnes or ~212.5 million tonnes per year (Fig. 3). This is a reduction of ~24% from the previous Mineral Planning Guidance Note 6 (MPG6, 1994). When compared with the 1994 MPG6 estimate, this represents a reduction of 29% in crushed rock but only 23% in land-won sand and gravel nationally. Although it will probably prove unimportant because production has been below the 1994 estimates, this does theoretically increase the contribution of sand and gravel to the overall provision of aggregate. The most recent government statistics derived from the 2007 monitoring exercise as reported in a current draft consultation by the Department of Communities and Local Government (DCLG, 2008) suggest a modest decline in forecast national demand, but this hides a significant fall in the North East and South East but an increase in London. This may be exacerbated by a fall in primary aggregate reserves reported to the RAWP Secretaries Committee in 2007 itself, probably due to a lack of applications for extraction permission. It is also sensitive

to economic activity and so will be expected to fall in response to the reduction in economic growth currently being experienced, although this does not appear to have fed through to individual aggregate companies as yet (Bardon Aggregates, March 2009, personal commun.).

The revised MPG6 advice to RAWPs includes compatibility with environmental objectives, but no specific mention of heritage or archaeological constraints, and in practice, the government expects apportionment to follow previous apportionments. Government estimates of future demand (aggregate consumption or AGGCON) are based on a demand forecasting model:

$$AGGCON = f(IC, LIC, trend),$$

where IC is aggregate-intensive construction, and LIC is less-aggregate-intensive construction, and trend is the general observed trend of aggregate use. The growth in construction was derived from a model provided by Cambridge Econometrics. The forecasts were then adjusted to take into consideration the effect of the aggregates levy (at £1.60 per tonne). The modeling suggests that although there will be a moderate rise in construction between 2003 and 2016, aggregate demand will remain approximately constant. This is due to a reduction in the intensity of aggregate use, and so with the increased use in secondary aggregates, it follows that demand for primary aggregates should fall. However, as has already been stated, monitored output, which was falling well below the 1994 estimates, may fall further due to economic

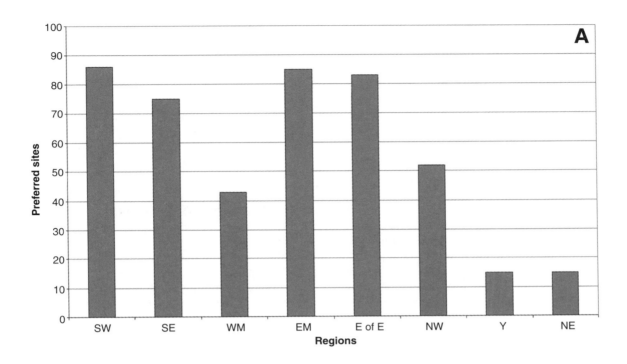

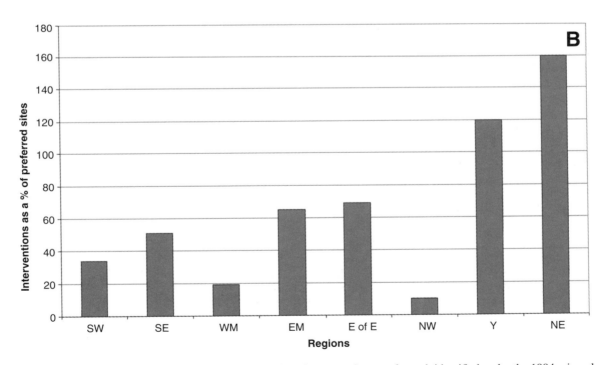

Figure 4. (A) Regional numbers of preferred sites, preferred areas, and areas of search identified under the 1994 mineral planning guidance. (B) The number of interventions 1999–2001 as a percentage of the total number of preferred sites identified in the mineral local plans. See the Figure 2 caption for an explanation of abbreviations.

slowdown, and so it is unlikely that the revised estimates will act in any way as a constraint on aggregate production because there are other more immediate constraints.

The second method of looking at future land-take is through the number of sites, and ideally the areas (land-take), that have been identified as preferred sites, or areas of search. Unfortunately, not all the MLPs include area data (or potential tonnage data), and so regional comparison is impossible and can only be based on the number of sites excluding areas of search. The statistics compiled in Figure 4A are based on preferred sites only, excluding active sites that are not also preferred future sites. Also excluded are sites that are not being currently worked but have outstanding permissions (including those that have not been identified as preferred sites and are unlikely to be worked). The analysis of the data using area would almost certainly increase the importance of both Yorkshire and the North East. However, it is noticeable that the East and the South East Regions have the third- and fourth-highest number of preferred sites, nearly all of which are sand and gravel sites, due to the low occurrence of hard aggregates—as reflected by low crushed-rock apportionments. This suggests that the impact on archaeology in the south and east of England is unlikely to diminish significantly, and will increase especially if there is a change in preferred sources (see later discussion) and economic revival.

These data also allow a calculation of the intervention ratio (ratio of number of interventions to number of preferred areas). Figure 4B should be treated with caution, because there are many different factors that could cause a low ratio (i.e., low percentage of interventions recorded by AIP to the number of preferred sites identified for quarrying), some of which are listed here:

1. The sites are large and phased over many years and so interventions will be phased.
2. Many of the sites are very small extensions to existing quarries and have been covered by existing assessments or evaluations.
3. There is a lack of completeness of the AIP data.
4. Some preferred areas are identified that are not economic or for some other reason are unlikely to be worked.
5. The Planning Authorities may view, on advice from the County Archaeologist, that some sites require no archaeological evaluation (e.g., some industrial sites), or there is a lack of prompting (sensu Darvill and Russell, 2002).
6. The interventions used only 1999–2001 AIP data, but although most MLPs were adopted around 1999–2000, some cover earlier and some later time periods.

From Figure 4B, it as can be seen that it is possible for the ratio to exceed 100%, because large preferred sites will require several interventions over a number of years. Indeed, given the status of the previous planning cycle (generally 1997–2006), the values are to be expected, with most regions having over 50% interventions approximately two thirds of the way through the time period. The exception is clearly the North West, which appears to have an unusually low ratio. Since the Cheshire MLP only identifies three preferred sites, although it lists existing quar-

ries (as of 1999), the main cause is Cumbria, which has a large number of existing sites with permissions, several areas of search for sand and gravel, and even more for hard rock aggregate, and, at least as recorded in the AIP, a low number of recorded interventions since 1997. This is not necessarily a serious heritage conservation issue, as Figure 2D showed that it has the highest rate of interventions recording "no archaeology" (33%) of all the regions, but it does suggest some targeting of resources to both investigate the situation and promote aggregate-related archaeology in the region, and particularly in Cumbria. This has to some extent been fulfilled by English Heritage's commissioning of research on the aggregate resources and archaeology of the Ribble catchment (Chiverrell et al., 2009).

THE CHANGING ENVIRONMENT

The changing environment of aggregate-related archaeology in the UK results from climate change (both direct and indirect effects) and changes in the legislative and planning environment. The planning, legal (including health and safety), and environmental constraints are important in that they affect the types of aggregates quarried, the locations they are taken from, and the methods of quarrying. There are many pieces of legislation and directives at both the national and European level that are now impacting, and will continue to impact, the industry in the next few years. One of the most important is the European Water Frameworks Directive, and its incorporation into UK legislation in the Water Act, which received Royal Assent in 2003. The Water Act makes nontemporary abstraction licenses a requirement for pumping over 27 liters per day. This legislation, and the operation of new European standards for water entering main rivers by the Environment Agency (EA), will impose limits on the quantity and quality of water that can be discharged into rivers, or recharge aquifers, during dewatering and continued pumping. The result may pose an additional cost on quarrying, causing a change in operations, or even a shift in the preferred sources of primary aggregates. The reason is that if water falls below the required standard, or it is believed that it will, then a license will not be granted by the EA. This could force wet working of sand and gravel pits (by drag-line), which is more expensive, by an estimated 10%–15% (QPA, 2006, personal commun.), and also is much more problematic for certain types of sites than dry working. These are the sites where the archaeology is intragravel and so includes mostly Paleolithic material but also prehistoric and even later archaeology in some river reaches, such as the Middle Trent and its tributaries (Knight and Howard, 2004; Brown and Salisbury, 2010). Since there is no way at present to identify such intragravel archaeology, no mitigation is possible, and the archaeological resource cannot be protected. A further, and possibly compounding, effect could be to force some limestone quarries out of operation. These would affect quarries operating below the regional water table, which have to pump either continuously or episodically. The minimum requirement will probably be for continuous hydrological monitoring, and field trials are under way at quarries in the Mendips and Pennines (Hobbs, 2002), and work on hydrological monitoring has been funded by ALSF through Minerals Research Organisation (MIRO). If some hard rock quarries were unable to dewater, they could not be worked, and/or if significant costs were added, then the result could be to shift aggregate provision toward sand and gravel reserves.

These pressures are combined with others, including increasingly strict health and safety legislation. While this paper is not the place to review this in detail, some comment is warranted on whether it will affect archaeology other than directly through on-site work. It could be presumed that it would affect the industry indirectly; however, this may not be the case, because the hazards posed by high hard rock quarry faces and lower sand and gravel faces are not equal (Charters and Duthie, 2002), and differential costs may well arise. A further area of legislation that could have a significant effect on aggregates is the regulations that relate to bird strikes on aircraft. The current legislation as specified in Town and Country Planning Aerodromes and Technical Sites Direction 1992 (Department of Transport, 1992), which delimits a 13 km radius around a prescribed list of airports within which local planning authorities must consult airport authorities over developments that could increase the likelihood of a bird striking an aircraft. Given the proximity of most UK airports to larger river valleys and interfluve gravels (i.e., plateau gravels), any extension of either the number of airports or the size of the safeguarded area could potentially affect both wet working and the form of restoration of worked areas. QPA has estimated that due to the location of airports in England (generally on the edge of large urban centers and frequently aligned along valleys and located on higher level terraces), this could potentially include 80% of all sand and gravel quarries. To some extent, this counteracts the problems associated with dewatering, but the restoration of quarries using landfill if they are beneath the water table is now unacceptable. It is not known what effect these regulatory pressures will have on the industry, and therefore archaeology; however, it is likely that their effect could be far greater than either the commercial pressures of demand or the national guidance set out by the UK government.

Aggregate archaeology will be affected by climate change alongside all archaeological procedures and mitigations (English Heritage, 2008; Howard et al., 2008). However, it is probably more susceptible than archaeology in nonalluvial environments and this is considered here. In order to do this, is it is necessary to set out the current consensus about future climate change scenarios for England. This will be done briefly using data provided by UKCIP (United Kingdom Climate Impacts Programme), the Hadley Centre, CEH (Centre for Hydrology and Ecology), and DEFRA (Department of Farming and Rural Affairs). The current consensus is summarized here:

1. Models are in general agreement that by 2050, the UK will have experienced an increase in mean annual temperatures of between 1 °C and 5 °C, dependent upon whether high or low greenhouse gas emissions occur (IPCC, UKCIP, 2002).

2. There is also a general consensus about the following seasonal changes: a decrease in summer precipitation, at least in south and east England, although there is some possibility of an increase in northern England; an increase in winter and spring precipitation; and increased variability and rainfall intensities.

3. Intense rainfall events become less frequent in summer all over England, while in winter and autumn, the situation is variable, but small increases are predicted over most of the country. The biggest increases are expected to occur in southeastern England (equivalent to a 20% increase in the 2 yr return period daily precipitation under the moderate to high emission scenario).

UKCIP08 is incomplete, but the trends report illustrates the changes to precipitation between the 1961–1990 and 1991–2000 periods. Most of midland and southern England has undergone an increase in average autumn precipitation by 5%–10%, and winter precipitation has also increased in southwest and northern England by a similar amount. There has only been a reduction in summer precipitation in northern England. The overall picture is also taking into consideration the distribution of change in rain days per season; the trend is toward an increasing disparity between western and eastern England, i.e., the west getting wetter and the east getting drier. Although there is a general consensus, there are major uncertainties, and the GCMs (Global Climate Models) do not agree, especially at the regional scale. In this respect, the situation is rather different in relation to sea-level rise, which is regarded as being certain, and which, it is believed, can be estimated to a relatively high degree of accuracy (UKCIP, 2002). Although relatively little primary aggregate is extracted from the coastal zone, there are some areas where the increased risk of marine flooding may prevent aggregate exploitation. Any possible mitigation of this threat by increased retention of floodwater upstream in catchments by small dams and retention ponds will reduce this threat.

Direct Effects of Climate Change

The most obvious direct effect on valley floor sites would be an increase in flooding of low sites in autumn and winter (Beven, 1993; Arnell, 1997). There is hydrological evidence that we are presently within a flood-rich period (Lane, 2008). While increased flooding could have some beneficial effects through increased floodplain soil moisture, it also could have some negative effects. One of these would be the increasing likelihood of breaches of bunds, allowing flooding of dry-worked gravel pits. This has happened in several quarries, including at Hemington in the Trent Valley, where in 2001 a flood inundated the quarry and displaced many of the wooden artifacts that were then under excavation. Indeed, it is now happening regularly along this reach (e.g., Aston was flooded in February 2004). The extent of additional flooding can be estimated using the revised Indicative Flood Maps, which have been produced by the Environment Agency. The likelihood of increased flooding is being incorporated into flood planning and so will have indirect effects (see following section). The increased temperatures may also have some effect on archaeology through an increase in evapotranspiration, and so a possible reduction in nonfloodplain recharge. This could lead to the further desiccation through a fall in the water table surrounding aggregate quarries, compounded by draw-down (French et al., 1999; French, 2004).

Indirect Effects of Climate Change

Indirect effects occur through governmental, institutional, public, and commercial responses to the perceived threats posed by climate change. These indirect effects will occur whether the climate change scenarios are correct or not. The data are taken from the EA Strategy for Flood Risk management (2003/4–2007/8) published in 2003, and from the DTI (Department of Trade and Industry) Foresight Programme (Flood and Coastal Defenses Project) as reported by Hall et al. (2006). They are summarized here:

1. The EA has taken as its working increase 20% (in flood frequency/magnitude), as this is above the current highest estimates and so incorporates a safety factor. This provides the basis for current planning of river defenses, etc.

2. Physical flood protection works remain an issue, with flood defense expenditure running at approximately £300 M per year to £479 M per year (2005–2006 estimate), which can be expected to rise further. During the last two years, 80 new schemes were approved. However, the increased risk associated with a general reluctance to increase expenditure, and a desire to seek less interventionist approaches, has encouraged the EA to change its approach from defending against floods to managing the flood risk (EA, 2003 in Thorndycraft et al., 2003). This may also, somewhat ironically, cause a threat to archaeology close to river channels. The reason is that part of this approach would be, in appropriate locations, not to maintain flood defenses; a result of this would be increased bank erosion caused by the increased flood magnitude and frequency. The scale of the potential threat here can be gauged from the Ribble Valley Project commissioned by the EA, which identified 807 archaeological sites within 10 m of the river edge (Lancaster Archaeological Unit, 2006, personal commun.). Overall, the effect of these measures is variable and will depend upon which strategy is pursued in each location. The archaeological response would also have to vary. Bank erosion on the Huntspill River in the Somerset Levels caused the potential destruction of an Iron Age–Romano–British saltern and led to its excavation in 2003 (Straker, 2006, personal commun.). However, this erosion has been halted by the planting of willows (*Salix* sp.) and common reed (*Phragmites* sp.) along the stream banks (Croft, 2006, personal commun.). It will be important to limit this erosion because recently geomorphologists and archaeologists have shown how the upper part of most alluvial floodplain sequences contains geochemical evidence of mining and industrial activity. This has been shown for metal contamination in the Tyne Basin and elsewhere in northern England (Lewin and

Macklin, 1986; Macklin et al., 1994), tin contamination around Dartmoor (Thorndycraft et al., 1999, 2003), and most recently in studies of the River Trent (Hudson-Edwards, 2006, personal commun.). In some cases, the concentrations can be several times higher than permitted levels for human health, thus preventing development without decontamination. Increased riverbank erosion could easily mobilize these contaminants back into the river, causing potential problems for water intake works.

3. There will most likely be an increase in soft bank protection methods (seeding and synthetic mats, etc.), and in most cases, these should be beneficial to the preservation of floodplain archaeology, as long as they are carried out sensitively and with care. The use of tree planting to reduce bank erosion is a contentious issue—because there are implications for downstream structures, fishing, and navigation—and, under current advice (EA), it is restricted.

4. Channel siltation is likely to increase due to increased soil erosion of agricultural land, although the UK government is seeking to reduce this through its "Soil Action Plan" (DTI, 2003 in Thorndycraft et al., 2003). A likely response in large rivers where navigation and flood control are issues may be to increase dredging. This has two archaeological implications: first, in the accidental discovery or displacement of artifacts from riverbeds (which, in certain areas, can be rich in later prehistoric artifacts); and, second, the burial of the floodplain under the spread of river silt adjacent to the channel. This could benefit the protection of buried alluvial archaeology.

5. Government and intergovernmental agencies will play a role in the development of integrated strategies for floodplain management (see following).

One of the most important indirect effects of climate change, or even perceived climate change, results from new environmental legislation, as discussed earlier in this section.

ARCHAEOLOGY AND INTEGRATED FLOODPLAIN MANAGEMENT

Due to the existing multiple pressures on floodplains and the additional burden of climate change, coupled with a desire to improve environmental quality, there is a general movement across Europe in favor of some form of integrated sustainable management of floodplains (EA, 2003 in Thorndycraft et al., 2003; *Wise Use of Floodplains* EU Life-Environment Project), reflected to some extent in the European Water Frameworks Directive. There are several ways in which integrated floodplain management could impact aggregate-related archaeology, for example, by increasing flood retention through the use of quarries and secondary channels for flood storage; maintaining high water tables by maintaining weirs; and through floodplain and terrace afforestation (with appropriate archaeological evaluation).

In England, as in most European regions, the responsibilities for the different functions of floodplains are dispersed across tens of governmental departments, agencies, and institutions. Flooding and drainage are typically separated from agriculture, economic development, and recreational management, both in terms of ministerial and departmental responsibilities and often in degrees of devolution to lower administrative units. This provides all European governments with an implementation problem. The management of floodplains is also only one part of sustainable catchment management. In the UK, there are two catchments that are part of a European study (www.floodplains.org) and practical program of integrated catchment management: one is the River Parrett in Somerset, and the other is the Fens Floodplain Project, which includes Wicken Fen and several aggregate quarries. At present, archaeology does not feature in either of these projects despite both being areas of exceptional importance for long environmental records and a long history of human activity.

THE FUTURE

The data presented here show most obviously that since 1990, interventions in aggregate quarries have increased due, almost certainly, to PPG16. The proposed revision of PPG16 into a new PP statement superseded in March of 2010 by PPS5 (Planning Policy Statement) has the potential to dilute these controls and reverse the progress made under PPG16 since 1990. Any new government guidance should be at least as strong as what has gone before, even though this might be politically difficult in a time of recession because archaeology is of course a finite and nonsubstitutable resource. In the short term, a combination of responsive mode and targeted expenditure by bodies such as English Heritage can be employed to both equal-out expenditure of ALSF resources and address spatial variations in past research into aggregate-related archaeology. The existing methodology for applications coming through the planning system in England is well suited to supragravel (i.e., superficial) archaeology through desk-based assessment, evaluations, watching briefs, and, where appropriate, excavation. However, for intragravel archaeology (within gravel archaeology, often but not always Paleolithic), this methodology is far less satisfactory. A very convincing argument can be made that even with adequate pre-permission assessment and evaluation, watching briefs are still important, and in some cases critical. Indeed, the sampling employed by assessments, typically 2% in the UK, is inadequate, and, in many cases, it would be far more productive to strip the topsoil and then evaluate the entire area and subsequently concentrate resources on watching briefs where appropriate (Waddington, undated). In the case of intragravel archaeology, the situation is even more problematic, and a review of recording techniques is urgently required. Most staff working for archaeological contractors have a sound training in archaeological techniques, including archaeological stratigraphy and context recording. However, intragravel archaeology generally sits within a natural sediment body, and the sedimentological features and structures that should be recorded can have direct bearing on the interpretation of the archaeology. Additionally, recording of the stratigraphy often does not take place until an archaeological find is made, and yet, by this time, most of the sediment body may have been removed, along with its contextual evidence. There are two possible remedies for this problem—one is to train enough archaeologists in geoarchaeological recording. However, even if this could be done on a sufficient scale, the "needle in a haystack problem" still remains, along with possible objections from developers, who would proffer that this is not archaeology under the terms of PPG16 or similar planning guidance. An alternative is to try and automate the recording of gravel stratigraphy at least to the extent that a large part of the contextual evidence is collected at minimal cost and can be archived. The development of ground laser scanning, which is being used extensively by the aggregates industry itself (MIRO, 2010, personal commun.), geologists (Buckley et al., 2008), and by archaeologists (English Heritage, 2006), is probably the best way forward and should be supported with resources generated by ALSF.

CONCLUSIONS

This study has quantified the regional variation in archaeological intervention, both pre- and post-PPG16 in England. This variation is only partly geological, and an element of it must have been the result of a variation in the application of guidance by local authorities, or prior to 1990, by the aggregates industry. This may well be warranted by local archaeological conditions, but the result is an uneven coverage of floodplain archaeology in England. Funding from environmental taxes such as the Aggregates Levy Sustainability Fund has helped alleviate this situation and may continue to do so, dependent upon the allocation of such funds by the UK government. It is also important that bodies responsible for preserving UK heritage should encourage the targeting of areas of low intervention. A very convincing argument can be made that even with adequate pre-permission assessment and evaluation, watching briefs are still important and, in some cases, critical. Indeed, the sampling employed by assessments, typically 2% in the UK, is inadequate, and, in many cases, it would be far more productive to strip the topsoil and then evaluate the entire area and subsequently concentrate resources on watching briefs where appropriate. However, for this to be practical, there is an urgent need for the techniques used in watching briefs to be upgraded, along with appropriate staff training. This paper has also shown that UK aggregate production, although largely predictable in terms of government policy, is less predictable when it comes to economic activity, substitution, and legislative and planning changes. An additional influence will be climate change, both directly and indirectly, and it is difficult to predict how this will impact the aggregates industry. A particular concern is that legislative pressure and climate change may cause a shift to more wet aggregate working, and this would inevitably have a negative impact on aggregate-related archaeology. In the medium to long term, aggregate-related archaeology should be seen as one component in the integrated management of floodplain environments.

ACKNOWLEDGMENTS

The data used in this paper were compiled with the assistance of all the County and Unitary Authority Environment Departments, to whom thanks are given. The assistance of Bronwen Russell and of the Archaeological Investigations Project has been invaluable. I must thank Sue Rouillard for drawing and Helen Jones for scanning and other assistance. Jen Heathcote and several other employees of English Heritage are thanked for discussion and advice, and many geoarchaeological and archaeological colleagues are thanked for their help and information. J. Thatcher was invaluable in the acquisition of the Mineral Local Plans. I must also thank B. Croft and an anonymous reviewer for helping to improve the paper. Finally, the views expressed in this paper are entirely personal and do not reflect any institutional position.

REFERENCES CITED

Arnell, N., 1997, Global Warming, River Flows and Water Resources: Chichester, Wiley, 224 p.

Benson, D., and Miles, D., 1974, The Upper Thames Valley: An Archaeological Survey of the River Gravels: Oxfordshire Archaeological Unit Survey 2: Oxford, 112 p.

Beven, K., 1993, Riverine flooding in a warmer Britain: The Geographical Journal, v. 159, p. 157–161, doi:10.2307/3451405.

British Geological Survey, 2005, Aggregates Minerals Survey of England and Wales: British Geological Survey Commissioned Report CR/07/041 N, 142 p.

Brown, A.G., 2008, Geoarchaeology, the four dimensional (4D) fluvial matrix and climatic causality: Geomorphology, v. 101, p. 278–297, doi:10.1016/j.geomorph.2008.05.021.

Brown, A.G., 2009, The Environment and Aggregate-Related Archaeology: Oxford, Oxbow Books & Heritage Marketing and Publications, 220 p.

Brown, A.G., and Salisbury, C., 2010, The geomorphology and environment of the Hemington reach, in Ripper, S., and Cooper, L., eds., The Hemington Bridges: The Excavation of Three Medieval Bridges at Hemington Quarry near Castle Donington, Leicestershire: Leicester Archaeological Monographs, University of Leicester Archaeological Services, p. 142–173.

Buckley, S.J., Howell, J.A., Enge, H.D., and Kurz, T.H., 2008, Terrestrial laser scanning in geology: Data acquisition, processing and accuracy: Journal of the Geological Society of London, v. 165, p. 625–638, doi:10.1144/0016-76492007-100.

Charters, A.C., and Duthie, B., 2002, Living with the 1999 Quarries Regulations: A practical approach, in Scott, P.W., and Bristow, C.M., eds., Industrial Minerals and Extractive Industry Geology: London, Geological Society of London, p. 269–274.

Chiverrell, R.C., Foster, G.C., Thomas, G.S.P., Marshall, P., and Hamilton, D., 2009, Robust chronologies for landform development: Earth Surface Processes and Landforms, v. 34, p. 319–328, doi:10.1002/esp.1720.

Darvill, T., and Russell, B., 2002, Archaeology after PPG16: Archaeological Investigations in England 1990–1999: Bournemouth University School of Conservation Sciences Research Report 10 and English Heritage, 82 p.

Department of Communities and Local Government, 2008, Draft Revised National and Regional Guidelines for Aggregates Provision in England: 2005–2020: Consultation: Communities and Local Government Publications, April 2008, 29 p.

Department of Transport, 1992, Safeguarding Aerodromes, Technical Sites and Military Explosives Storage Areas: Circular Regarding Amendments to the Town and Country Planning Order 1995: London, Office of the Deputy Prime Minister, 20 p.

English Heritage, 2006, Advice and Guidance to Users on Laser Scanning in Archaeology and Architecture: London, English Heritage, 57 p.

English Heritage, 2008, Climate Change and the Historic Environment: London, 17 p.

French, C.A.I., 2004, Hydrological monitoring of an alluviated landscape in the Lower Great Ouse Valley at Over, Cambridgeshire: Results of the gravel extraction phase: Environmental Archaeology, v. 9, p. 1–13.

French, C.A.I., Davis, M., and Heathcote, J., 1999, Hydrological monitoring of an alluviated landscape in the lower Great Ouse valley, Cambridgeshire: Interim results of the first three years: Environmental Archaeology, v. 4, p. 41–56.

Fulford, M., and Nichols, E., eds., 1992, Developing Landscapes of Lowland Britain. The Archaeology of the British Gravels: A Review: London, Society of Antiquaries Occasional Papers 14, 140 p.

Hall, J.W., Sayers, P.B., Walkden, M.J.A, and Panzeri, M., 2006, Impacts of climate change on coastal flood risk in England and Wales: 2030–2100: Philosophical Transactions of the Royal Society of London, ser. A, v. 364, p. 1027–1049.

Hobbs, S.L., 2002, The hydrogeological effects of quarrying karstified limestone: Operational requirements for monitoring and mitigation, in Scott, P.W., and Bristow, C.M., eds., Industrial Minerals and Extractive Industry Geology: London, Geological Society of London, p. 161–168.

Howard, A.J., and Macklin, M.G., 1999, A generic geomorphological approach to archaeological interpretation and prospection in British river valleys: A guide for archaeologists investigating Holocene landscapes: Antiquity, v. 73, p. 527–541.

Howard, A.J., Challis, K., Kincey, M., and Passmore, D.G., 2008, The impact of climate change on archaeological resources in Britain: A catchment scale assessment: Climatic Change, v. 91, p. 405–422, doi:10.1007/s10584-008-9426-9.

Knight, D., and Howard, A.D., 2004, Trent Valley Landscapes: Kings Lynn, Heritage Marketing and Publications Ltd, 202 p.

Lane, S., 2008, Climate change and the summer 2007 floods in the UK: Geography (Sheffield, England), v. 93, p. 91–97.

Lewin, J., and Macklin, M.G., 1986, Metal mining and floodplain sedimentation in Britain, in Gardiner, V., ed., International Geomorphology, Part I: Chichester, Wiley, p. 1009–1027.

Macklin, M.G., Ridgway, J., Passmore, D., and Rumsby, B.T., 1994, The use of overbank sediment for geochemical mapping and contamination assessment: Results from selected English and Welsh floodplains: Applied Geochemistry, v. 9, p. 689–700, doi:10.1016/0883-2927(94)90028-0.

Office of National Statistics, 2005, Annual Minerals Raised Enquiry: Her Majesty's Stationary Office.

Office of the Deputy Prime Minister (ODPM), 2002, Consultation Paper on Draft National and Regional Guidelines for Aggregate Provision in England, 2001–2016: London, Office of the Deputy Prime Minister, 14 p.

Thorndycraft, V., Pirrie, D., and Brown, A., 1999, Tracing the record of early alluvial tin mining on Dartmoor, UK, in Pollard, A.M., ed., Geoarchaeology: Exploration, Environments, Resources: Geological Society of London Special Publication 165, p. 91–102.

Thorndycraft, V.R., Pirrie, D., and Brown, A.G., 2003, An environmental approach to the archaeology of tin mining on Dartmoor, in Murphy, P., and Wiltshire, P., eds., The Environmental Archaeology of Industry: Oxford, Oxbow Books, p. 19–28.

UKCIP (United Kingdom Climate Impacts Programme), 2002, Climate Change Scenarios for the United Kingdom: Bracknell, Hadley Centre.

Waddington, C., undated, Mineral Extraction and Archaeology: A Practical Guide: London, English Heritage/DEFRA (Department of Farming and Rural Affairs), 120 p.

Ward, I., 2011, this volume, The contribution of English Heritage Aggregates Levy Sustainability Fund research to geoarchaeology and sustainability, in Brown, A.G., Basell, L.S., and Butzer, K.W., eds., Geoarchaeology, Climate Change, Sustainability: Geological Society of America Special Paper 476, doi:10.1130/2011.2476(13).

Wymer, J., 1999, The Lower Palaeolithic Occupation of Britain, Volumes 1 and 2: London, Wessex Archaeology and English Heritage.

MANUSCRIPT ACCEPTED BY THE SOCIETY 3 AUGUST 2010